LABORATORY
MANUAL
IN PHYSICAL
GEOLOGY

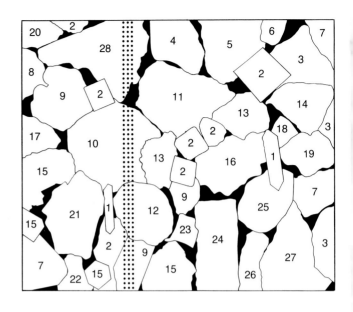

Front cover. View looking north near Fremont Peak, Bridger Wilderness of the Wind River Range, Wyoming (photographed by Lauret E. Savoy, Mount Holyoke College). The Wind River Mountain Range was uplifted during the Laramide Orogeny, a phase of crustal deformation that occurred in the Rocky Mountains from Late Cretaceous through Oligocene time (about 80–30 million years ago). Subsequent weathering and erosion of uplifted crust has added to the formation of the present landscape. 2.6-billion-year-old Precambrian metamorphic rocks now crop out in the area of the photograph, which is in Titcomb Basin (part of the Green River Drainage Basin).

Note that all subsystems (spheres) of Earth's dynamic system are represented by the photograph: lithosphere (rocks, soil), hydrosphere (stream), cryosphere (ice, snow), atmosphere (sky, clouds), and biosphere (yellow lichen, algae, other plants, photographer).

Back cover. A colorful collection of minerals and rocks (photographed by Rich Busch). The minerals can be identified using the numerical cover sketch above and the key below.

1. gypsum
2. fluorite
3. banded agate
4. chalcopyrite
5. malachite (green) on azurite
6. microcline (potassium feldspar) var. amazonite
7. golden calcite
8. calcite with pyrite
9. sulfur
10. quartz with hematite inclusions
11. rose quartz
12. amethyst geode
13. quartz crystals on chrysocolla
14. galena with white quartz
15. pyrite
16. pyrite crystals on galena
17. anhydrite
18. malachite
19. azurite
20. chrysocolla
21. turquoise
22. rhodochrosite
23. microcline (potassium feldspar)
24. covellite
25. tourmaline var. rubellite (pink) and var. verdelite (green)
26. orpiment (yellow) with realgar (red)
27. sodalite (blue) with nepheline (white)
28. kyanite

THIRD EDITION

LABORATORY MANUAL IN PHYSICAL GEOLOGY

Produced under the auspices of

AMERICAN GEOLOGICAL INSTITUTE

and

NATIONAL ASSOCIATION OF GEOLOGY TEACHERS

Edited by
RICHARD M. BUSCH
West Chester University

Illustrated by
DENNIS TASA
Tasa Graphic Arts, Inc.

Macmillan Publishing Company
New York

Maxwell Macmillan Canada
Toronto

Maxwell Macmillan International
New York   Oxford   Singapore   Sydney

Editor: Robert A. McConnin
Production Editor: Rex Davidson
Art Coordinator: Peter A. Robison
Cover Designer: Robert Vega
Production Buyer: Pamela D. Bennett
Page Layout: Ellen Robison

This book was set in Palatino by York Graphic Services,
Inc. and was printed and bound by R. R. Donnelley &
Sons Company. The cover was printed by Phoenix Color
Corp.

Macmillan Publishing Company
866 Third Avenue
New York, New York 10022

Macmillan Publishing Company is part of the
Maxwell Communication Group of Companies.

Maxwell Macmillan Canada, Inc.
1200 Eglinton Avenue East, Suite 200
Don Mills, Ontario M3C 3N1

Printing: 1 2 3 4 5 6 7 8 9   Year: 3 4 5 6 7

PREFACE

This laboratory manual was designed for use in a course on Introductory Geology or Physical Geology. It was produced under the auspices of the American Geological Institute and the National Association of Geology Teachers. The idea of such a jointly-sponsored laboratory manual was proffered by Robert W. Ridky (past president of NAGT and past member of the AGI Education Advisory Committee), who envisioned a manual made up of the "best laboratory investigations written by geology teachers." To that end, this third edition of the manual consists of nineteen exercises developed primarily with input from thirty-six contributing authors. The authors are nationally prominent Earth science educators and/or specialists in the geologic subject areas of their contributions.

The first edition of this laboratory manual was planned in 1984, when Merrill Publishing Company became interested in the Ridky concept. AGI initiated negotiations with a proposal developed by AGI Education Director, Andrew J. Verdon, Jr., and Ridky. Verdon directed the project and chaired a Laboratory Manual Project Steering Committee. The Committee was charged to design the manual, select exercises, and choose an editor. The Committee included Brewster Baldwin, Robert L. Bates, William E. Bonini, Jeffrey G. Callister, Marvin E. Kauffman, Julia A. Jackson, William H. Matthews III, Robert W. Ridky, and A. G. Unklesbay. Robert L. Bates was named Editor, and the "best exer-

cises" were acquired by sending notices to NAGT members and to geology departments in the United States and Canada. The exercises were screened by Robert L. Bates, Marvin E. Kauffman, Constantine Manos, Kenneth J. Van Dellen, and Andrew J. Verdon, Jr.

In 1985, AGI signed the publishing agreement with Merrill and the jointly-shared royalty agreement with NAGT. Royalties support the education programs of both organizations. Special thanks are due to Marvin E. Kauffman (NAGT President 1984–1985, AGI Executive Director 1985–1990), Kathy Nee (then of Merrill), and the many reviewers for ensuring the success of the innovative first edition, published in 1986.

Preparation for a second edition began in 1987, when Richard M. Busch (then of Kansas State University) was named Editor. For the second edition, nearly all of the exercises were reorganized and rewritten according to a standardized style and format, and five new exercises were added. Both metric and English systems of measurement were used (as in this latest edition), because Earth scientists generally use both systems on a daily basis. The second edition manuscript was subjected to rigorous peer review and was field tested at West Chester University (Department of Geology and Astronomy) and the University of Delaware (Department of Educational Development). The second edition was published in 1990.

Macmillan Publishing Company acquired Merrill in 1989 and initiated the planning process for this third edition. AGI Executive Director, Chip Groat, AGI Education Director, Andrew J. Verdon Jr., and the Editor, Richard M. Busch, met at AGI headquarters in July 1991 to develop a revision plan. A limited survey was also developed and conducted of Earth science educators who helped develop the first and/or second editions of the manual. This meeting and survey made possible the development of a specific revision plan for this edition. Dennis Tasa and William Fox Munroe added valuable input on issues pertaining to revision of figures and manual layout.

NEW FEATURES

The third edition reflects the strengths and features of previous editions: consistent exercise format, concise background information, full-color photographs, Dennis Tasa art pieces and charts, and the six tear-out structural models at the end of the book. The following features make this new edition an even more effective teaching tool:

- Several short, related exercises are now combined.

- Greater emphasis is placed on student understanding of the Earth as a complex, evolving system having interacting processes and cycles of change.

- Concept emphasis has been modified based on the results of a four-year nationwide study of Earth science educational goals for the 21st century by AGI.

- New Exercise One introduces the science of geology from a planetary perspective. Students briefly explore the evolution of Earth's dynamic system as it relates to the other terrestrial planets. They also explore the practicality of the global Plate Tectonics Model relative to determinations of plate motions, news reports of geologic phenomena, and mineral resource exploration.

- New Exercise Three introduces rocks and the rock cycle.

- Better examples, better directives, and more supporting information make this edition more user-friendly than ever before.

- There are more full-color figures than previous editions; including more Dennis Tasa art pieces and charts, maps, stereograms, sample photo-

graphs, outcrop photographs, computer-enhanced images, and photomicrographs.

- There are more process-oriented, inquiry-type questions and fewer questions emphasizing recall of terms and information.

- The Instructor's Resource Guide has been enhanced and expanded by Timothy Lutz, LeeAnn Srogi, and the Editor.

- A slide set is available to instructors using the manual.

We sincerely appreciate the assistance and contributions made by those individuals and institutions who have helped in the preparation of this edition. Lauret E. Savoy (Mount Holyoke College) provided the front-cover photograph. Other new photographs were supplied by Mary Dale-Bannister (Washington University in St. Louis), Jody Swann (U.S. Geological Survey, Branch of Astrogeology), Michael F. Hochella, Jr. and C. M. Eggleston (Stanford University), and J. van der Woude (Jet Propulsion Laboratory, California Institute of Technology). Thomas R. Watters and Rose Steinet (Smithsonian Institution, Center for Earth and Planetary Science) provided data and assisted with photographic research.

Joyce Young cheerfully typed the manuscript, and Fred C. Schroyer again provided outstanding copy editing. Revision comments were volunteered by Sally V. Beaty (on behalf of the Southern California Consortium, Pasadena), Deborah Casey (Lamar University), Ronald Corey (Baldwin Wallace College), Cydney Faul-Halsor and Sid P. Halsor (Wilkes University), Lawrence B. Gillett (State University of New York, Plattsburgh), Pamela J. W. Gore (Dekalb College), Gary Houlette (Oklahoma City College), Donal M. Ragan (Arizona State University), Stephen Simpson (Highland Community College), Richard C. Stenstrom (Beloit College), Gene C. Ulmer (Temple University), and Kenneth J. Van Dellen (Macomb Community College).

We thank the North Museum of Franklin and Marshall College, Omni Resources (formerly Geoscience Resources, Inc.), West Chester University (Department of Geology and Astronomy, Mineral Museum), and David B. Saja for providing many of the mineral and rock samples that appear as photographs in the manual. Photographs and data related to St. Catherines Island, Georgia, were made possible by grants to the Editor from the St. Catherines Island Research Program of the American Museum of Natural History, supported by the Edward J. Noble Foundation.

For maps, map data, and aerial photographs we thank the U.S. Geological Survey's EROS Data Center; National Aeronautics and Space Administration; National Space Science Data Center; U.S. Department of Agriculture; Mitchell Beazley Publishers, London; Department of Energy, Mines, and Resources, Ottawa; Bureau of Topographic and Geologic Survey of Pennsylvania; Surveys and Resource Mapping Branch, Ministry of Environment, Government of British Columbia; Grand Canyon Natural History Association; and Washington State Department of Natural Resources, Division of Geology and Earth Resources. Additional input to text and figures was provided by Cambridge University Press, Princeton University Press, *Scientific American, Paleobiology, Journal of Geological Education,* and the American Association of Petroleum Geologists.

The efforts of many persons at Macmillan Publishing Company are also appreciated. We thank Rex Davidson, Chuck Healy, Robert Vega, and Sue Bonito. Special thanks are also extended to Robert McConnin, whose extraordinarily effective and unique direction as Senior Editor made a complex revision process easy and wonderfully successful.

The continued success of this laboratory manual depends most on comments from colleagues. Therefore, we would welcome any and all comments regarding this edition and suggestions regarding a future edition. Please submit comments and suggestions directly to the Editor: Richard M. Busch, Department of Geology and Astronomy, West Chester University, West Chester, PA 19383.

Marcus E. Milling
Executive Director, AGI

Andrew J. Verdon, Jr.
Director of Education, AGI

Richard M. Busch
Editor

CONTRIBUTING AUTHORS

HAROLD E. ANDREWS
Department of Geology
Wellesley College
Wellesley, MA 02181

JAMES R. BESANCON
Department of Geology
Wellesley College
Wellesley, MA 02181

JANE L. BOGER
Department of Geological Sciences
SUNY, College at Geneseo
Genesco, NY 14454

PHILLIP D. BOGER
Department of Geological Sciences
SUNY, College at Geneseo
Geneseo, NY 14454

JONATHAN BUSHEE
Division of Geology
Northern Kentucky University
Highland Heights, KY 41076

MARY DALE-BANNISTER
Department of Earth and Planetary
Sciences
Washington University in St. Louis
St. Louis, MO 63130-4899

CHARLES I. FRYE
Department of Geology and
Geography
Northwest Missouri State
University
Maryville, MO 63501

PAMELA J. W. GORE
Department of Geology
Dekalb College
555 North Indian Creek Drive
Clarkston, GA 31993

EDWARD A. HAY
Division of Physical Sciences and
Mathematics
De Anza College
Cupertino, CA 95014

CHARLES G. HIGGINS
Department of Geology
University of California at Davis
Davis, CA 95616

MICHAEL F. HOCHELLA, JR.
Department of Geology
Stanford University
Stanford, CA 94305-2115

MICHAEL J. HOZIK
Geology Program
Stockton State College
Pomona, NJ 08240

SHARON LASKA
Department of Geology
Acadia University
Wolfville, Nova Scotia
BOP 1XO Canada

RICHARD W. MACOMBER
Department of Physics
Long Island University—Brooklyn
Brooklyn, NY 11201

GARY D. MCKENZIE
Department of Geology and
Mineralogy
Ohio State University
Columbus, OH 43210

CHERUKUPALLI E. NEHRU
Department of Geology
Brooklyn College (CUNY)
Brooklyn, NY 11210

CHARLES G. OVIATT
Department of Geology
Kansas State University
Manhattan, KS 66506

**DEPARTMENT OF GEOLOGY AND
PLANETARY SCIENCE**
University of Pittsburgh
Pittsburgh, PA 15260

WILLIAM R. PARROTT, JR.,
Geology Program
Stockton State College
Pomona, NJ 08240

JAMES H. SHEA
Department of Geology
University of Wisconsin—Whitewater
Whitewater, WI 53190

JOHN A. SHIMER
Department of Geology
Brooklyn College (CUNY)
Brooklyn, NY 11210

RAMAN J. SINGH
Division of Geology
Northern Kentucky University
Highland Heights, KY 41076

JOHN C. STEWART
Department of Geology
Brooklyn College (CUNY)
Brooklyn, NY 11210

KENTON E. STRICKLAND
288 Dwyer Hall
Wright State University
Lake Campus
7600 State Route 703
Celina, OH 45822

RICHARD N. STROM
Department of Geology
University of South Florida—Tampa
Tampa, FL 33620

JODY SWANN
Planetary Data Facility
Branch of Astrogeology
U.S. Geological Survey
2255 North Gemini Drive,
MS 9580
Flagstaff, AZ 86001-1698

RAYMOND W. TALKINGTON
Geology Program
Stockton State College
Pomona, NJ 08240

MARGARET D. THOMPSON
Department of Geology
Wellesley College
Wellesley, MA 02181

EVELYN M. VANDENDOLDER
Arizona Geological Survey
845 N. Park Ave. #100
Tucson, AZ 85719

NANCY A. VAN WAGONER
Acadia University, Nova Scotia

JOHN R. WAGNER
Department of Earth Sciences
Clemson University
Clemson, SC 29634-1908

CHARLES P. WALTERS
Department of Geology
Kansas State University
Manhattan, KS 66506

DONALD W. WATSON
Department of Geology
Slippery Rock University
Slippery Rock, PA 16057

PATRICIA A. WEISSE
Department of Geology
Wellesley College
Wellesley, MA 02181

JAMES R. WILSON
Department of Geology
Weber State College
Ogden, Utah 84408

MONTE D. WILSON
Department of Geosciences
Boise State University
Boise, ID 83725

CONTENTS

ITEMS REQUIRED TO COMPLETE EXERCISES IN THIS MANUAL

1. Sharp #2 or #3 pencils, with eraser
2. Graph paper: 10 divisions to the inch
3. Colored pencils
4. Hand lens
5. Ruler calibrated in metric and English units
6. Pocket stereoscope
7. Drafting compass
8. Protractor
9. Steel knife or masonry nail (provided by instructor)
10. Streak plate (provided by instructor)
11. Copper penny
12. Small magnet
13. Dilute hydrochloric acid (HCl) in dropper bottle (provided by instructor)
14. Calculator

QUANTITATIVE CONVERSIONS, UNIT SYMBOLS, AND ABBREVIATIONS

1 kilometer (km) = 1000 meters (m)   = 0.621 mile (mi)
1 meter (m)   = 100 centimeters (cm)   = 3.28 feet (ft)
1 centimeter (cm) = 0.01 meter (m)   = 0.394 inch (in.)
1 mile (mi)   = 1.6 kilometers (km)   = 5280 feet (ft)
1 foot (ft)   = 30.48 centimeters (cm) = 0.305 meters (m)
1 inch (in.)   = 2.54 centimeters (cm) = 25.4 millimeters (mm)

360 degrees (°) = a complete circle
1 degree (°)   = 60 minutes (')
1 minute (')   = 60 seconds (")

EXERCISE ONE
Earth—A Planetary Perspective

Mary Dale-Bannister
Washington University in St. Louis

Cherukupalli E. Nehru
John A. Shimer
John C. Stewart
Brooklyn College (CUNY)

Edward A. Hay
De Anza College

Jody Swann
Branch of Astrogeology
U. S. Geological Survey

PURPOSE

This exercise introduces the science of geology from a *planetary perspective*. The first part helps you see Earth as a unique planetary system compared to other planets in our solar system. We will ask you to consider how Earth is evolving, both as a result of its position in the Solar System and because of its processes of change. In the second part, we introduce you to the Plate Tectonics Model. We will ask you to examine the practicality of this model relative to limited investigations of lithospheric plate motions, 1991 news reports of volcanic activity and earthquakes, and mineral resource exploration.

MATERIALS

Pencil, eraser, metric ruler, and calculator (optional).

INTRODUCTION

Science is a logical and methodological process of investigation that people use to answer questions and solve problems. The branch of science that deals with Earth is **geology**. Its name comes from two Greek words, *geo* = Earth and *logos* = study of. Thus, geologists are Earth scientists. They work in field settings, laboratories, aircraft, spacecraft, and submersibles in the ocean. They make careful observations and collect data (information) about Earth materials, events, and processes of change.

These careful observations have provided geologists with a fast-growing body of knowledge and understanding of Earth. This knowledge and understanding is used:

- to form new **hypotheses** (ideas to be tested and evaluated)
- to devise **experiments** to test the hypotheses
- to make **inferences** (conclusions based on evidence)
- to design **models** (tentative concepts of cause-and-effect relationships or how observations and processes are related).

Therefore, geologists are uniquely qualified to explain Earth's origin and geologic history in reasonable and qualified terms, to locate Earth resources used by people, to evaluate the impact of human actions on the environment, to recommend governmental policies related to Earth science, to analyze the feasibility of land-development projects, to predict certain events, and so on. But geologists are not Earth-bound. There is no reason to restrict the science of geology to a single *place*, such as Earth. Principles discovered by geologists apply to other astronomical bodies as well!

1

Technological innovations from space exploration enable geologists to play an ever-increasing role in scientific investigations of the Moon, other planets, and moons of other planets. Modern geology has grown to be the science of Earth and other rocky bodies of the Solar System.

PART 1—EARTH AS A SYSTEM

Earth scientists generally conceptualize Earth as a dynamic system composed of five interacting *subsystems* or *spheres*. These are the lithosphere, hydrosphere, atmosphere, cryosphere, and biosphere.

Earth's **lithosphere** is the solid, outermost layer of the planet. It consists of solid bedrock, fragmented rock (regolith), and soil (regolith mixed with organic debris sufficient to support plant growth). The lithosphere is 60–100 km thick (40–60 mi). It rests on the **asthenosphere,** a weak zone of the upper mantle where rocks flow plastically due to intense heat and pressure. The lithosphere is not a single, rigid, eggshell-like covering. It is a mosaic of numerous rigid plates that are moved by the slow plastic flow of the asthenosphere. Zones between adjacent plates, called **plate boundaries,** are regions of common earthquakes and occasional volcanic activity.

Earth's **hydrosphere** is all of the liquid water on the planet's surface and in the ground (lithosphere). Most of the hydrosphere is salt water, contained in oceans that cover about 70% of our planet. The U. S. Geological Survey has noted that, if all of the water on Earth could be put into a 55-gallon drum, then slightly more than 53 gallons of that water would be ocean water. Only about one-fourth of a gallon would be water in the ground. Only about one-hundredth of a gallon would be the water in lakes and streams. The remainder would be water vapor in the atmosphere (about one-eighth of a gallon) and water frozen in the cryosphere (slightly over a gallon).

Earth's **atmosphere** is the mass of gases (air) that surrounds the planet. It consists of about 75% nitrogen, 20% oxygen, and small amounts of other gases including argon, carbon dioxide, and water vapor. Air pressure is created as gravity pulls this air mass against the planet's surface. Atmospheric currents (winds) form due to regional variations in the air pressure, air convection (motion caused by unequal heating), and Earth's rotation. Atmospheric temperatures on Earth's surface range from recorded extremes of $+58°C$ $(+136°F)$ in the Libyan desert (September 13, 1922) to $-89°C$ $(-129°F)$ at Vostok, Antarctica (July 21, 1983).

Earth's **cryosphere** is the ice and frost that form due to freezing of portions of the hydrosphere or atmosphere. Therefore, the cryosphere is water ice on Earth's surface. Most of it exists in the polar ice sheets, plus permafrost (permanently frozen moisture in the ground).

The **biosphere** is the living part of Earth's system, the part that is organic and self-replicating. It is the total of all organisms (plants and animals) living in the other four spheres.

All of Earth's subsystems, except for the biosphere, are evident from space as distinct entities (Figure 1.1). Yet, these distinct systems interact and influence one another to form the integrated, dynamic planetary system. Any significant change in one subsystem generally causes changes in other subsystems.

PROCESSES AND CYCLES OF CHANGE

Changes in Earth's planetary subsystems are caused by numerous physical and chemical processes. These involve inorganic and organic materials in solid, liquid, or gaseous states (*phases*). Figure 1.2 reviews some of these processes and the changes they cause. Note that many processes have opposite effects: melting and freezing, evaporation and condensation, dissolution and chemical precipitation, photosynthesis (food production) and respiration (food consumption or "burning"). The process called sublimation also is reversible: a solid changing directly to a gas, or a gas changing directly to a solid. Such effects cause chemical materials to be endlessly cycled and recycled between two or more states and between two or more subsystems.

Hydrologic Cycle

The **hydrologic cycle** (water cycle) involves several processes and changes related to all three phases of water and all subsystems of Earth (Figure 1.3). Thus it is among Earth's most important cycles.

The cycle operates like this: water (hydrosphere) evaporating from Earth's surface produces water vapor (atmospheric gas). The water vapor eventually condenses to form aerosol water droplets (clouds). The droplets can combine to form raindrops or snowflakes (atmospheric precipita-

FIGURE 1.1 *Apollo 17* photograph of Earth. Note brown land areas (lithosphere), white Antarctic ice sheet (cryosphere), white clouds (atmosphere), and blue ocean (hydrosphere). (Photo courtesy of NASA)

COMMON PROCESSES OF CHANGE		
Process	Kind of Change	Example
Melting	Solid phase changes to liquid phase.	Water ice turns to water.
Freezing	Liquid phase changes to solid phase.	Water turns to water ice.
Evaporation	Liquid phase changes to gas (vapor) phase.	Water turns to water vapor or steam (hot water vapor).
Condensation	Gas (vapor) phase changes to liquid phase.	Water vapor turns to water droplets.
Sublimation	Solid phase changes directly to a gas (vapor) phase, or gas (vapor) phase changes directly to solid phase.	Dry ice (carbon-dioxide ice) turns to carbon dioxide gas, or the reverse.
Dissolution	A substance becomes evenly dispersed into a liquid (or gas). The dispersed substance is called a solute, and the liquid (or gas) that causes the dissolution is called a solvent.	Table salt (solute) dissolves in water (solvent).
Vaporization	Solid or liquid changes into a gas (vapor), due to evaporation or sublimation.	Water turns to water vapor or water ice turns directly to water vapor.
Reaction	Any change that results in formation of a new chemical substance (by combining two or more different substances).	Baking soda (sodium bicarbonate) and vinegar (acetic acid) react to form water, sodium, and carbon dioxide gas.
Atmospheric precipitation	A physical change in the atmosphere whereby a gas phase turns to droplets of liquid, or a liquid phase turns to solid particles.	Water vapor turns to rain, snow, or hail in the atmosphere.
Chemical precipitation	A solid that forms when a liquid solution evaporates or reacts with another substance.	Salt forms as ocean water evaporates. Table salt forms when hydrochloric acid and sodium hydroxide solutions are mixed.
Photosynthesis	Sugar (glucose) and oxygen are produced from the reaction of carbon dioxide and water in the presence of sunlight (solar energy).	Plants produce glucose sugar and oxygen.
Respiration	Sugar (glucose) and oxygen undergo combustion (burning) without flames and change to carbon dioxide, water, and heat energy.	Plants and animals obtain their energy from respiration.
Transpiration	Water vapor is produced by the biological processes of animals and plants (respiration, photosynthesis).	Plants release water vapor to the atmosphere through their pores.
Evolution	Change through time.	Biological evolution, change in the shape of Earth's landforms through time.

FIGURE 1.2 Common processes of change on Earth.

tion). Snowflakes can accumulate to form ice (cryosphere) that sublimates back into the atmosphere or melts back into water. Both rainwater and meltwater soak into the ground, evaporate back into the atmosphere, drain back into the ocean, or are consumed by plants and animals (which release the water back to the atmosphere via transpiration).

This endless recycling of water undoubtedly has occurred since the first water bodies formed on Earth billions of years ago. Your next drink may include water molecules that once were part of a glacier or that once were consumed by a thirsty dinosaur!

The water cycle doesn't just run by itself. It is driven by energy, which must come either from the Sun or from Earth's interior. This energy keeps the processes of the cycle (evaporation, etc.) functioning like machinery in a sort of water-recycling factory. Heat energy from the Sun, during daytime and especially in summer, causes evaporation, melting of ice, and sublimation of ice to gas. Heat energy from volcanic activity causes the same phenomena. The absence of solar heat during night

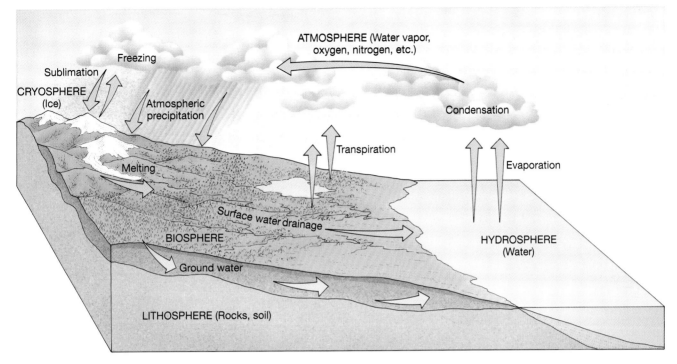

FIGURE 1.3 The hydrologic cycle (water cycle). Note the relation of processes of change in water (evaporation, condensation, freezing) to Earth's subsystems (lithosphere, cryosphere, hydrosphere, atmosphere, biosphere).

and winter, or the absence of volcanic activity, can cause condensation, freezing of water, and sublimation to solid.

Photosynthesis

The process of **photosynthesis** is also driven by the Sun's energy, in the form of light. It is the process by which plants convert carbon dioxide and water into their own sugar food, using energy from sunlight. A byproduct of photosynthesis is oxygen, which is used by animals to burn food and release energy.

Therefore, photosynthesis enables the exchange (cycling) of oxygen and carbon dioxide between plants and animals. This oxygen-carbon dioxide exchange involves both the biosphere and atmosphere. It ensures that oxygen is present for animals to breathe, that carbon dioxide does not reach levels toxic to animals, and that Earth's greenhouse effect does not fluctuate dramatically.

Greenhouse Effect

The **greenhouse effect** is an insulation effect. Atmospheric gases like carbon dioxide and water

vapor absorb heat energy that otherwise would be radiated back into space. By storing this heat energy, they maintain the warmth of Earth's surface. However, too much insulating atmospheric gas undoubtedly would cause global warming, and too little insulating gas undoubtedly would cause global cooling.

Volcanoes

Volcanoes also notably influence Earth's planetary system. They explosively eject into the atmosphere molten rock material (liquefied lithosphere), rock fragments (cinders, ash), and gases (Figure 1.4). Large rock fragments then settle to the ground, where they combine with lava flows to build up the surface of the lithosphere. Dust-sized rock fragments can remain suspended in the atmosphere for many years, along with water vapor, sulfur dioxide gas, nitrogen gas, carbon dioxide gas, and hydrogen gas from the eruption.

When Mt. Pinatubo in the Philippines erupted on 12 June 1991, an immense plume of ash, dust, and gases shot nearly 30 km into the atmosphere. Shortly thereafter, ash fell on Singa-

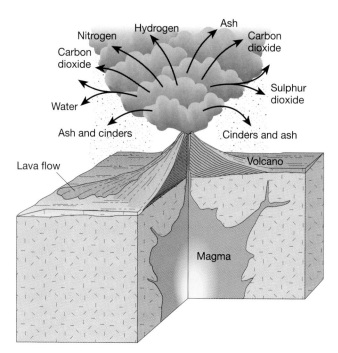

FIGURE 1.4 A typical volcano erupting on Earth, showing liquid (lava), solid (ash, cinders), and common gaseous components (water vapor, carbon dioxide, nitrogen, hydrogen, sulfur dioxide).

pore and other cities 3200 km (2000 mi) away (Figure 1.17). By mid-July a hazy band of dust and gas blanketed equatorial parts of the entire Earth! Sulfur dioxide had by then combined with atmospheric water vapor to produce tiny droplets of sulfuric acid, a sort of sulfuric acid aerosol spray. These tiny droplets act as billions of tiny prisms. They bend solar light rays enough to scatter many of them back into space, so the amount of solar energy reaching Earth's surface decreases and global cooling occurs.

The full effects of the Mt. Pinatubo eruption were not fully determined when this was written, but some atmospheric cooling and acid rain can be predicted on the basis of historical evidence. When Mt. Tambora in Indonesia erupted massively in 1815, atmospheric haziness caused the historic 1816 "year without a summer." Northern Hemisphere temperatures during that famous summer fell 2–3°C (3–6°F) below normal, and early frosts destroyed crops in New England.

OTHER PLANETARY SYSTEMS

Earth's planetary system is unique compared to other planets of our Solar System. To appreciate

this uniqueness, consider the three other terrestrial planets (i.e., the inner rocky planets): Mercury, Venus, and Mars.

FIGURE 1.5 Photographic mosaic of the planet Mercury, constructed from *Mariner* data. (Photo courtesy of NASA)

Mercury

Mercury is a tiny planet, only about 1/3 the diameter of Earth. Most data available for Mercury were obtained by NASA's *Mariner 10* spacecraft, which photographed the planet in 1974 only 19,000 km (12,000 mi) from its surface. A mosaic of *Mariner* photographs (Figure 1.5) reveals that most of its surface is heavily cratered and shattered from meteorite bombardment. Notably absent are Earthly features such as volcanic cones, clouds, ice, water bodies, and a recognizable atmosphere.

Mercury's very thin atmosphere contains only traces of helium, hydrogen, neon, and argon. The thin atmosphere and closeness to the Sun also cause Mercury to undergo dramatic day-night temperature changes. Surface temperatures range from about +320°C during the day to −170°C at night (+608°F to −274°F). In addition to extensive cratering, such extremes of hot and cold undoubtedly have helped produce a barren landscape of rocky ridges, boulder fields, and regolith patches.

Venus

Venus is the closest planet to Earth in both distance and size. Its diameter is only 5% smaller than Earth's. Nevertheless, remote sensing and robotic sensing indicate that Venus possesses a very dense atmosphere of about 96% carbon dioxide, plus small amounts of nitrogen, neon, argon, and water vapor. Sulfur dioxide gas from erupting volcanoes mixes with the water vapor to produce aerosol droplets and yellowish clouds of sulfuric acid that hide the planet's surface (Figure 1.6A).

Both the United States and the former Soviet Union launched probes to penetrate the thick Venusian clouds, and both projects provided valuable data. NASA's *Mariner 6* probe traveled within about 34,000 km (21,000 mi) of the planet, discovering that the surface reaches 480°C (900°F). The probe also found water vapor in the Venusian atmosphere. This was determined by spectroscopic analyses of electromagnetic radiation from the planet, including light.

Subsequent *Pioneer-Venus* spacecraft launched by NASA (1978, 1979) used radar reflections to map the planet. They also dropped probes into the Venusian atmosphere and onto the Venusian lithosphere. One probe indicated sulfuric acid droplets in the atmosphere, but such droplets were not found at the surface. Apparently, the sulfuric acid droplets and raindrops evaporate before falling onto the lithosphere.

By this time, the Soviets also had obtained valuable data. In 1975 and 1982, their robotic probes *Venera 9* and *10* each transmitted a black-and-white photograph of the Venusian surface. *Venera 13* and *14* returned color images in 1982. However, none of the Pioneer-Venus or Venera probes survived long in the harsh Venusian environment. *Venera 14* transmitted data for only 68 minutes before it succumbed! One of the Venera photographs (Figure 1.7) shows a rocky, cracked, arid surface with regolith. The robotic probe found that the rocks have the composition of basalt, a common volcanic rock on Earth (Figure 4.9).

On 4 May 1989, the four-ton *Magellan* radar-mapping spacecraft was launched toward Venus from the Space Shuttle *Atlantis*. The spacecraft arrived at Venus in August 1990 and continues to image the planet at the time of this writing. NASA released *Magellan's* vivid radar images of Venus like the mosaic in Figure 1.6B and the oblique view in Figure 1.7.

Compared to Earth, Venus's surface is generally smooth, interrupted by volcanoes and deep cracks (rifts). The perspective radar image in Figure 1.7 reveals fractured lava plains and volcanoes. On the left in the image is Gula Mons volcano, about 3 km high (1.8 mi). A lava flow extends hundreds of kilometers from Gula Mons to the foreground of the image.

In the planetary mosaic (Figure 1.6B), well-defined craters are absent, despite the likelihood that Venus has undergone the same meteoritic bombardment as Mercury, Earth, the Moon, and Mars. Perhaps the craters were obliterated by volcanic processes. It also is probable that many meteorites were pulverized in the Venusian atmosphere due to its intense air pressure (90–100 times that on Earth). Such pressure probably is sufficient to crush meteorites smaller than 100 m in diameter, showering a shotgun-like blast of rocky debris into the Venusian lithosphere. Such a model may account for the dark, circular blotches scattered sparsely over the planet, instead of craters.

Mars

Mars is about half the diameter of Earth and is much farther from the Sun. It also has received much study by NASA and the U. S. Geological Survey. As early as 1962, NASA's *Mariner 2* spacecraft passed within 34,800 km (21,600 mi) of the planet. That was followed by flyby and orbiting spacecraft in 1965 *(Mariner 4)*, 1969 *(Mariner 6 and 7)*, and 1971 *(Mariner 9)*.

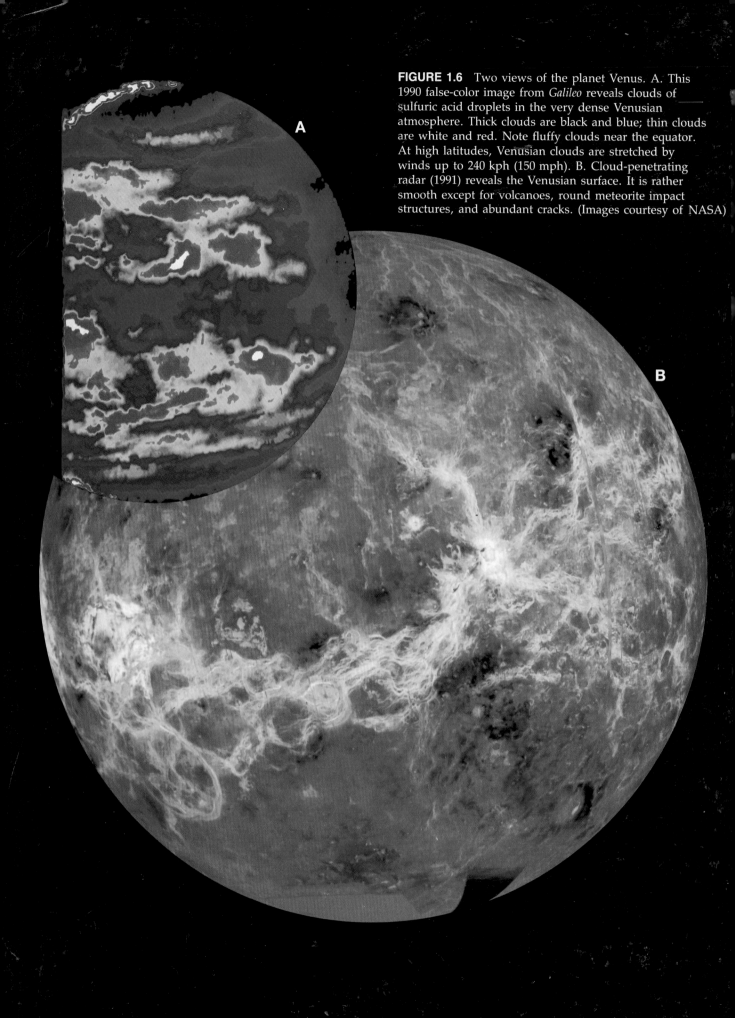

FIGURE 1.6 Two views of the planet Venus. A. This 1990 false-color image from *Galileo* reveals clouds of sulfuric acid droplets in the very dense Venusian atmosphere. Thick clouds are black and blue; thin clouds are white and red. Note fluffy clouds near the equator. At high latitudes, Venusian clouds are stretched by winds up to 240 kph (150 mph). B. Cloud-penetrating radar (1991) reveals the Venusian surface. It is rather smooth except for volcanoes, round meteorite impact structures, and abundant cracks. (Images courtesy of NASA)

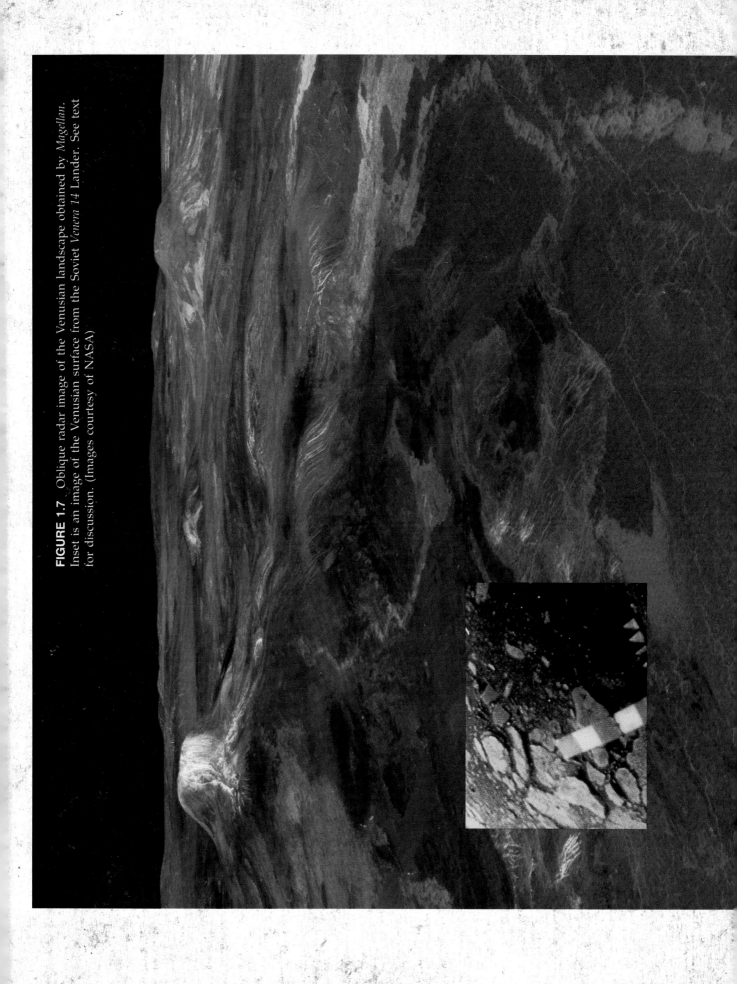

FIGURE 1.7 Oblique radar image of the Venusian landscape obtained by *Magellan*. Inset is an image of the Venusian surface from the Soviet *Venera 14* Lander. See text for discussion. (Images courtesy of NASA)

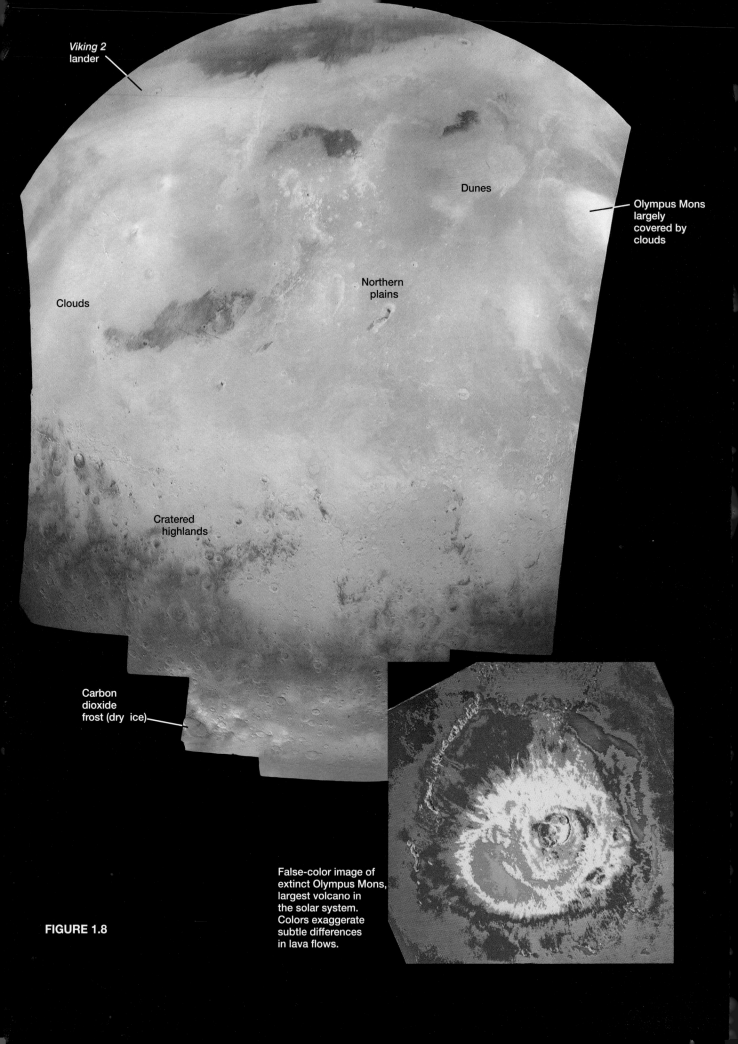

Viking 2 lander

Dunes

Olympus Mons largely covered by clouds

Clouds

Northern plains

Cratered highlands

Carbon dioxide frost (dry ice)

False-color image of extinct Olympus Mons, largest volcano in the solar system. Colors exaggerate subtle differences in lava flows.

FIGURE 1.8

The most spectacular data from Mars, however, came from NASA's *Viking 1* (1977–1982) and *Viking 2* (1976–1980). Both spacecraft orbited the planet and sent robotic landers to the Martian surface. Figure 1.8 is a mosaic of 104 *Viking 1* orbiter photographs composed by Jody Swann of the U. S. Geological Survey's Branch of Astrogeology. Note the location of the *Viking 2* lander, which transmitted the Martian-landscape photograph in Figure 1.9B.

Also note the cratered highlands, northern plains, dunes, clouds, and the extinct Olympus Mons volcano, largest known in the Solar System. Its area is larger than the state of Missouri. Its volume is about 50 times greater than Earth's largest volcano (Hawaii's Mauna Loa, Figure 1.16). The false-color photograph of Olympus Mons in Figure 1.8 was taken by the *Viking 1* orbiter and exaggerates subtle color differences in lava flows.

Mars has seasonal and geographic temperature variations that range from about $-128°C$ to $+26°C$ ($-200°F$ to $+80°F$). The entire planet is characterized by thick water-ice permafrost. The northern pole has a cap of water-ice, and the southern pole has a cap of water ice plus carbon dioxide frost (partly visible in Figure 1.8). The Martian atmosphere is about 95% carbon dioxide and 2–3% nitrogen, with traces of argon, oxygen, and water vapor. No liquid is present on the Martian surface *at this time*. However, ancient stream beds and shoreline features are evident on Mars (Figure 1.8).

Photographs taken by the *Viking* landers (Figure 1.9) reveal an arid landscape with rocks, regolith, sand dunes, and occasional frosts of carbon dioxide and water. The dark rocks probably are basalt (see Figure 4.9). The reddish regolith is caused by oxidation (rusting) of iron in the rocks. Free oxygen is rare in today's Martian atmosphere because most of it is bonded with carbon in the 95% carbon dioxide atmosphere. Thus, oxidation of the iron probably is a very slow process.

QUESTIONS—PART 1, EARTH AS A SYSTEM

1. Note the color differences between images of the Martian surface at the *Viking 2* Lander site in Figures 1.9B and 1.9C. What color do you think geologist Edward Guinness added to Figure 1.9C to make the Martian materials look as they would on Earth? Explain your reasoning.

2. In the Venera photograph (Figure 1.7), why do you think the rocky Venusian surface is colored yellow? Infer what color the rocky surface would appear to be on Earth, and explain your reasoning.

3. Complete the chart in Figure 1.10 with data about subsystems of Mercury, Venus, Earth, and Mars (the "terrestrial planets"). Write OCCURS or ABSENT in each square, and note brief evidence or information to justify your inference. (Refer to examples already completed on the chart.)

4. Note and briefly explain what kinds of problems you encountered when filling in the chart in Figure 1.10. Be prepared to discuss this with other class members.

5. Refer to your completed chart in Figure 1.10. In what ways is Earth a unique planetary system, compared to the other inner planets? Be prepared to discuss this with other class members.

6. Propose a hypothesis or model to explain why Earth has evolved into such a unique planet, compared to the other inner planets.

7. Geologists have compiled data on changes in Earth's subsystems that occurred over the past 600 million (0.6 billion) years. Some of this information has been summarized in Figure 1.11. Notice how the following have varied through time: composition of the atmosphere, sea level, extent of glaciers, numbers of plant and animal families, and amount of volcanism. With this in mind, consider these questions:
    a. What relationship through geologic time do you observe between sea level (hydrosphere) and amount of volcanism (lithosphere)? Propose an explanation for this relationship.

FIGURE 1.8 Digital mosaic showing the Martian early northern summer. The mosaic was produced by Jody Swann from *Viking 1* Orbiter images taken in 1980 (using an image-processing technique developed by the U.S. Geological Survey, Branch of Astrogeology). Color variations have been enhanced and solar reflection has been reduced. Latitude limits of the image are about 65° N and 65° S. Center of the image is at 3° N latitude, 185° W longitude. Inset is a false-color image of the extinct Olympus Mons volcano, largest in the Solar System. Image was obtained by the *Viking 1* Orbiter to detect differences in lava flows for mapping purposes. See text for discussion. (Images courtesy of U.S. Geological Survey and NASA)

FIGURE 1.9 Synthetic high-resolution images of Mars (see text for discussion). Image A data were acquired at the *Viking 1* Lander site. Images B and C are differently colored forms of an image from the *Viking 2* Lander site. A and B have been tinted to show how they would appear on Mars. Image C was modified to show how Martian surfaces would look on Earth. (Image processing by Mary A. Dale-Bannister and Edward A. Guinness, Washington University, St. Louis)

A.

B.

C.

FIGURE 1.10 Chart for compiling data on subsystems of the inner planets (terrestrial planets).

SUBSYSTEMS (SPHERES) OF THE INNER PLANETS				
Mercury	Venus	Earth	Mars	
				Lithosphere
OCCURS: thin, poorly developed. Only traces of helium, hydrogen, neon, and argon.		OCCURS: well developed, with 75% nitrogen, 20% oxygen, argon, carbon dioxide, water vapor, etc.		Atmosphere
				Cryosphere
				Hydrosphere
ABSENT?: Conditions on planet could not support Earth-type life.		OCCURS: many kinds of plants and animals are known.		Biosphere

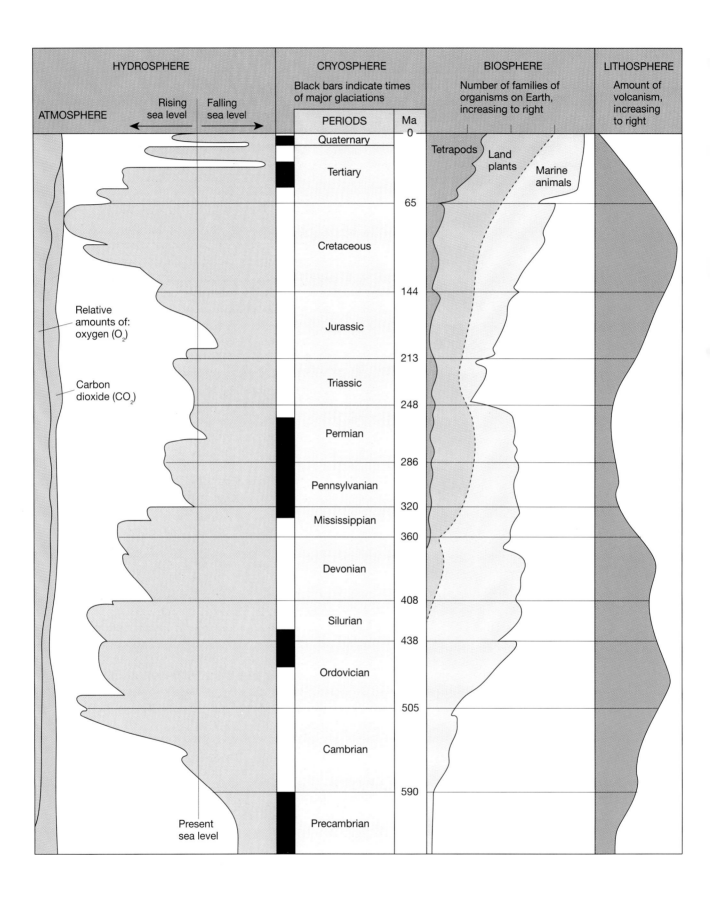

b. Compare the abundance of plants through geologic time with the composition of the atmosphere. What relationship do you observe between the abundance of oxygen in the atmosphere and the abundance of plants? Propose an explanation for this relationship.

c. What relationship through geologic time do you observe between the evolution/extinction patterns of families of animals (biosphere) and sea level (hydrosphere)? Propose an explanation for this relationship.

8. Venus often is referred to as a "sister planet" to Earth, because it is about the same size and is nearest Earth in the Solar System. On the other hand, Venus has a very different kind of atmosphere. It evolved an atmosphere composed almost entirely of carbon dioxide, giving the planet a "runaway" greenhouse effect and surface temperatures that would be lethal to life on Earth. Earth once had an atmosphere much richer in carbon dioxide than today (see Figure 1.11), but over the past 600 million years it has evolved an oxygen-rich/carbon dioxide-poor atmosphere. Propose an explanation for why these two planets evolved such different atmospheres, even though they seem in other ways to be sister planets.

9. Notice that Mars also has an atmosphere rich in carbon dioxide, yet it is a cold planet with global permafrost, lacking significant greenhouse effect. Propose an explanation for why Mars has evolved such an atmosphere compared to Earth and Venus (in terms of composition and temperature).

10. Reconsider your hypothesis/model from question 6. Is it still reasonable? If not, propose a new hypothesis/model to explain why Earth has evolved into such a unique planetary system. Be prepared to discuss your reasoning with other class members.

FIGURE 1.11 (Opposite page) Some changes in Earth's subsystems over the past 600 million years. (Data assembled from Vail, P. R., Mitchum, R. M., Jr., and Thompson III, S., 1977, American Association of Petroleum Geologists Memoir 26:83–97; Benton, M. J., 1988, *The Beginning of the Age of Dinosaurs*, New York: Cambridge Univ. Press, 303–20; Sepkoski, J. J., 1981, *Paleobiology* 7:36–53; Niklas, K. J., and others, 1985, *Phanerozoic Diversity Patterns*, Princeton, NJ: Princeton Univ. Press; and Cloud, P., 1970, *Adventures in Earth History*, San Francisco: W. H. Freeman & Co.)

PART 2—PLATE TECTONICS

Ever since the first reasonably accurate world maps were constructed in the 1600s, people have speculated on global models to explain the origin of Earth's continents and ocean basins. Some thought that surficial processes, like catastrophic floods of Biblical proportions, had carved ocean basins and deposited rocky materials to form mountainous continents. Others thought that global relief was the result of what is now called **tectonism:** large-scale movements and deformation of Earth's crust. One of the latter was a German scientist, Alfred Wegener. He argued (1915) that all continents once were part of a supercontinent, *Pangaea,* and that the continents subsequently drifted apart. This idea became widely known as the **continental drift** hypothesis.

Wegener's idea of continental drift was favored by "mobilists," for it helped them explain the large masses of rock in the Alps that had been pushed horizontally for many kilometers. The pushing (compression) caused huge folds to develop in the layered rock. However, "antimobilists" rejected Wegener's ideas because he provided no model to explain how continental drift occurred.

The antimobilists argued that it was impossible for continents to "drift" through solid oceanic rocks. They felt that *vertical* displacements of blocks of Earth's crust were the main elements of tectonism. Also, they were preoccupied with developing models of changes in Earth's size. They reasoned that, if Earth were cooling from a semimolten state, it should be contracting. This would cause the continents to compress together and the oceans to disappear. Conversely, if Earth were heating up and expanding, the rigid crust and continents would split apart and ocean basins would expand. This seemed reasonable initially, but it did not explain mountain ranges caused by compression, as in the Alps. Wegener died in 1930, as debates about tectonism and continental drift continued.

By the 1950s new data on continental drift had emerged. Paleontologists (geologists who mostly study fossils) observed identical fossil organisms on two or more continents, despite their separation by oceans. Did these organisms swim or float across the oceans? Or were the continents joined at the time these plants and animals were alive?

Study of paleoclimates (ancient climates) indicated that glacial deposits from at least four different continents once were part of a single deposit on a supercontinent centered near the South Pole. And studies of paleomagnetism (ancient magnetism) indicated that either (1) Earth's magnetic poles had wandered about the globe, or (2) the poles were stationary and the continents had moved.

During the 1960s still more data emerged. Earthquake data indicated that Earth has a thin, rigid lithosphere underlain by a plastic asthenosphere. Studies revealed that volcanoes and severe earthquakes are mostly concentrated along cracks in the lithosphere; these are the "plate boundaries" mentioned earlier in this exercise. By the end of the 1960s a new model of global tectonics had emerged, called **plate tectonics.**

With the Plate Tectonics Model, there is no problem of having continents "plow" through more rigid rock. Instead, the continents are portions of rigid plates that simply move about relative to one another. Because of the amount of supporting evidence, plate tectonics has gained more widespread acceptance in the scientific community, and is now a widely used model.

Considerable crustal deformation develops along plate boundaries, because they are the contact areas between massive plates. Therefore, plate boundaries are characterized by earthquakes, some volcanism, and distinctive topography. Geologists now recognize three basic types of plate boundaries. Before introducing these, we need a quick review of rock deformation: Earth's forces and the types of faulting they produce.

EARTH'S FORCES AND FAULTS

Three kinds of force (stress) can be applied to a solid mass such as rock: (1) **compression** or squeezing, (2) **tension** or pulling apart, and (3) **shear** or sliding past. Each force produces a distinctive break in the rock, called a **fault.** Figure 1.12 depicts these three forces and the faults they produce in rocks.

Note that tensional forces cause **normal faulting.** As rocks are pulled apart (tension), gravity pulls the **hanging block** downward, causing it to slide off the other subjacent block. Normal faulting gets its name because it is a *normal* response to gravity. By contrast, compressional force pushes the hanging block upward, opposing Earth's gravity. This is the *reverse* of a normal response, and so it is called **reverse faulting.**

Shear forces cause lateral movements of blocks of rock. This is called **strike-slip faulting** because the rocks move ("slip") past one another

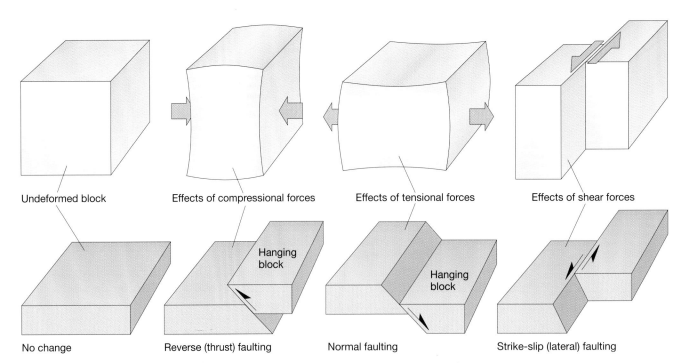

FIGURE 1.12 Schematic block diagrams illustrating the effects of stress and resulting types of faulting. Top row shows stresses (applied forces are indicated by large arrows). Bottom row shows the resulting types of faulting in rocks.

along the direction of strike (explained in Exercise Fourteen).

THREE TYPES OF PLATE BOUNDARIES

Although scientists have previously suggested Earth expansion (extension) and Earth contraction (compression) models to explain global deformation observed in Earth's crust, modern data indicate that Earth's volume has changed very little in the last 4 billion years. Normal faulting (extension), reverse faulting (compression), and strike-slip faulting (shear) presently occur throughout the world. However, on a global scale, each type of fault does not occur randomly. Instead, each of the three boundary types between lithospheric plates is primarily characterized by only one type of faulting. We will now look at these three plate boundary types.

Divergent Plate Boundaries

This type of plate boundary occurs primarily along ocean ridges, such as the Mid-Atlantic Ridge and the East Pacific Rise. Here basaltic lavas well up from Earth's mantle through cracks in the oceanic crust. As the lavas rise and occasionally pour onto the seafloor, they solidify to form new oceanic crust (Figure 1.13, left half). The rising lavas also force aside older crust, making it spread horizontally away from both sides of the ridge (i.e., to the left and right in the figure). Therefore, there is a continuing supply of new crust that forms a ridge along the boundary. Such plate boundaries also are known as **spreading ridges,** or **mid-ocean ridges,** or **rises.** Their equivalent on land areas is a **rift.**

Crustal expansion at divergent plate boundaries causes abundant normal faults to develop along the ridge. However, crustal extension does not occur at the same rate everywhere along divergent boundaries. Differential extension rates lead to shear, development of strike-slip faults, and offsets of ridge segments (Figure 1.13). These particular strike-slip faults are called **transform faults,** because they form where the motion of the seafloor is transformed from spreading (at the ridge) to shearing between offset segments of ridges.

Convergent Plate Boundaries

Where does the old crust eventually end up as it migrates away from the spreading ridge? If it stayed on the surface, Earth would indeed grow larger and larger. But geologists discovered that the formation of new crust along ridges is balanced by **subduction:** descent of the old crust back down into the mantle, where it is remelted. Plate subduction typically occurs where dense oceanic crust and less-dense continental crust slowly collide, forcing the denser oceanic crust to descend beneath the continental crust. Regions of Earth where plate collision and subduction occur are called **subduction zones** (Figure 1.13, right half).

Where rocks of similar density converge (for example, continental crust colliding with other continental crust), simple subduction cannot occur. Instead, it's like sliding two rugs together: both rumple. A zone of intense deformation and mountain building may develop, called a **suture zone** because the two plates become sutured together. Both subduction zones and suture zones are plate boundaries, and they are collectively called **convergent plate boundaries.**

Convergent plate boundaries are zones of dramatic crustal compression. Therefore, they are primarily zones of reverse faulting.

Transform Plate Boundaries

Although crust may be formed at one side of a moving plate and remelted (subducted) at another, there are additional plate boundaries where compensating motions take place without either plate formation or remelting. Two plates simply slide past one another along huge strike-slip faults or transform faults. Such boundaries are called **transform plate boundaries.**

EARTH'S EIGHT MAJOR LITHOSPHERIC PLATES

Eight major lithospheric plates form Earth's rigid outer shell (Figure 1.14). There are a dozen smaller plates, plus some ambiguous regions, but for this exercise we'll limit our attention to the eight major ones. Notice the extent of the Eurasian, Indo-Australian, Pacific, Antarctic, Nazca, South American, North American, and African plates. Also note the kinds of plate boundaries distributed among them (see key at bottom of Figure 1.14). In the following problems, we ask you to evaluate the practicality of the Plate Tectonics Model by examining several interacting plates and boundaries.

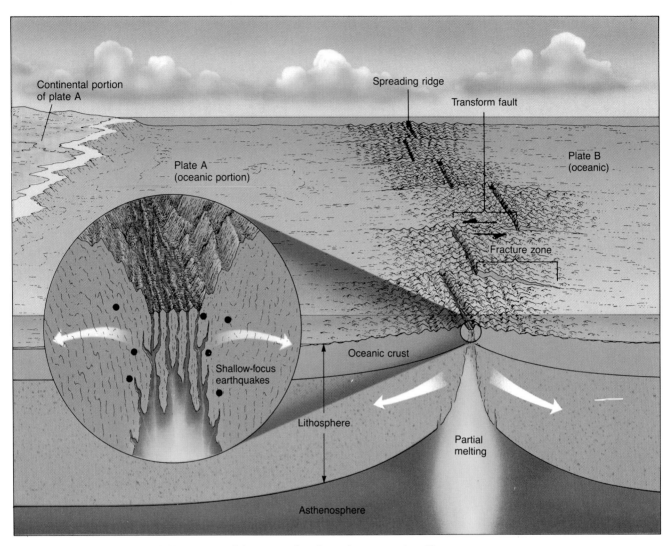

FIGURE 1.13 Hypothetical illustration of features related to plate tectonics. Shown are two different types of continental margins (edges of continents). On the opposite page, the continental margin is called an *active margin* because tectonism (subduction) occurs there. On the left side, the continental margin is called a *passive margin* because no tectonism currently occurs there.

QUESTIONS—PART 2, PLATE TECTONICS

Figure 1.15 is a geologic map of southern California showing the San Andreas Fault. As is well known to all who live on or near it, this active fault zone is marked by frequent earthquakes.

11. What clues tell you how the lithosphere has moved? Draw arrows along opposite sides of the San Andreas Fault to show the relative sense of movement. What type of fault is it?

12. Estimate the average annual rate of movement along the San Andreas Fault. You can do so by recognizing older rocks that have been offset

by the fault. In Figure 1.15, note that Miocene rocks have been offset by the fault. These rocks have been dated as being 25 million years old. What is the average annual rate of fault movement in centimeters per year (cm/yr)? In feet per year (ft/yr)?

13. The average yearly rate of movement on the San Andreas Fault is very small. Does this mean that the residents of southern California have nothing to worry about from this fault? Explain.

14. An average movement of about 5 m (16 ft) along the San Andreas Fault was associated with the 1906 San Francisco earthquake. As-

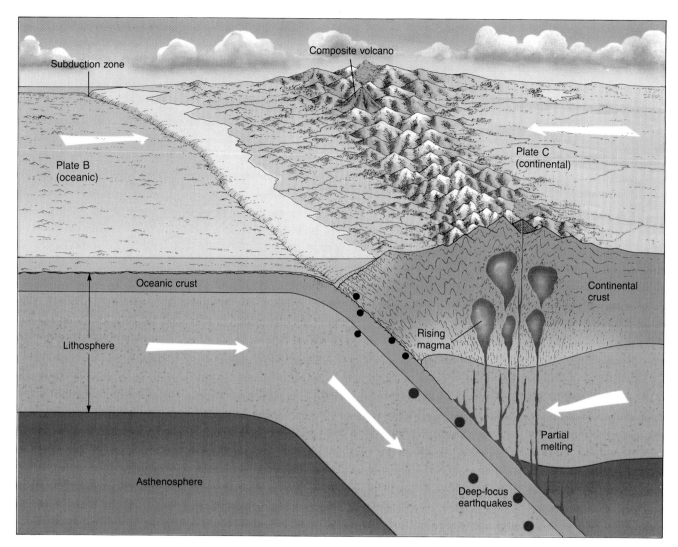

Subduction zone

Composite volcano

Plate B (oceanic)

Plate C (continental)

Oceanic crust

Lithosphere

Continental crust

Rising magma

Asthenosphere

Partial melting

Deep-focus earthquakes

FIGURE 1.13 *(continued)*

suming that all displacement along the fault was produced by Earth motions of this magnitude, how often must such earthquakes have occurred in order to account for the total displacement?

Mantle **plumes** may be important tectonic phenomena. They are believed to result from slowly rotating convection cells in molten material deep in the mantle. On the surface of the lithosphere, they are expressed as "hot spots," or sites of volcanic activity. Plumes may develop beneath plate boundaries or within plates.

As a lithospheric plate migrates across a stationary hot spot, a volcano develops directly above the hot spot. As the plate lumbers on, the volcano

that was over the hot spot becomes dormant, and over time migrates many kilometers from the hot spot. A new volcano arises as new material passes over the hot spot. The result is a string of volcanoes, with one end of the line located over the hot spot and quite active, and the other end distant and inactive. In between is a succession of volcanoes which are progressively older with distance from the hot spot. The Hawaiian Islands are thought to represent such a line of volcanoes.

15. Figure 1.16 shows the distribution of the Hawaiian Islands. The numbers show the age of each island in millions of years, obtained from the basaltic igneous rock of which each island is composed. On the basis of this information,

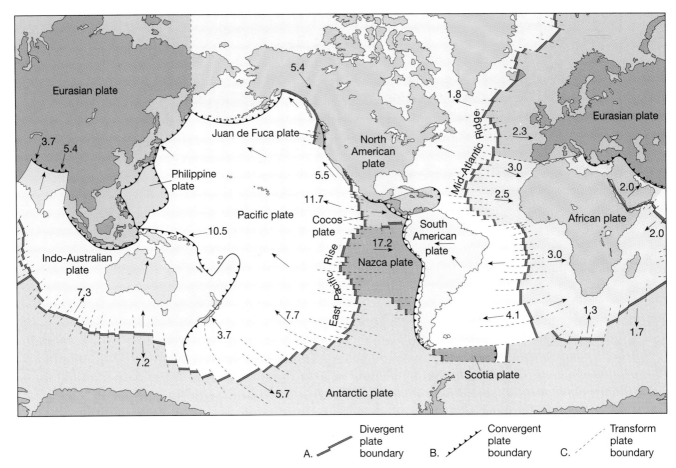

A. ⎯⎯⎯ Divergent plate boundary   B. ⎯⊢⊢⊢⎯ Convergent plate boundary   C. ⎯ ⎯ ⎯ Transform plate boundary

FIGURE 1.14 Earth's lithospheric plates and their boundaries. Numerals indicate the current rate of plate movement in centimeters per year. (Map after Lutgens, F. K., and Tarbuck, E. J., 1986, *Essentials of Geology,* 2d ed., Fig. 1.6, p. 6–7, Columbus: Macmillan Publishing Company; movement rates after McKenzie, D. P., and Richter, F., 1976, *Convection Currents in the Earth's Mantle,* Copyright by Scientific American, Inc.)

what was the average rate in centimeters per year (cm/yr) of plate movement here during the last 4.7 million years? Add this data to Figure 1.14.

16. Now compare the rate and direction of Pacific plate movement through segments of geologic time:

   a. What was the rate and direction of plate motion in the Hawaiian region from 4.7 to 1.6 million years ago?

   b. What was the rate and direction of plate motion from 1.6 million years ago to the present time?

   c. How do the rate and direction of Pacific plate movement during the past 1.6 million years differ from the older rate and direction (4.7–1.6 m.y.) of plate motion?

17. Locate the Hawaiian Island Chain and the Emperor Seamount Chain (submerged volcanic islands) in Figure 1.17.

   a. How are the two island chains related?

   b. Based on the distribution of the two island chains, suggest how the direction of Pacific plate movement has generally changed over the past 60 million years.

   Thousands of earthquakes and volcano-related events occurred on Earth in 1991, and some of the more notable events are indicated on Figure 1.17. Particularly newsworthy were violent earthquakes and the volcanic eruptions of Mt. Unzen in Japan, Mt. Pinatubo in the Philippines, and Kilauea volcano in Hawaii. Less dramatic volcanic eruptions occurred in the United States (Mount St. Helens), Guatemala, and Colombia.

FIGURE 1.15 Generalized geologic map of southern California.

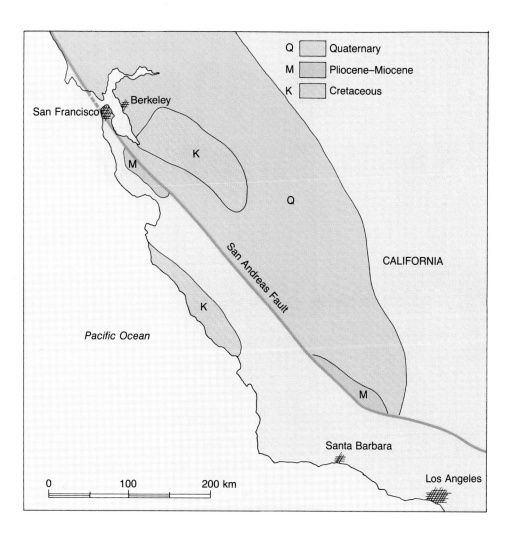

During 1991, geologists used submersibles to observe volcanic eruptions along a segment of the East Pacific Rise, but at least one escaped direct observation. Boulders of pumice (porous volcanic rock that floats, Figure 4.17) were observed floating in the southwest Pacific Ocean near Fiji. The pumice must have formed from an unseen submarine volcanic eruption.

To the geologically uninformed, the events noted on Figure 1.17 may seem unrelated and random. However, many noted the coincidence of events during June: eruptions of Japan's Mt. Unzen and Hawaii's Kilauea volcano, and the June 12 eruption of Mt. Pinatubo in the Philippines, hailed as among the largest eruptions of the century. People were generally curious about the possibility that these events somehow were related. Earthquakes occurred globally throughout June, as they do in all months, but one person was killed on June 28 in an earthquake associated with Cali-

fornia's San Andreas Fault zone, reinforcing the impression of a possible connection.

18. Imagine that you are a geologist who has been asked by a news journalist to comment on earthquakes and volcanic events of 1991. Answer the following questions, and be prepared to discuss them with other class members:
   a. Many geologic events of 1991 made news headlines. Were the events related? Briefly explain your answer.
   b. The geologic events of June, 1991 were particularly newsworthy. Is it likely, from your reasoning as a geologist, that those events signal the impending cataclysmic end of Earth? Briefly explain your answer.

Geologist Peter Rona published a series of articles in the 1970s suggesting that the Plate Tectonics Model can be used to explain the distribution of

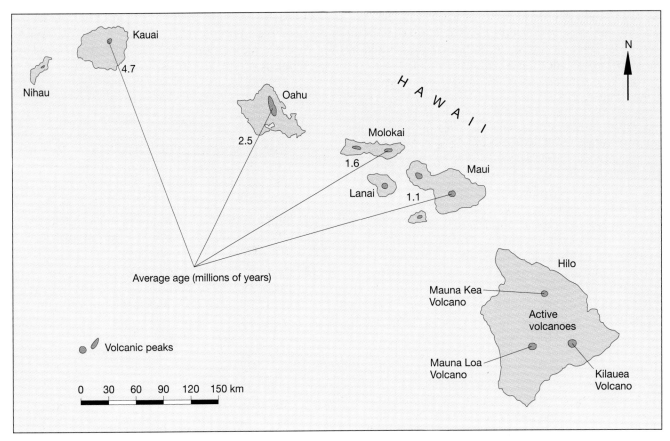

FIGURE 1.16 Map of the Hawaiian Islands, showing volcanic peaks. Absolute ages were determined from basalts that form the islands.

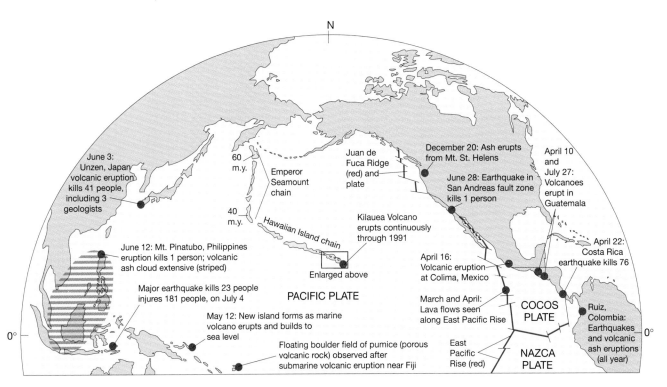

FIGURE 1.17 Northern Pacific Ocean and adjacent land areas, showing 1991's notable volcanic and earthquake events. Events adapted from *Geotimes*, reports of geologic phenomena (1991–1992).

some mineral deposits. If this is true, then the model might be used to predict where new mineral deposits could be found. An often-cited example of the possible relation between plate tectonics and mineral occurrences is in the central Andes Mountains (Figure 1.18).

According to the Plate Tectonics Model, the Andes currently are forming as a result of Nazca plate subduction. The position of the subducting plate is known from earthquake data, as earthquakes occur along and above subducting plates. As the plate descends, it melts from the intense heat and pressure, and the molten rock (magma) rises to form a volcanic mountain range.

Note that the volcanoes form over the point where the subducting plate is about 150 km deep. An adjacent folded range to the east also has developed in response to compressional forces associated with the rising magma and plate subduction. Note how the four belts of metal occurrences are distributed in Figure 1.18.

Now examine the map of Washington State in Figure 1.19, which shows locations of metal deposits, volcanoes, and a vertical cross-section *Y–Y'*. The volcanoes are part of the Cascade Range and are the result of magma rising upward from the subducting and melting Juan de Fuca plate (JFP).

19. Based on the Andean example in Figure 1.18, where melting occurs 150 km below the volcanic range, sketch the position of the subducting JFP in cross-section *Y–Y'*. How does the Cascade Range subduction zone seem to differ from the central Andes subduction zone?

20. Try to plot the position of Cascade Range metal belts on the cross-section in Figure 1.19 (analogous to the way it was done in Figure 1.18). Suggest how the distribution of metals in the Cascade Range is the same as the distribution of metals in the Andes Mountains.

21. Suggest how the distribution of metals in the Cascade Range is different from the distribution of metals in the Andes.

22. Based on your understanding of the plate tectonics and metal occurrences of the Washington region, what kind of metals would you expect to find:
    a. On Vancouver Island, Canada?
    b. On the Yakima Indian Reservation?
    c. Under the Columbia River basalt plateau around point *Y'*?

23. How practical is the Plate Tectonics Model for explaining geologic events and relationships on Earth?

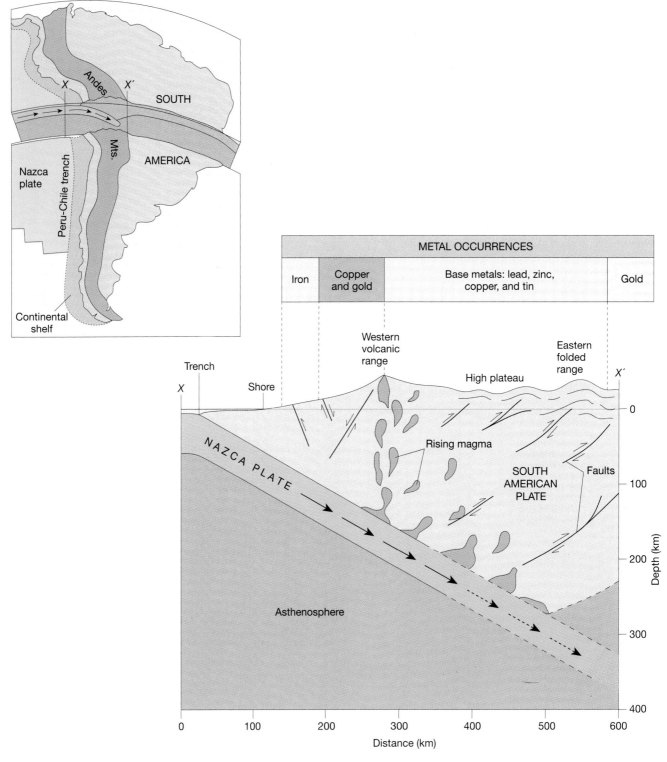

FIGURE 1.18 Geologic cross section showing plate subduction, mountain building, and metal occurrences in the central Andes Mountains of South America. (Metal occurrences after Rona, P., 1973, *Scientific American*, 229(1):86–95)

FIGURE 1.19 Map of Washington State showing mineral resource occurrences, section line *Y–Y'*, and grid for a geologic cross section of the subduction zone developed beneath line *Y–Y'*. (Mineral resource occurrences after Moen, W. S., 1986, *Mineral Resource Maps of Washington*, Olympia: Washington State Department of Natural Resources, Division of Geology and Earth Resources, GM–22).

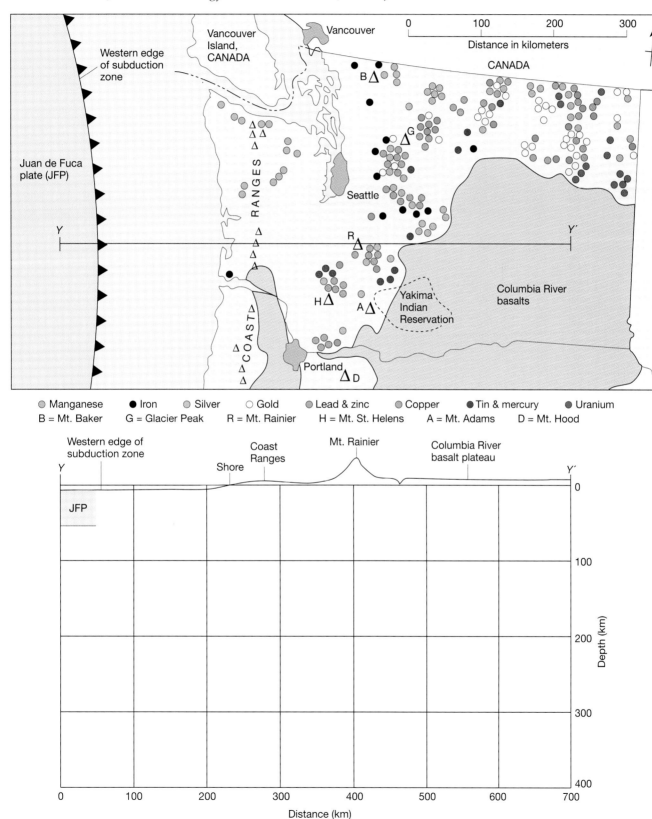

EXERCISE TWO

Mineral Properties, Uses, and Identification

Jane L. Boger
Philip D. Boger
SUNY, College at Geneseo

Charles I. Frye
Northwest Missouri State University

Michael F. Hochella, Jr.
Stanford University

PURPOSE

People use many different minerals in different ways, because of their beneficial properties. Some minerals are used in their natural forms. Others are industrially *refined,* or separated, into their constituent elements. The most commonly refined mineral compounds are the ores of metals. For example, the metal lead is refined from the mineral galena (lead sulfide) by separating the lead from the sulfur. Indeed, we use so many minerals and mineral products daily that you would have difficulty listing them all!

Some minerals can produce adverse effects upon people's lives. For example, refining of sulfide minerals (such as refining galena for lead) may release large amounts of sulfur into the atmosphere. There it can combine with rainwater to form sulfuric acid, creating a type of acid rain that deteriorates Earth materials and disrupts the life cycles of organisms. The burning of coal that contains sulfate minerals has a similar result.

This exercise presents systematic procedures for identifying minerals by their physical properties. Your ability to determine these properties by careful *observation* and *testing* is more important than merely being able to recognize and name minerals. Later exercises will show how *minerals* combine to form *rocks.* Thus it is essential for you to learn the common minerals and their properties so that you will be able to complete the rock identification exercises.

MATERIALS

Pencil, eraser, steel knife or steel masonry nail, wire nail, glass plate, streak plate, copper penny, small magnet, dilute (1–3%) hydrochloric acid (HCl) in a dropper bottle, and mineral samples provided by your instructor.

INTRODUCTION

A **mineral** is a naturally occurring, inorganic substance with crystalline structure, a characteristic chemical composition, and characteristic physical properties. Crystalline structure refers to an orderly, predictable arrangement, or pattern, of the atoms in a substance (Figure 2.13). Substances possessing crystalline structure are called **crystals.** Chemical composition and crystalline structure determine the physical properties of a mineral: its color, hardness, shape, feel, and how it reflects or refracts light. Different minerals therefore have different properties, and these can be used to distinguish one mineral from another.

A **mineraloid** is a naturally occurring, inorganic substance with a characteristic chemical composition and physical properties. However, mineraloids lack crystalline structure (i.e., they are amorphous). For example, opal (Figure 2.23) and limonite (Figure 2.24) are mineraloids. Some common minerals and mineraloids are shown in Figures 2.1 through 2.25.

MINERAL PROPERTIES

Crystal form is the external, geometrical appearance of a perfectly formed crystal. The flat external surfaces of the crystal are called *crystal faces* (Figures 2.1, 2.2, 2.3). Individual crystals that are perfectly bounded by all of their natural faces are

FIGURE 2.2 Amethyst quartz. This quartz variety has a violet-to-purple color caused by small amounts of *ferric iron* as an impurity. These crystals formed in a very large bubble of gas trapped within a solidifying body of molten rock material (magma) inside Earth. The amethyst formed secondary crystals on top of primary crystals of transparent-to-milky quartz.

FIGURE 2.1 Quartz crystals. Because quartz consists of the two most abundant elements of Earth's crust, silicon (Si) and oxygen (O), it is one of the most common minerals in the crust. Angles between crystal faces of individual quartz crystals are always the same.

called *euhedral* crystals, and are rare. Mineral grains that exhibit some of their natural faces are called *subhedral* crystals, and are common. Some mineral grains do not exhibit any of their natural crystal faces (i.e., they lack external crystal form), and are called *anhedral* crystals.

Color of a mineral, usually its most noticeable property, may be one of the least-accurate diagnostics in mineral identification. For example, quartz can be colorless (Figure 2.1), violet (Figure 2.2), white (Figure 2.4), rose (Figure 2.5), gray, blue, green, red, yellow, brown, and more. However, most minerals do have a typical color that can be used as a clue in identification. For example, the majority of quartz specimens are colorless, white, or gray. The color of a mineral also may be a clue to its chemical composition.

Streak is the color of a mineral after it has been ground to a fine powder. The easiest way to do this is simply to scratch the mineral across the surface of a square of unglazed porcelain (called a *streak plate*). Then, blow away the excess powder and broken fragments. The color of the powder remaining on the plate is the streak (Figure 2.7).

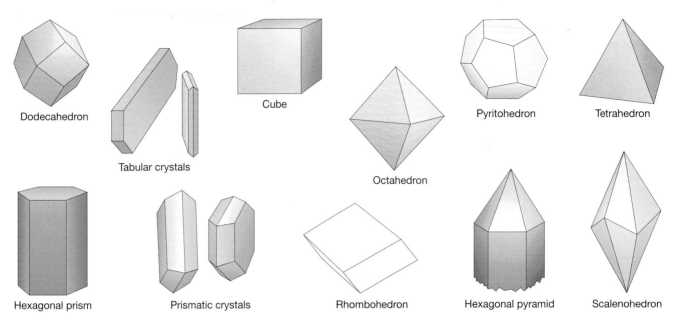

Dodecahedron

Tabular crystals

Cube

Octahedron

Pyritohedron

Tetrahedron

Hexagonal prism

Prismatic crystals

Rhombohedron

Hexagonal pyramid

Scalenohedron

FIGURE 2.3 Some external forms of mineral crystals.

FIGURE 2.4 Milky quartz. This quartz variety forms when quartz contains microscopic fluid inclusions, commonly water. The sample displays essentially no crystal faces, because many crystals developed simultaneously in a crowded area, resulting in this "massive" form. Note the greasy luster of the fracture surfaces.

FIGURE 2.5 Rose quartz. This quartz variety is rose-to-pink because it contains small amounts of the element *titanium* as an impurity. Rose quartz generally occurs in massive form like this example.

FIGURE 2.6 Agate. This quartz variety may contain chert (white to gray), opal (any color), flint (black), jasper (yellow, brown, red), or chalcedony (any color) in alternating bands, blotches, stripes, or mosslike patterns. It is commonly found lining fractures and solution cavities in the bedrock of arid regions.

FIGURE 2.7 Hematite. This mineral is an oxide of iron that takes several forms. Hematite always has a characteristic red-brown *streak* (its color in powdered form) as shown here for four samples of hematite having different lusters and textures. (Photo by R. Busch)

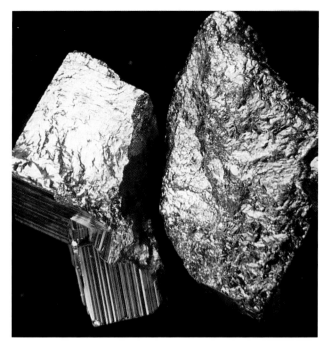

FIGURE 2.8 Pyrite (left) and chalcopyrite (right). Both of these iron sulfide minerals are informally known as "fool's gold" because they are pale brassy-yellow and have a metallic luster. Pyrite often has striated crystal faces, but not always. It lacks the iridescent play of colors so typical of chalcopyrite. (Compare to the unstriated pyrite crystals in Figure 2.25.) (Photo by R. Busch)

Streak color is representative of a mineral's true color, which often is different from the apparent color of an unground specimen.

Luster is the manner in which the surface of a substance reflects light. Terms used to describe luster include earthy (like concrete), glossy (like auto paint), metallic (like silver, gold, or copper), pearly (like a pearl), greasy (like grease), waxy (like a candle), and vitreous (like glass). Sphalerite (Figure 2.9) has metallic luster only when viewed in certain directions, so its luster is described as submetallic.

Cleavage planes are flat surfaces along which some crystalline substances break because of weakness in their crystalline structure. That is, they are parallel surfaces of weak chemical bonding (attraction) between repeating, parallel layers of atoms in the crystal. Each different set of parallel cleavage planes has an orientation relative to the crystalline structure, and is referred to as a *cleavage direction* (Figure 2.10). For example, muscovite mica (Figure 2.12) has one cleavage direction. Galena (Figure 2.11) and halite (Figure 2.14) have three prominent cleavage directions developed at right angles to

FIGURE 2.9 Sphalerite. This mineral is zinc sulfide, and it is commonly mined as zinc ore. Sphalerite has a characteristic luster called submetallic, as in the sample shown. It also has dodecahedral cleavage (see Figure 2.10), a white-to-yellow-brown streak, and is commonly yellow, red, brown, or black.

one another, so they break either into cubes (cubic cleavage), or into fragments that have sides at right angles to one another. Other common cleavage patterns are described in Figure 2.10.

A mineral with *good cleavage* reflects light from very obvious, parallel flat surfaces that are extensive on large crystals:

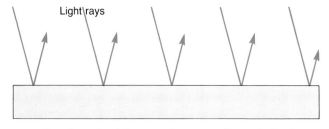

A mineral with *poor cleavage* reflects light from many flat, parallel surfaces that are not so obvious because the flat surfaces are relatively small:

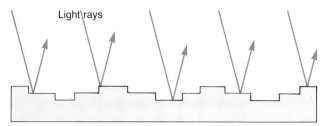

Fracture surfaces are nonplanar, nonparallel surfaces along which minerals and other substances may break in addition to cleavage, or in the absence of cleavage. Quartz and volcanic glass are examples of materials that fracture and lack cleavage. They break along smoothly curved surfaces called *conchoidal fractures*. "Splintery" (like wood) and "irregular" (like concrete) are other terms that describe the fracture appearance of particular minerals. Unlike cleavage surfaces, fracture surfaces reflect light in many different directions:

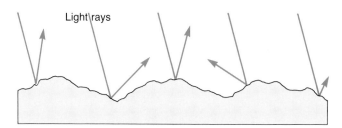

Feldspar is a mineral that has both cleavage and fracture (Figures 2.20, 2.21, 2.22). It has two directions of cleavage at nearly right angles, plus a fracture direction.

Striations are straight "hairline" grooves on the cleavage faces of some minerals. This can be helpful in mineral identification. For example, we will use the striations of plagioclase feldspar to distinguish it from potassium feldspar:

Plagioclase feldspars (Figures 2.20, 2.22) have striations, which appear as straight parallel lines or grooves on the faces of one cleavage direction, and which are parallel to the faces of the second cleavage direction.

Potassium feldspars (Figures 2.21, 2.22) may have lines on their surfaces that resemble striations. However, these are thin, discontinuous, subparallel lamellae (thin, discontinuous layers) of plagioclase, called exsolution lamellae.

Tenacity is the manner in which a substance resists breakage. Terms such as brittle (like glass), malleable (like modeling clay), flexible (like a plastic comb), and elastic (like a rubber band) are all used to describe tenacity.

Reaction to acid differs among minerals. Cool, dilute (1–3%) hydrochloric acid (HCl) applied from a dropper bottle is a common "acid test." Many carbonate minerals such as calcite (Figure 2.15) will effervesce ("fizz") when a drop of such dilute HCl is applied to a freshly exposed surface. Another carbonate mineral, dolomite, appears al-

Number of Cleavage Directions	Shapes that Crystal Breaks Into	Sketch	Ilustration of Cleavage Directions
0 No cleavage, only fracture	Irregular masses with no flat surfaces	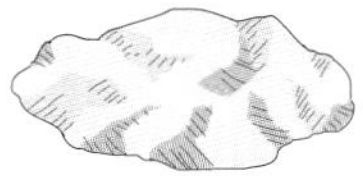	None
1	"Books" that split apart along flat sheets	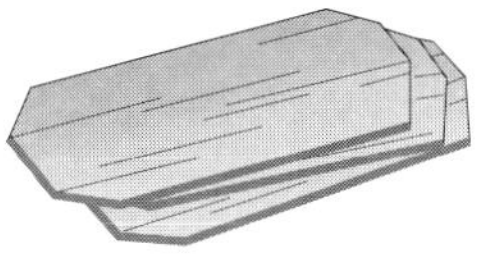	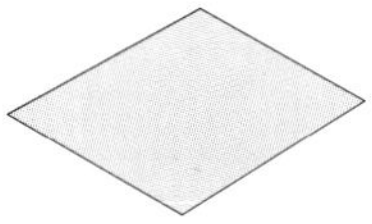
2 at 90°	Elongated form with rectangular cross sections (prisms) and parts of such forms	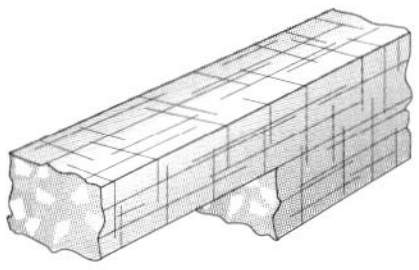	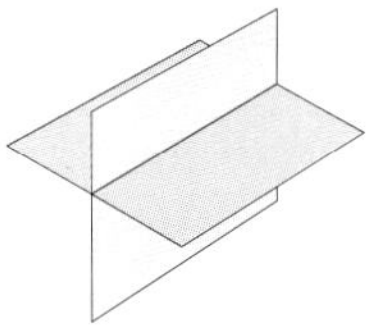
2 not at 90°	Elongated form with parallelogram cross sections (prisms) and parts of such forms	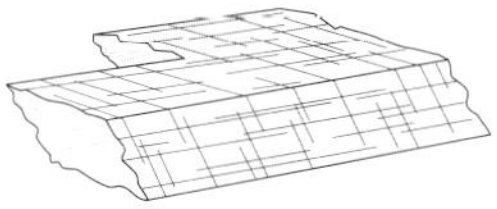	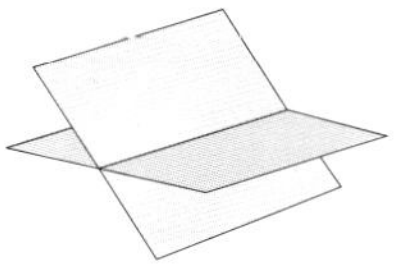
3 at 90°	Shapes made of cubes and parts of cubes	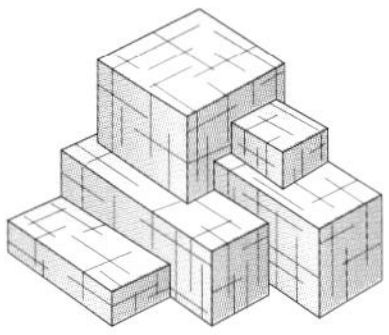	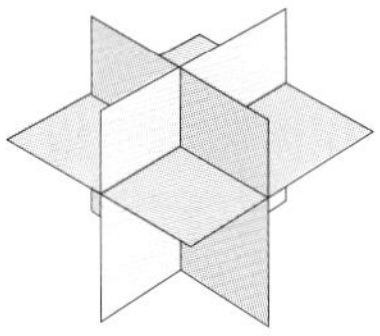
3 not at 90°	Shapes made of rhombohedrons and parts of rhombohedrons	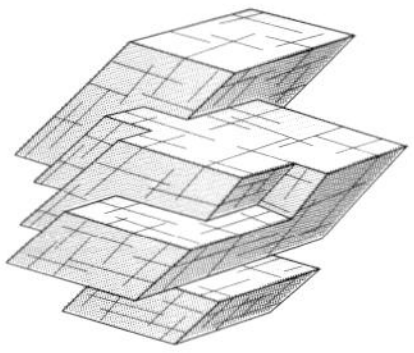	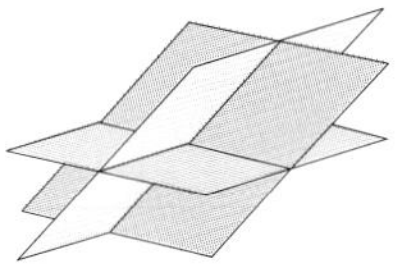
4	Shapes made of octahedrons and parts of octahedrons	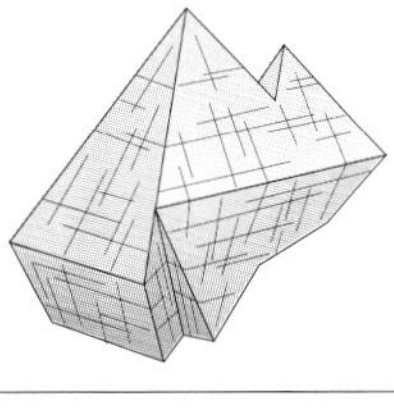	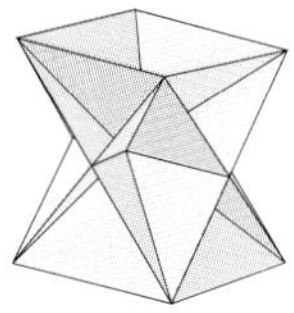
6	Shapes made of dodecahedrons and parts of dodecahedrons	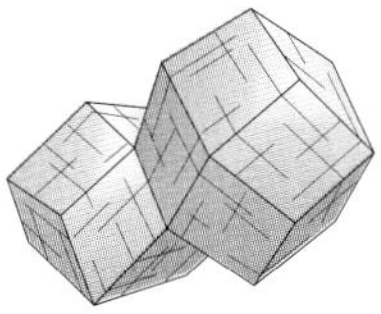	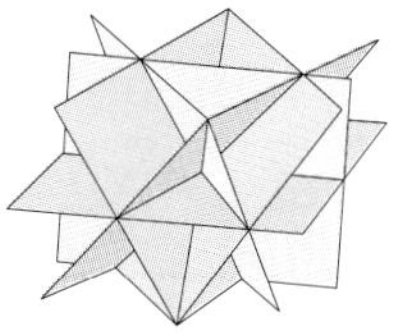

FIGURE 2.10 Common *cleavage patterns* of minerals, which cause minerals to break into preferred shapes.

most identical to calcite, but it will effervesce in dilute HCl only if the mineral is first powdered. (It can be powdered for this test by simply scratching the mineral's surface with the tip of a rock pick or pocket knife.) If HCl is not available, undiluted vinegar can be used for the acid test, for it contains acetic acid.

Magnetism is exhibited by some minerals, such as magnetite. The test is simple: magnetite is attracted to a magnet. Lodestone is a variety of magnetite that is itself a natural magnet. It will attract steel paperclips.

Double refraction occurs when light passes through the crystalline structure of some minerals.

The light is refracted (bent) into two rays, so that a double image is produced. Clear calcite displays excellent double refraction (Figure 2.15).

Specific gravity (SG) is the ratio of the weight of a substance to the weight of an equal volume of water. For example, the mineral quartz (SG = 2.65) is 2.65 times heavier than an equal volume of water. *Hefting* is an easy way to judge the specific gravity of one mineral relative to another. This is done by holding a piece of the first mineral in one hand and holding an equal-sized piece of the second mineral in your other hand. Feel the difference in weight between the two samples (i.e., heft the samples). The sample that feels heavier has a higher specific gravity than the other. Most metallic minerals have higher specific gravities than nonmetallic minerals.

Hardness (H) is a measure of resistance to scratching. A harder substance will scratch a softer one. A German mineralogist, Friedrich Mohs (1773–1839), developed a quantitative scale of mineral hardness on which the softest mineral (talc) has a hardness of 1 and the hardest mineral (diamond) has a hardness of 10. Higher-numbered minerals will scratch lower-numbered minerals (e.g., diamond will scratch talc, but talc cannot scratch diamond). *Mohs Scale of Hardness* (Figure

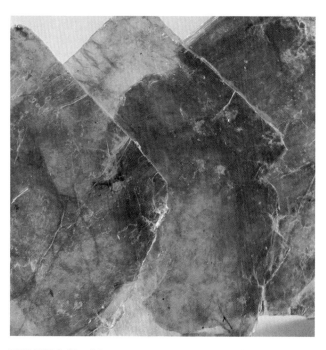

FIGURE 2.12 Muscovite mica. Micas are aluminum silicate minerals which form stout crystals that split easily into paper-thin, flexible sheets, parallel to the flat base of the crystals. This splitting is called *basal cleavage*. Muscovite is a light-colored, silvery-brown mica, in contrast to biotite mica, which is black.

2.26) is now widely used by geologists and engineers.

There are many other properties of minerals that we have not described here. Keep this in mind as you continue this exercise, so that you can increase your understanding of mineral identification and uses. Refer to Figures 2.13–2.26 before you proceed.

MINERAL IDENTIFICATION

The ability to identify minerals is one of the most fundamental skills of an Earth scientist. It also is fundamental to identifying rocks, for you must first identify the minerals composing them. Only after minerals and rocks have been identified can their origin, classification, and alteration be adequately understood.

To identify a mineral, you must first list as many of its properties as you can determine, using available tools and your senses. Then, identify the mineral using the mineral identification tables (Figures 2.27, 2.28) or flow charts (Figures 2.29, 2.30).

Use this procedure for each mineral:

FIGURE 2.11 Galena is lead sulfide, so it has a notably high specific gravity. It forms cubic crystals, has cubic cleavage (see Figure 2.10), and its metallic luster resembles that of lead, for which galena is an ore.

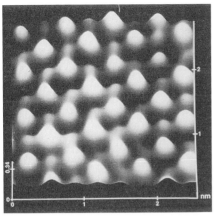

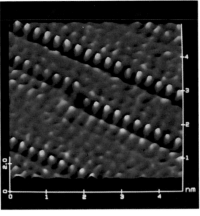

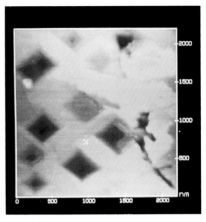

A. Galena   B. Hematite   C. Calcite

FIGURE 2.13 *Atomic-resolution images* of galena, hematite, and calcite. Scales are in nanometers (nm). There are 1000 nanometers in 1 micron, and 1000 microns in 1 millimeter, so 1 nanometer is 1 millionth of a millimeter (or 1 billionth of a meter). (Images courtesy of Stanford University)

A. Scanning tunneling microscope (STM) image of galena (PbS), tilted back 30° to give better perspective. High bumps are electrons tunneling from sulfur atoms, and low bumps represent fewer electrons tunneling from the individual lead atoms. Nevertheless, the surface is atomically flat. Each *sulfur* atom is bonded to four lead atoms in the image, plus another lead atom beneath it. Similarly, each *lead* atom is bonded to four sulfur atoms in the image, plus a sulfur atom beneath it. (Image collected by C. M. Eggleston, Stanford University)

B. STM image of hematite (Fe_2O_3) fracture surface, also tilted back 30° for perspective. Because of the conditions under which electrons were tunneled onto the surface, only the oxygen atoms (and not the iron atoms) are visible in the image. The blue bumps represent oxygen atoms on atomically flat surfaces. The pink bumps highlight oxygen atoms located at the edges of steps that are one atom high. (Image collected by C. M. Eggleston, Stanford University)

C. Scanning force microscope (SFM) image of a surface of calcite ($CaCO_3$). It has been immersed in water and partly dissolved by hydrolysis, a decomposition reaction involving water. This image is not tilted and was collected from a relatively large area; however, the vertical scale is small. The highest point on the image (lightest color) is only about 15 nm above the lowest point (darkest color). The two markers on the image are on the top and bottom of a step that is only one atom high. (Image collected by M. F. Hochella, Jr., Stanford University)

A. Separate metallic from nonmetallic minerals. If you are uncertain about a mineral's luster, then it is probably nonmetallic.

B. For the *metallic* minerals, determine:
  1. hardness
  2. color
  3. cleavage qualities, quantities, and angles between cleavage directions
  4. streak
  5. other properties as needed
  6. name from Figure 2.27

C. For the *nonmetallic* minerals:
  1. separate light from dark colors
  2. determine hardness
  3. determine cleavage qualities, quantities, and angles between cleavage directions
  4. determine streak
  5. determine other properties as needed
  6. determine name from Figure 2.28

Mineral tables and flow charts are extremely helpful, but they are cumbersome in the field, and their use is time consuming. Therefore, the ability to identify common minerals without tables and charts is an important asset to the field-oriented Earth scientist.

FIGURE 2.16 Fluorite is calcium fluoride. It commonly forms cubic crystals that are purple, blue, yellow, green, or colorless. Fluorite has very well-developed octahedral cleavage, as shown (see Figure 2.10). Its common crystal form is a cube (Figure 2.3). (Photo by R. Busch)

FIGURE 2.14 Halite has a characteristic cubic cleavage, meaning that it breaks into cubes (blocks) or pieces with numerous flat surfaces that are all perpendicular to one another (see Figure 2.10). Halite is common table salt.

FIGURE 2.15 Calcite has a characteristic rhombohedral cleavage (see Figure 2.10), meaning that it breaks into rhombohedra (leaning blocks) or shapes composed of rhombohedra. Also note the golden colored crystal of calcite (lower left) that is easily scratched by an iron nail; it exhibits external crystal faces rather than cleavage surfaces. Calcite is a carbonate mineral that *effervesces* (fizzes) in dilute, cool hydrochloric acid (HCl) squeezed from a dropper bottle (upper left). It also exhibits double refraction; note how the X behind the top-center sample appears as two overlapping letters. Calcite is the chief mineral in the rocks limestone and marble. (Photo by R. Busch)

FIGURE 2.17 Garnet is a hard mineral (H = 6.5–7.5). It is used as an abrasive (in garnet paper, a form of sandpaper) and as a gemstone. It is commonly red, black, or green, but its streak is white. Garnet is brittle and has no cleavage, instead commonly breaking along slightly curved, subparallel surfaces called *parting surfaces* (as in this sample showing the broken end of a large crystal).

FIGURE 2.18   Augite pyroxene. Pyroxenes are a group of complex silicates. Because they contain some proportion of iron (Fe) and magnesium (Mg), they are *ferromagnesian silicates*. Augite is a pyroxene containing both iron and magnesium. It forms short, stout crystals which are dark green to black and have a pearly luster. Augite also has two prominent cleavage directions, which intersect at 87° and 93° and are difficult to detect in hand samples.

FIGURE 2.19   Hornblende amphibole. Amphiboles are another group of complex silicates containing some proportion of iron (Fe) and magnesium (Mg), so they too are *ferromagnesian silicates*. Hornblende is generally green to black and has two prominent cleavage directions, intersecting at 56° and 124°.

FIGURE 2.20   Albite feldspar. Albite is a sodium plagioclase feldspar. Like other feldspars, it has two obvious directions of cleavage, one of which has parallel, closely spaced *hairline striations* (also see Figure 2.22). The striations are caused by twinning, which is the intergrowth of symmetrically paired microcrystalline portions of the large crystal. Albite is usually colorless, white, or gray.

FIGURE 2.21   Microcline feldspar. Microcline is a potassium-rich feldspar (or "K-spar"), so it is commonly pink or red. However, green-to-blue-green microcline is encountered, and is called amazonite. Like other feldspars, microcline has two obvious cleavage directions (also see Figure 2.10). It typically contains thin, discontinuous, subparallel lamellae of plagioclase feldspar, called *exsolution lamellae*. They are visible on the front cleavage surface of this sample.

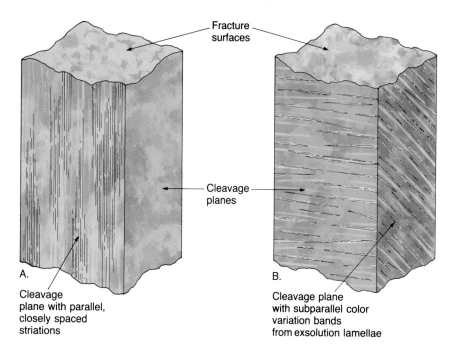

FIGURE 2.22 Common feldspars and rock.
A. This piece of plagioclase feldspar crystal shows *hairline striations* on a cleavage surface. These striations are caused by *twinning*. Twinning occurs when microscopic intergrowths develop between symmetrically paired microcrystalline portions of the larger crystal. The striations occur only along one of the two cleavage directions.
B. This piece of potassium feldspar (K-spar) crystal shows intergrowths of thin, discontinuous, subparallel lamellae of plagioclase, called *exsolution lamellae*. Such texture is called *perthitic* texture.
C. This hand specimen formed as an aggregate of intergrown plagioclase mineral crystals. Individual mineral crystals are discernible within the rock, particularly the cleavage surfaces of plagioclase with their characteristic hairline striations.

FIGURE 2.23 Opal is a *mineraloid*, a mixture of quartz molecules and water molecules that forms massive opal without crystalline structure. Opal has a characteristic conchoidal fracture, waxy luster, and low specific gravity. It also can have a play of colors, called *opalescence,* in which case it is called "precious opal." The opal shown formed on brown rock, and it has been fractured throughout.

FIGURE 2.24 Limonite is an amorphous, hydrous oxide of iron (mineraloid), commonly known as the "rust" that forms on iron objects. It generally forms earthy masses, although it also may replace iron-bearing minerals that are in contact with air (containing oxygen).

FIGURE 2.25 Pyrite crystals and limonite pseudomorphs after pyrite.

QUESTIONS

1. Examine Figures 2.1 and 2.2 (or laboratory examples, if available). How many crystal faces form the end (terminus) of each quartz crystal? What kind of crystal form is it (See Figure 2.3)?

Mohs Scale of Hardness	Hardness of Some Common Objects
10 DIAMOND	
9 CORUNDUM	
8 TOPAZ	
7 QUARTZ	
6 ORTHOCLASE	
	5.5 Glass, steel knife, masonry nail
5 APATITE	
	4.5 Wire nail
4 FLUORITE	
	3.5 Copper penny
3 CALCITE	
	2.5 Fingernail
2 GYPSUM	
1 TALC	

FIGURE 2.26 Mohs Scale of Hardness and the hardness of some common objects.

2. Biotite mica and muscovite mica have the same crystalline structure. (Examine laboratory samples of both, if available.)
   a. Why are they different materials?
   b. What physical properties distinguish biotite from muscovite?

3. Other than the properties already discussed in this exercise, name two properties of halite that can be used to distinguish it from colorless calcite. (Examine laboratory samples of both, if available.)

4. What products in your house or dormitory might be made from these minerals? (Examine laboratory samples of them, if available. Also refer to Figure 2.31 as needed for information about the uses of some common minerals.)
   a. muscovite
   b. gypsum
   c. hematite, magnetite, or limonite
   d. graphite
   e. galena
   f. feldspar
   g. garnet
   h. talc

5. Which property is more reliable in mineral identification, color or streak? Why?

6. Both magnetite and pyrite can be ores for iron. Based upon their chemical composition, which

one of these minerals would you choose for this purpose? Why?

7. Describe the chemical changes that take place to form limonite pseudomorphs after pyrite (Figure 2.25). (Examine laboratory samples, if available.)

8. Why are so many minerals pseudomorphic after the mineral halite?

9. Imagine that you have found a large vein of white calcite in a quarry that mines limestone (a type of rock composed of calcite).
   a. Why is the calcite white?
   b. Describe how the white calcite formed at that location. (Hint: normal rainwater is a weak acid.)

10. What kind(s) of crystal form do the pyrite crystals and limonite pseudomorphs have in Figure 2.25? (Also see Figure 2.3.)

11. Obtain a set of minerals from your instructor, if available. Identify each of the minerals using the information provided in this exercise.

ATOMIC-RESOLUTION MINERALOGY

Two modern technologies now allow mineralogists to obtain images of the atoms and atomic structures of minerals and other Earth materials. These new technologies are described here, along with images of three minerals for you to interpret.

Scanning tunneling microscopy (STM) was invented in IBM's laboratory at Zurich, Switzerland, between 1979 and 1981 by Gerd Binnig and Henrich Rohrer. This revolutionary discovery earned Binnig and Rohrer the Nobel Prize in physics in 1986.

STM works by scanning a sharp metal tip over the surface of a sample. If the sample can conduct electricity and the tip is brought to within a few atomic diameters of the surface, then applying a small voltage allows electrons to "tunnel" across this extremely small gap. Most tunneling electrons are exchanged only between the last atom on the end of the tip and the first atom on the sample surface directly beneath it. As the tip scans over the surface, the variation in tunneling current is measured, in effect mapping the position of each atom (Figure 2.13A).

In most cases, however, not all surface atoms contribute to the image. Atoms that contribute to tunneling depend on the applied voltage and their exact electronic structure (Figure 2.13B). At atomic resolution, images are most easily interpreted when the surface composition is known and the types of chemical bonds are understood. At lower resolution (larger scan areas), surface shape can be mapped precisely by requiring a constant tunneling current between the tip and sample. This keeps the gap constant. The image then is formed by the up-and-down motion of the tip as it scans over the surface.

Scanning force microscopy (SFM), also called atomic force microscopy (AFM), is a direct descendant from STM technology. It was first built and used in 1985 by Gerd Binnig and Calvin Quate, respectively of IBM and Stanford University. SFM is similar to STM, except the image is produced by moving the sample laterally under a hard, sharp tip that is free to move up and down.

Unlike STM, the tip is in actual physical contact with the surface. However, the force holding it down is approximately a billion times less than the force used to hold a stylus against a phonographic record. These extremely light tracking forces keep the sharp tip from damaging the surface. The motion of the tip usually is measured by an optical laser system that is sensitive to movement on the atomic scale. Consequently, images with nearly atomic resolution can be obtained. Because this type of microscopy does not require electrical current, insulating surfaces can be imaged as well as those that are conducting (Figure 2.13C).

STM and SFM have become important tools for studying mineral growth and breakdown. Atomic structure and bonding can be studied (Figures 2.13A, 2.13B), along with minute surface topographic features (Figures 2.13B, 2.13C). Structure, bonding, and topography determine what may or may not adsorb to a mineral (this is the process by which ions in water attach to a mineral's surface). If the attachment reaction is strong, the attracted ions may be effectively removed from solution. Or, if attachment is weak, they may stay in solution. These processes are extremely important in water purification. They also may be important in ore deposit formation and hazardous waste migration.

ADDITIONAL QUESTIONS

12. In Figure 2.13A, what is the approximate distance between sulfur and lead atoms? (Note that this is the length of the sulfur-lead atomic bond.)

METALLIC MINERALS			
Hardness	Streak	Other Properties	Mineral
Not scratched by steel nail or knife — 6.5–6	Dark gray	brass yellow, may tarnish brown; brittle, no cleavage, cubic crystals common, S.G. = 5.0.	PYRITE ("fool's gold") FeS_2 iron sulfide
6.5–6	Dark gray	pale brass yellow to whitish gold; brittle, no cleavage, radiating masses and "cockscombs," S.G. = 4.9.	MARCASITE FeS_2 iron sulfide
6	Dark gray	dark gray to black; magnetic, no obvious cleavage, S.G. = 5.2.	MAGNETITE Fe_3O_4 iron oxide
6.5–5	Red to red-brown	silver to gray, may be tiny glittery flakes, may tarnish red, S.G. = 4.9–5.3.	HEMATITE Fe_2O_3 iron oxide
Scratched by steel nail or knife — 5.5–5	Yellow-brown	dark brown to black, in radiating layers, S.G. = 4.3.	GOETHITE FeO(OH) hydrous iron oxide
5.5–5	Yellow-brown	yellow-brown to dark brown; amorphous, but may be pseudomorphic after pyrite, S.G. = 4.1–4.3.	LIMONITE $Fe_2O_3 \cdot nH_2O$ hydrous iron oxide
Scratched by wire nail — 4–3.5	Dark gray	golden yellow, may tarnish purple; brittle, no cleavage, S.G. = 4.1–4.3.	CHALCOPYRITE $CuFeS_2$ copper-iron sulfide
4–3.5	White to yellow-brown	brown to yellow, or black; submetallic, dodecahedral cleavage, S.G. = 3.9–4.0.	SPHALERITE ZnS zinc oxide
Scratched by penny — 3–2.5	Copper	copper to dark brown, may oxidize green; malleable, S.G. = 8.8–8.9.	NATIVE COPPER Cu copper
2.5	Gray to dark gray	silvery gray, tarnishes dull gray; cubic cleavage, not scratched by fingernail, S.G. = 7.4–7.6.	GALENA PbS lead sulfide
Scratched by fingernail — 1	Dark gray	gray to black, marks paper easily; greasy feel, S.G. = 2.1–2.3.	GRAPHITE C carbon

FIGURE 2.27 Characteristics of metallic minerals. SG = specific gravity.

13. In Figure 2.13B, why might the oxygens at the step edges produce different height bumps in the STM image than oxygens on the terraces?

14. Cleavage or parting planes on mineral surfaces often look perfectly flat to the unaided eye.

How do you think they look on the nanometer scale (e.g., Figure 2.13A, 2.13B)?

15. What features in Figure 2.13C show that this mineral surface has been dissolving?

NONMETALLIC MINERALS				
	Hardness	Streak	Other Properties	Mineral
Not scratched by steel nail, knife	9	White	gray, red, brown, blue; greasy luster, commonly in six-sided crystals with striated flat ends; no cleavage, S.G. = 3.9–4.1.	CORUNDUM Al_2O_3 aluminum oxide
	8	White	colorless, yellow, blue, or brown; one perfect cleavage, crystal faces often striated, S.G. = 3.5–3.6.	TOPAZ $Al_2SiO_4(OH,F)_2$ hydrous fluoro-aluminum silicate
	7.5–7	White	green, yellow, pink, blue, brown, or black slender crystals with rounded triangular cross sections; striated crystal faces, no cleavage, S.G. = 3.0–3.2.	TOURMALINE complex silicate
	7	White	any color to colorless, transparent to translucent, greasy luster, no cleavage, conchoidal fracture, S.G. = 2.7.	QUARTZ SiO_2 silicon dioxide
	7	White	white, light colors; waxy luster, translucent, often banded masses, cryptocrystalline, S.G. = 2.5–2.8.	CHALCEDONY SiO_2 cryptocrystalline quartz
	7	White	black, cryptocrystalline, waxy, conchoidal fracture, translucent to opaque, S.G. = 2.5–2.8.	FLINT SiO_2 cryptocrystalline quartz
	7	White	gray, brown, yellow; cryptocrystalline, waxy luster, opaque, conchoidal fracture, S.G. = 2.5–2.8.	CHERT SiO_2 cryptocrystalline quartz
	7	White	red, opaque, waxy luster, cryptocrystalline, conchoidal fracture, S.G. = 2.5–2.8.	JASPER SiO_2 cryptocrystalline quartz
	7	White	green, black, or yellow; conchoidal fracture, no cleavage, S.G. = 3.3–3.4.	OLIVINE $(Fe,Mg)_2SiO_4$ ferromagnesian silicate
	7	White	dark red, brown, pink, green, or yellow; transparent to translucent, no cleavage, S.G. = 3.4–4.3.	GARNET complex silicate

FIGURE 2.28 Characteristics of nonmetallic minerals. SG = specific gravity.

NONMETALLIC MINERALS			
Hardness	Streak	Other Properties	Mineral
Not scratched by steel nail, knife 7–6	White	green to yellow-green, striated crystals or dull granular masses, one cleavage, S.G. = 3.3–3.5.	EPIDOTE complex silicate
6	White	blue-gray, black, or white; striations on some cleavage planes; two cleavages at nearly 90°; S.G. = 2.6–2.8.	PLAGIOCLASE FELDSPAR $NaAlSi_3O_8$ to $CaAl_2Si_2O_8$ calcium-sodium aluminum silicate
6	White	white, pink, brown, green; exsolution lamellae are present and subparallel, two cleavages at 90°, S.G. = 2.6.	POTASSIUM FELDSPAR $KAlSi_3O_8$ potassium aluminum silicate
6	White	colorless, white, orange, gray, yellow, green, red, blue; may have play of colors (opalescence), amorphous, greasy luster to earthy luster; conchoidal fracture, S.G. = 1.9–2.3.	OPAL $SiO_2 \cdot nH_2O$ hydrated silicon dioxide
Scratched by steel nail, knife 5.5	White	green to black, dull, stout crystals; two cleavage directions that intersect at about 87° and 93°; S.G. = 3.2–3.5.	PYROXENE (AUGITE) calcium ferromagnesian silicate
5.5	White	green to black, opaque, two cleavage directions at 60° and 120°, slender crystals, may be splintery or fibrous, S.G. 3.0–3.3.	AMPHIBOLE (HORNBLENDE) calcium ferromagnesian aluminum silicate
5	White	brown, green, blue, yellow, purple, or black; one poor cleavage, common as six-sided crystals, S.G. = 3.1–3.2.	APATITE $Ca_5F(PO_4)_3$ calcium fluorophosphate
5–2	White	green, yellow, gray, or variegated green, gray, and brown; dull masses or asbestos fibrous crystals, no cleavage, S.G. = 2.2–2.6.	SERPENTINE $Mg_6Si_4O_{10}(OH)_8$ hydrous magnesian silicate
5.5–1.5	Red to red-brown	red, opaque, earthy luster, S.G. = 4.9–5.3.	HEMATITE Fe_2O_3 iron oxide
5.5–1.5	Yellow-brown	yellow-brown to dark brown, amorphous, but may be pseudomorphic after pyrite, S.G. = 3.6–4.0.	LIMONITE $Fe_2O_3 \cdot nH_2O$ hydrous iron oxide

FIGURE 2.28 *(continued)*

			NONMETALLIC MINERALS		
	Hardness	Streak	Other Properties		Mineral
Scratched by wire nail	4	White	colorless purple, blue, yellow, or green; dioctahedral cleavage, crystals usually cubic, S.G. = 3.0–3.3.		FLUORITE CaF_2 calcium flouride
	4–3.5	Light blue	vivid royal blue, earthy masses or tiny crystals, effervesces in dilute HCl, S.G. = 3.7–3.8.		AZURITE $Cu_3(CO_3)_2(OH)_2$ hydrous copper carbonate
	4–3.5	Green	green to gray-green laminated crusts or masses of tiny, granular crystals; effervesces in dilute HCl, S.G. = 3.9–4.0.		MALACHITE $Cu_2CO_3(OH)_2$ hydrous copper carbonate
	4–2.0	Very light blue	pale blue to blue-green crusts or massive, amorphous, conchoidal fracture, S.G. = 2.0–2.4.		CHRYSOCOLLA $CuSiO_3 \cdot 2H_2O$ hydrated copper silicate
	4–3.5	White	white, gray, pink, or brown; opaque; rhombohedral cleavage; effervesces in dilute HCl only if powdered, S.G. = 2.8–2.9.		DOLOMITE $CaMg(CO_3)_2$ magnesian calcium carbonate
Scratched by penny	3	White	colorless, white, yellow, gray, green, brown, red, blue; transparent to translucent, rhombohedral cleavage; effervesces in dilute HCl, S.G. = 2.7.		CALCITE $CaCO_3$ calcium carbonate
	3	White	colorless, white, red, brown, yellow, blue; platy crystals, massive, or in rose-like shapes; three cleavages, one perfect and at right angles to others; very heavy, S.G. = 4.5.		BARITE $BaSO_4$ barium sulfate
	3–2.5	Gray-brown	very dark brown to black, one perfect cleavage; flexible, very thin sheets, S.G. 2.7–3.1.		BIOTITE MICA ferromagnesian potassium, hydrous aluminum silicate
	2.5	White	colorless, white, yellow, red, blue, brown; cubic crystals and cubic cleavage, salty taste, S.G. = 2.1–2.6.		HALITE $NaCl$ sodium chloride

FIGURE 2.28 *(continued)*

NONMETALLIC MINERALS			
Hardness	Streak	Other Properties	Mineral
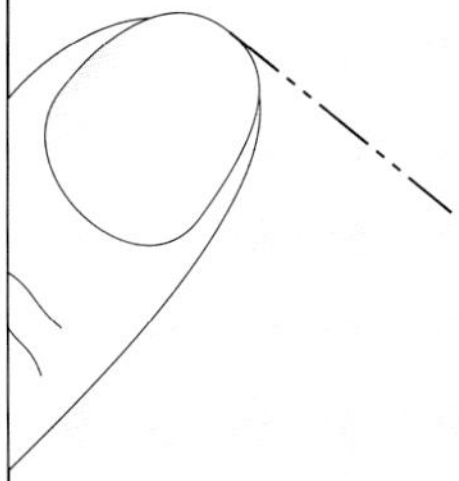 2.5–1.5	Pale yellow	yellow to red, bright crystals or earthy masses, brittle, no cleavage, conchoidal fracture, S.G. = 2.1.	NATIVE SULFUR S sulfur
2.5–2	White	colorless, yellow, brown, red-brown; one perfect cleavage; flexible, elastic sheets, S.G. = 2.7–3.0.	MUSCOVITE MICA potassium hydrous aluminum silicate
2	White	dark green, one perfect cleavage; S.G. = 2.6–3.0.	CHLORITE ferromagnesian aluminum silicate
2	White	one good cleavage (two poor cleavages); nonelastic sheets, colorless to white; H = 2, easily scratched with fingernail, S.G. = 2.3.	GYPSUM $CaSO_4 \cdot 2H_2O$ calcium sulfate
2–1	White	white to very light brown, one perfect cleavage, common as earthy, microcrystalline masses, S.G. = 2.6.	KAOLINITE $Al_4(Si_4O_{10})(OH)_8$ hydrous aluminum silicate
1	White	white, gray, green, pink, brown, yellow; soapy feel, pearly to greasy luster, massive or foliated, S.G. 2.7–2.8.	TALC $Mg_3Si_4O_{10}(OH)_2$ hydrous magnesian silicate

Scratched by fingernail

FIGURE 2.28 *(continued)*

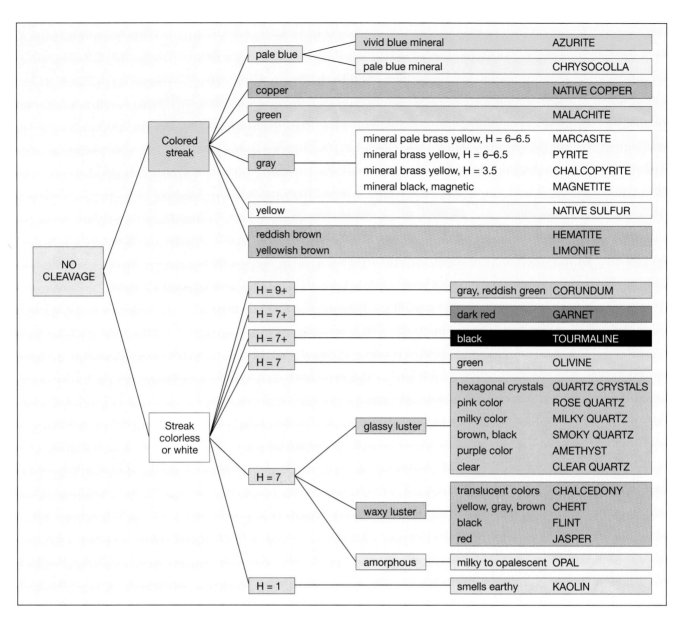

FIGURE 2.29 Flow chart for identification of minerals and mineraloids that have *no obvious cleavage.*

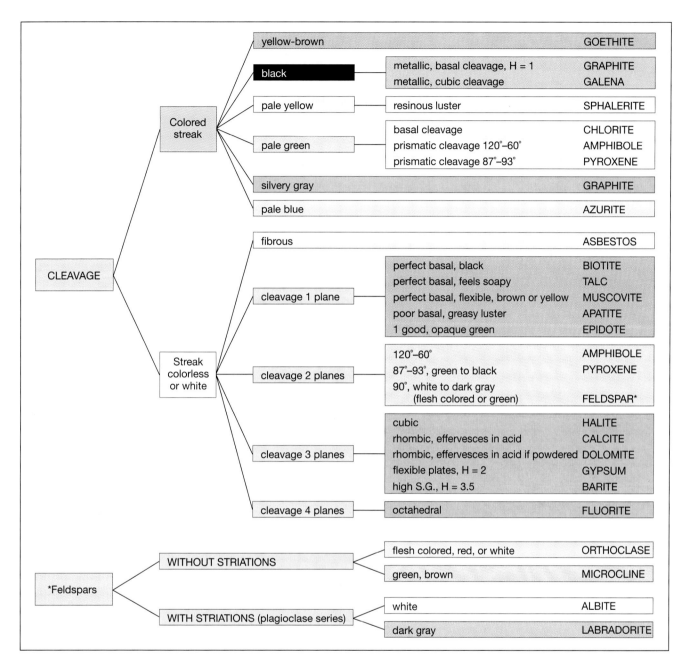

FIGURE 2.30 Flow chart for identification of minerals that have *obvious cleavage*.

Mineral	Formula	Uses
Calcite	$CaCO_3$	In the form of limestone, used as fertilizer, soil conditioner, a source of lime, and in Portland cement In the form of limestone, marble, travertine, and Mexican onyx, used as ornamental stone
Chalcopyrite	$CuFeS_2$	Ore of copper
Feldspar	Aluminosilicates of K, Na, Ca	Major use in manufacture of porcelain, glass, ceramics Minor use as gemstones: amazonite, moonstone, sunstone
Galena	PbS	Chief ore of lead
Garnet	Ca, Fe, Mg, Al silicate	Abrasive powder and sandpaper; gem variety is January birthstone
Graphite	C	Machinery lubricant; heat-resistant material in foundries; pencil "lead"
Gypsum	$CaSO_4 \cdot 2H_2O$	Wallboard, plaster of Paris, drywall, sheetrock, some ornamental use in form called alabaster
Halite	NaCl	Table salt, road salt, and source of sodium and chlorine chemicals; old salt mines used as storage sites
Hematite	Fe_2O_3	Major ore of iron; minor use as a pigment (cave paintings often were done with hematite)
Limonite	$Fe_2O_3 \cdot nH_2O$	Ore of iron; minor use as pigment
Magnetite	Fe_3O_4	Ore of iron
Muscovite	$KAl_2(AlSi_3)O_{10}(OH)_2$	Used in sheets as electrical insulation; ground for use in wallpaper and paint; computer chip substrate
Olivine	$(Fe, Mg)_2SiO_4$	Gem variety called peridot is August birthstone; source of silicon for computer chips
Pyrite	FeS_2	"Fool's gold"; ore of sulfur used to make sulfuric acid; also mined for iron, and for associated real gold or copper
Quartz	SiO_2	In form of pure sand, used in making glass; minor importance as gemstones: amethyst, tiger's eye, agate, onyx

FIGURE 2.31 Economic significance of some common minerals and mineraloids.

EXERCISE THREE

Introduction to Rocks and the Rock Cycle

PURPOSE

This exercise helps you understand what rocks are and how they are formed. It also shows how all rock-forming materials are part of a *rock cycle* that has igneous, sedimentary, and metamorphic components.

MATERIALS

Pencil, paper, and mineral identification materials of your choice.

INTRODUCTION

A **rock** is any natural aggregate of minerals, mineraloids, glass, or organic particles. For example: granite is a rock composed of several minerals. Rock salt is a rock that is a mass of intergrown halite crystals. Rock opal is a rock composed of the mineraloid opal. Obsidian is a rock made of volcanic glass. Coal is a rock composed of organic particles.

Rocks form as a result of several different Earth processes. These rock-forming processes interact in a continuous rock cycle (Figure 3.1). Rock-forming processes produce three general types of rocks: igneous, sedimentary, and metamorphic. Each of these rock types forms character-istic rock bodies (Figure 3.2). Each rock type also has characteristic textures (Figure 3.3).

ROCK PROPERTIES

Rocks have many different properties. The properties you can observe in a rock are clues to its origin and are used to classify it.

The most obvious properties of rocks are their general forms and colors. Most rocks are irregular aggregates of Earth materials such as mineral crystals, organic particles (shells, wood, stems, bones), or fragments of other rocks. However, some rocks have distinctive shapes. For example, they may have flat layers, icicle shapes, teardrop shapes, smooth spherical shapes, or be rounded shards with sharp edges (glass shards).

Rocks vary in color, depending on their chemical composition or the colors of their constituent parts. For example, dark rocks often are rich in iron, magnesium, or carbon; light-colored rocks lack significant amounts of these elements. Multicolored crystalline rocks generally contain several kinds of mineral crystals; uniformly colored crystalline rocks generally contain a single kind of mineral crystal.

A very important property of rocks is **texture.** Texture describes the constituent parts of a rock—their size, shape, and arrangement. Some rocks are

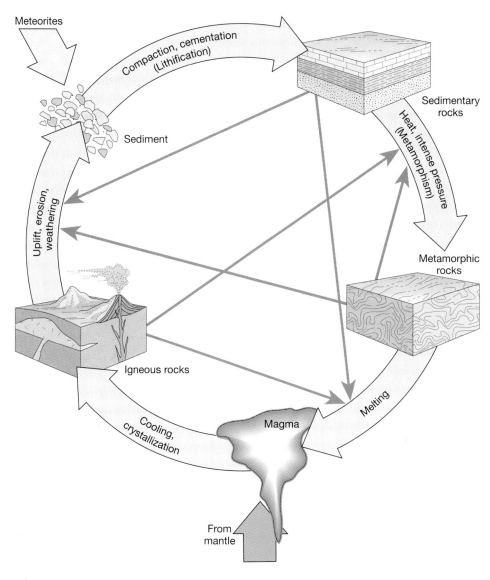

FIGURE 3.1 The rock cycle. The typical path is shown. However, any type of rock can be transformed into any other kind of rock, depending on conditions. For example, sedimentary rock can be melted and cooled to form new igneous rock; metamorphic rock can be weathered and its particles cemented to form a new sedimentary rock.

Meteorites

Compaction, cementation (Lithification)

Sediment

Sedimentary rocks

Heat, intense pressure (Metamorphism)

Uplift, erosion, weathering

Metamorphic rocks

Igneous rocks

Melting

Cooling, crystallization

Magma

From mantle

dense, solid masses. Others are a mixture of solid particles (called **grains**) and spaces (called **void spaces**). The void spaces may contain air, natural gas, or liquids. The grains in a rock can be inorganic or organic.

We describe grain size with the terms **fine-grained** (grains <1 mm, too small to identify without a hand lens) or **coarse-grained** (grains >1 mm, large enough to identify with your unaided eye). Some dense materials, like glass **(glassy texture)**, completely lack grains (Figure 3.3A). Void spaces may be **vesicles** or bubbles (B), solution cavities (cavelike spaces), fractures, or irregular spaces between **poorly sorted** grains of diverse size.

Rocks having grains that are mineral crystals are said to have **crystalline textures,** and they are glittery when rotated in bright light. The mineral

crystals may be arranged into oriented patterns and layers that cause the rock to break into specific, regular shapes. Or, the mineral crystals may be randomly arranged, in which case the rock breaks randomly and irregularly. Rock textures also can be described as **equigranular** (having grains all about the same size, H) or **heterogranular** (having grains of distinctly different sizes, K).

Sedimentary rocks often contain **clasts** (fragments of minerals, other rocks, plants, or animals) and thus have a **clastic texture** (I, J, L). They may include **fossils,** which are parts of ancient plants, animals, or other evidence of life such as animal tracks.

Metamorphic rocks have undergone **deformation**—a change in shape and/or texture, caused by an applied force. These properties include frac-

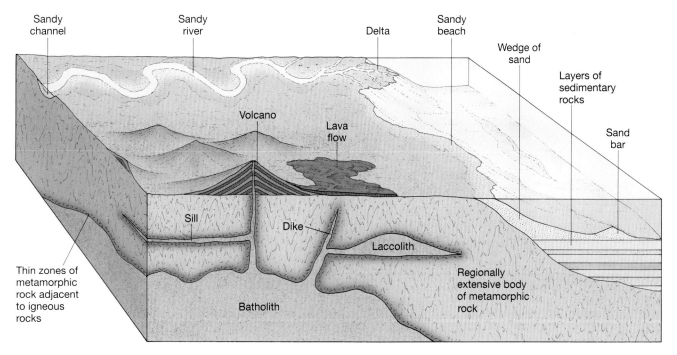

FIGURE 3.2 Common igneous, sedimentary, and metamorphic rock bodies. All result from rock-forming processes in the rock cycle.

tures, faults, folds, deformed fossils (E), and foliated textures. **Foliated texture** is the alignment of flat-sided mineral grains so they are parallel to one another, giving the appearance of folio-like (leaf-like) layers. Foliated texture causes rocks to break along the parallel layers of flat-sided minerals, so the rocks have **rock cleavage** (so-called because the breaks resemble mineral cleavage). Foliated rocks that contain abundant mica minerals typically have a shiny, somewhat metallic, luster.

ROCK CLASSIFICATION

All rocks are classified as igneous, sedimentary, or metamorphic, based on their properties (Figure 3.4). Some properties are characteristic of more than one rock type—for example, igneous, sedimentary, and metamorphic rocks all can be dark, or light, or shiny, or granular. Therefore, it is essential to classify rocks from multiple properties.

Igneous rocks form by the cooling of molten rock (which was liquefied by heat and pressure deep in the mantle). Molten rock exists both below Earth's surface (where it is called magma) and at the surface (where it is called lava). The cooling of molten rock can occur in either place, forming igneous rocks of different characters. When magma cools underground, it forms various rock bodies

(Figure 3.2). Large bodies are *batholiths*. Where magma has flowed parallel to bedrock layering, it solidifies in a *sill*. Where magma cuts across bedrock layers, it solidifies in a *dike* or a blisterlike *laccolith*. When molten rock cools above ground, it forms *lava flows*.

Igneous rocks can have various textures, including crystalline, glassy, or fine-grained vesicular (bubbly). They commonly contain mineral crystals of olivine, pyroxene, or feldspars. Igneous rocks from cooled lava flows may have ropy, streamlined shapes or layers (from repeated flows of lava). Igneous rocks lack fossils and organic grains.

Sedimentary rocks form in two ways. **Lithification** is the hardening of sediments—loose, fragmented Earth materials. **Precipitation** produces crystals in water that collect in aggregates.

The lithification process occurs as rocks are **compacted** (pressure-hardened) or **cemented** (glued together by tiny crystals precipitated from fluids in the pores of sediment). Thus, most sedimentary rocks have clastic textures and are layered. The clasts are arranged in layers due to sorting by wind or water. Clasts often include fragments of life forms, so fossils are a diagnostic property of sedimentary rocks.

Other sedimentary rocks are layered aggregates of crystals precipitated from water. This includes the icicle-shaped stalactites that hang from

COMMON IGNEOUS ROCK TEXTURES

A   Glassy   B   Vesicular (bubbly)   C   Randomly oriented small crystals   D   Randomly oriented large crystals

COMMON METAMORPHIC ROCK TEXTURES

Deformed fossil fern

E   Deformed fossils   F   Folded   G   Foliated small crystals and shiny reflection   H   Equigranular large crystals

COMMON SEDIMENTARY ROCK TEXTURES

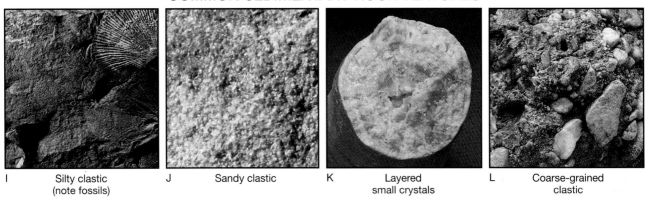

I   Silty clastic (note fossils)   J   Sandy clastic   K   Layered small crystals   L   Coarse-grained clastic

FIGURE 3.3 Some common rock textures of igneous, metamorphic, and sedimentary rocks.

the roofs of caves (Figure 8.3). Common minerals in such sedimentary rocks include calcite, dolomite, gypsum, or halite.

Most sedimentary rocks occur in bodies that record the shape of the original sediment deposits: river beds, deltas, beaches, sand bars, or extensive flat layers (Figure 3.2).

Metamorphic rocks have been altered (changed) physically and/or chemically due to the effects of intense heating, intense pressure, or the chemical action of hot fluids. Therefore, metamorphic rocks have textures indicating deformation (folds, extensive fracturing, faults, and foliation). Fossils, if present, also are deformed (stretched or

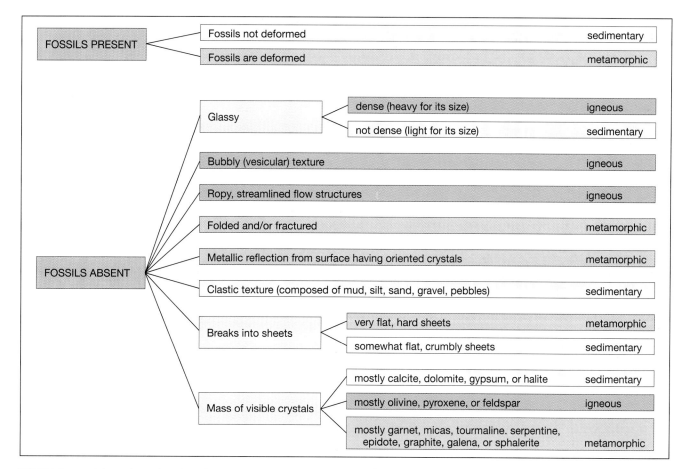

| FOSSILS PRESENT | Fossils not deformed | | sedimentary |
| | Fossils are deformed | | metamorphic |

FOSSILS ABSENT	Glassy	dense (heavy for its size)	igneous
		not dense (light for its size)	sedimentary
	Bubbly (vesicular) texture		igneous
	Ropy, streamlined flow structures		igneous
	Folded and/or fractured		metamorphic
	Metallic reflection from surface having oriented crystals		metamorphic
	Clastic texture (composed of mud, silt, sand, gravel, pebbles)		sedimentary
	Breaks into sheets	very flat, hard sheets	metamorphic
		somewhat flat, crumbly sheets	sedimentary
	Mass of visible crystals	mostly calcite, dolomite, gypsum, or halite	sedimentary
		mostly olivine, pyroxene, or feldspar	igneous
		mostly garnet, micas, tourmaline. serpentine, epidote, graphite, galena, or sphalerite	metamorphic

FIGURE 3.4 Flow chart for classification of rocks as igneous, sedimentary, or metamorphic.

crushed). Metamorphic rocks often contain garnet, micas, or tourmaline. Serpentine, epidote, graphite, galena, and sphalerite occur only in metamorphic rocks. Metamorphism can occur over large regions, or in thin "contact" zones (Figure 3.2).

ROCK CYCLE

Rock-forming processes all are part of the rock cycle (Figure 3.1). For example, a common chain of events is for magma to cool and form an igneous rock. It becomes weathered (physically and chemically broken down) to form sediment and chemicals in solution. The sediment can become lithified, or the chemicals can precipitate from the solution as mineral crystals, to form sedimentary rock. The sedimentary rock, in turn, can be altered by intense heat, pressure, or the chemical action of hot fluids, to form a metamorphic rock. If heating continues, the metamorphic rock can melt to form another body of magma and begin the rock cycle anew.

Of course, not all rock materials undergo such complete cycling and recycling. Small arrows in Figure 3.1 indicate alternate routes in the cycling process. Igneous rocks can be directly metamorphosed or remelted. Metamorphic rocks can be remetamorphosed or weathered directly. Sedimentary rocks can be weathered back into sediment or directly melted.

Figures 3.5–3.14 are photographs of rocks. For each Figure, do the following:

1. List the properties of the rock that you can observe.
2. Classify the rock as igneous, sedimentary, or metamorphic.
3. Describe, as best as you can, how the rock may have formed.
4. Predict from the rock cycle (Figure 3.1) what changes the rock could undergo next if left in a natural setting. (There are *at least* three changes that each rock could undergo.)

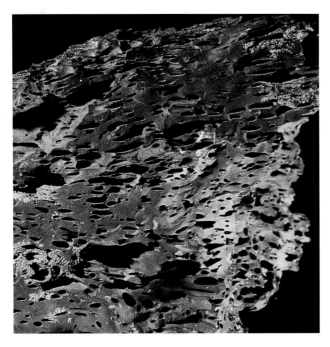

FIGURE 3.5 Rock sample for analysis, classification, and evaluation. (Photo by R. Busch)

FIGURE 3.7 Rock sample for analysis, classification, and evaluation. (Photo by R. Busch)

FIGURE 3.6 Rock sample for analysis, classification, and evaluation. (Photo by R. Busch)

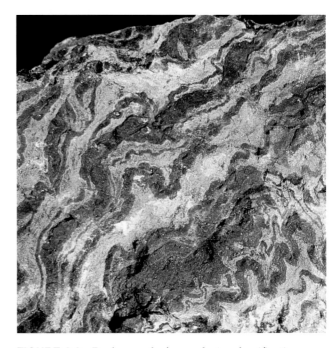

FIGURE 3.8 Rock sample for analysis, classification, and evaluation. (Photo by R. Busch)

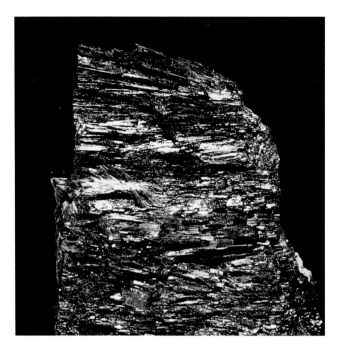

FIGURE 3.9 Rock sample for analysis, classification, and evaluation. (Photo by R. Busch)

FIGURE 3.11 Rock sample for analysis, classification, and evaluation. (Photo by R. Busch)

FIGURE 3.10 Rock sample for analysis, classification, and evaluation. (Photo by R. Busch)

FIGURE 3.12 Rock sample for analysis, classification, and evaluation. (Photo by R. Busch)

FIGURE 3.13 Rock sample for analysis, classification, and evaluation. (Photo by R. Busch)

FIGURE 3.14 Rock sample for analysis, classification, and evaluation. (Photo by R. Busch)

Igneous Processes and Rocks

Patricia A. Weisse
Harold E. Andrews
James R. Besancon
Margaret D. Thompson
Wellesley College

PURPOSE

This exercise introduces you to igneous processes, igneous rock textures, and igneous rock classifications.

MATERIALS

Hand lens, mineral-identification materials of your choice (see Exercise Two), ruler, and samples of igneous rocks provided by your instructor.

INTRODUCTION

As you learned in Exercise Three, a **rock** is any natural aggregate of minerals, mineraloids, glass, or organic particles. For example, granite is a rock composed of several minerals, rock salt is a rock composed of halite crystals, rock opal is a rock composed of the mineraloid opal, obsidian is a rock composed of volcanic glass, and coal is a rock composed of organic particles.

MAGMA, LAVA, AND IGNEOUS ROCKS

Magma is molten rock beneath Earth's surface that has been liquified by the intense heat and pressure within the planet. When magma flows onto the land surface or the seafloor, it is termed **lava.**

Igneous rocks form by the cooling of magma or lava. Those that form from the cooling of magma inside Earth are called *intrusive* igneous rocks, because they intrude into existing rock. Those that form at Earth's surface are called *extrusive* igneous rocks, because they are extruded onto the surface. Some examples of intrusive and extrusive igneous rocks are illustrated in Figures 4.4 through 4.19.

IGNEOUS ROCK TEXTURES

Igneous rock classification is based partly on texture, so it is important to know the different textures and what causes them. The size of mineral crystals in an igneous rock generally indicates the rate at which the lava or magma cooled to form a rock. Large crystals require a long time to grow, so their presence means the molten rock cooled very slowly. Tiny crystals, or none at all, tell us that the rock cooled more rapidly. If lava or magma is cooled abruptly **(quenched),** there is no time for mineral crystals to form. Instead, an amorphous volcanic glass called **obsidian** is produced (Figure 4.14). Thus, if you observe a glassy rock with no evident crystals, it may have cooled very quickly from lava on the surface.

The crystallization process also depends on the ability of atoms in the lava or magma to *nucleate*. Nucleation is the formation of an initial tiny crystal, to which other atoms progressively bond. This is how a crystal grows. If the magma cools slowly, crystals have time to grow, sometimes to many centimeters in length. However, if a magma is very viscous (thick and resistant to flow), atoms may be unable to reach nucleation sites, and crystals may not form even though the magma cools slowly.

Several terms describe igneous rock texture, based on crystal size: igneous rocks composed of volcanic glass (no crystals) have a **hyaline texture** (from the Greek word for glass). Igneous rocks composed of crystals too small to see without a hand lens (generally <1 mm) have an **aphanitic texture** (from the Greek word for invisible). Those composed of visible crystals (generally 1–10 mm and larger) have a **phaneritic texture** (from the Greek word for visible). Phaneritic igneous rocks with very large grains (generally >1 cm) have a **pegmatitic texture.**

Some igneous rocks mix two distinct crystal sizes; this is called **porphyritic texture.** The large crystals are **phenocrysts,** and the smaller, more

Composition / Texture[1]	Felsic (Light)	Intermediate	Mafic (Dark)	Ultramafic
	≥5% quartz. Potassium feldspar > plagioclase. 15% ferromagnesian minerals.	<5% quartz. Plagioclase > potassium feldspar. 15–40% ferromagnesian minerals.	No quartz. plagioclase ≈ 50%, no potassium feldspar. 40% ferromagnesian minerals.	Nearly 100% ferromagnesian minerals
Pegmatitic[2]	GRANITE-PEGMATITE	DIORITE-PEGMATITE	GABBRO-PEGMATITE	
Phaneritic[2]	GRANITE (SYENITE[3])	DIORITE	GABBRO (DIABASE[5])	PERIDOTITE
Aphanitic[2]	RHYOLITE (TRACHYTE[4])	ANDESITE	BASALT	
Glassy	OBSIDIAN		OBSIDIAN	
Frothy or cellular	PUMICE		SCORIA	
Pyroclastic or fragmental	VOLCANIC TUFF (fragments ≤ 2 mm)			
	VOLCANIC BRECCIA (fragments > 2 mm)			

[1]For porphyritic textures, simply qualify the basic rock name with *porphyry* or *porphyritic*. For example, a granite with phenocrysts can be called *porphyritic granite* or *granite porphyry*.

[2]These grain-size designations refer to the groundmass (matrix) of the rock: glassy (hyaline, but not frothy or cellular); aphanitic (crystals generally less than 1 mm); phaneritic (crystals generally 1–10 mm); pegmatitic (crystals generally larger than 1 cm).

[3]Name applied to felsic rocks resembling granite, but containing no quartz.

[4]Name applied to felsic rocks resembling rhyolite, but containing no quartz.

[5]Name applied to gabbros composed almost totally of plagioclase and pyroxene mineral crystals, about 1–2 mm in size.

[6]Peridotite consisting chiefly of olivine is called *dunite*.

FIGURE 4.1 Classification of igneous rocks is based upon three qualities: texture, composition, and darkness (color index). This chart shows how these three qualities are used to identify igneous rocks. Composition is the percentage abundance of quartz, potassium feldspar, plagioclase feldspar, and ferromagnesian minerals. Color index is the percentage of mafic (dark) minerals present in a coarse-grained (phaneritic or pegmatitic) igneous rock. The term *felsic* is shorthand for *feldspar-silicate* rocks; *mafic* is shorthand for *magnesium-ferric* (ferromagnesian) rocks.

numerous crystals form the **matrix,** or **groundmass.** Combinations of textures also occur: porphyritic-aphanitic textures (phenocrysts occur within an aphanitic matrix) and porphyritic-phaneritic textures (phenocrysts occur within a phaneritic matrix).

Vesicles are gas bubbles trapped in a rock, giving the rock a **vesicular** texture. Some lavas contain so many vesicles that they become frothy, like whipped egg whites. Upon cooling, a frothy texture can form scoria (Figure 4.13) or pumice (Figure 4.17). Pumice has so many tiny vesicles— so many air pockets—that it floats on water!

Pyroclasts (from the Greek, "fire broken") are fragmented rocky materials that have been hurled through the air and quickly cooled during explosive volcanic eruptions. They include volcanic ash fragments (pyroclasts <2 mm), lapilli or cinders (pyroclasts 2–64 mm), and volcanic bombs or blocks (pyroclasts >64 mm; Figure 4.15). Igneous rocks composed of pyroclasts have a **pyroclastic texture.** They include *tuff* (made of volcanic ash, Figure 4.16) and *volcanic breccia* (made chiefly of cinders and volcanic bombs, Figure 4.18).

CLASSIFICATION OF IGNEOUS ROCKS

Igneous rocks are classified using three properties: the minerals they contain (composition), their texture, and color index. Figure 4.1 shows how these three factors are related.

Note the upper row in the figure that shows the percentage abundance of quartz, feldspar, and ferromagnesian minerals. This is the most important mineralogical information used to classify igneous rocks. Igneous rocks composed mostly of quartz, potassium feldspar, and plagioclase are called **felsic** and are light-colored. Igneous rocks composed mostly of dark-colored ferromagnesian minerals (i.e., minerals containing much iron and magnesium) are called **mafic** and are dark.

In between the felsic and mafic rocks are **intermediate** igneous rocks, mixtures of both felsic and mafic minerals. Darkest are the **ultramafic** igneous rocks, composed entirely of ferromagnesian minerals.

These generalizations about mineral composition can be approximated for phaneritic and pegmatitic samples (large crystals) by using the **color index.** This index (top of Figure 4.1) is the visually estimated percentage of dark minerals in a rock.

To classify hand samples of igneous rocks, follow this procedure, with the aid of Figure 4.1:

1. Identify the rock's texture.
2. If the rock is coarse-grained (phaneritic or pegmatitic), estimate the color index and percentage abundances of quartz, feldspars, and ferromagnesian minerals. This lets you characterize the rock as felsic, intermediate, mafic, or ultramafic, so you can identify it in Figure 4.1.
3. If the rock is essentially fine-grained (aphanitic or porphyritic-aphanitic), or if you cannot identify its minerals, you'll have to approximate the composition. *Felsic* fine-grained rocks tend to be pink, white, or pale brown; *intermediate* fine-grained rocks tend to be greenish gray; and *mafic* fine-grained rocks tend to be dark gray to black.
4. Use textural terms, such as porphyritic or vesicular, as adjectives. For example, you might identify a pinkish, fine-grained, igneous rock as a rhyolite. If it contains scattered phenocrysts, then you would call it a *porphyritic rhyolite.* Similarly, you would call a basalt with vesicles a *vesicular basalt.*

ORIGIN OF IGNEOUS ROCKS

Most scientists reason that Earth formed simultaneously with the other planets in our Solar System. The oldest meteorites and Moon rocks that have been precisely dated are 4.6 billion years old, so this also may be the age of Earth. Scientists also reason that the young Earth probably contained abundant, newly formed radioactive elements. The energy released as these elements decayed would have produced much more heat than is presently generated by radioactive decay within Earth. Therefore, the interior of the young Earth probably had a much larger proportion of molten material (magma) than today, and the lithosphere probably was less stable and less rigid than it is now.

The oldest rocks on Earth are about 3.8 billion years old, and they include some crystalline grains 4.1 billion years old. This may mean that Earth did not develop a relatively rigid and stable lithosphere until some 4 billion years ago.

The body of Earth is now significantly cooler than it was 4 billion years ago, and a thin, rigid lithosphere covers the entire planet. Nevertheless, some of Earth's interior remains molten or semi-molten, and this hot magma (and associated gases) rises through cracks in the lithosphere to create

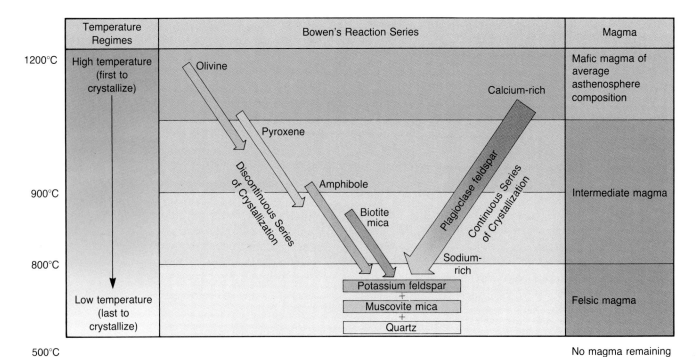

FIGURE 4.2 Bowen's Reaction Series. The diagram suggests the sequence in which minerals crystallize from an average magma in the asthenosphere when it is slowly cooled. Note the relation between temperature and mineral composition/stability. (This is approximate, because pressure also affects mineral composition/stability.) Viewing the diagram in reverse (bottom to top) also suggests the sequence in which minerals will melt to form magma when rocks are heated. See discussion in text. (After Lutgens, F. K., and Tarbuck, E. J., 1989, *Essentials of Geology,* 3d ed., Fig. 2.6, p. 40, Columbus: Macmillan Publishing Company)

lava flows, volcanoes, and intrusives. Thus igneous rocks are forming today, wherever magma and lava are cooling (the Hawaiian Islands, Iceland, the seafloors, and many other places).

In fact, igneous processes still dominate Earth. Catastrophic events such as volcanoes and earthquakes cause rapid changes, while gradual tectonic movements slowly form major features such as mountain chains and ocean basins.

COOLING DOWN—THE SEQUENCES OF CRYSTALLIZATION

American petrologist N. L. Bowen used laboratory experiments to study magmas and crystallization. He showed that, as magmas cool, two different series of silicate minerals (SiO_4) crystallize in predictable sequences (Figure 4.2). One series is the continuous crystallization of plagioclase feldspar (on the right in the figure). The other series is the discontinuous crystallization of various ferromagne-

sian silicate minerals (left). At the lowest temperatures—where the last crystallization occurs—the remaining elements commonly form potassium feldspar, muscovite mica, and quartz.

Bowen's Reaction Series clearly suggests a relation between temperature and the composition of magmas and rocks. Therefore, composition terms such as felsic (feldspar-silicate) and mafic (ferromagnesian) are used to describe magmas in Figure 4.2. For example, high-temperature magmas derived from Earth's asthenosphere (the top of the mantle) generally are mafic. If such magmas are erupted directly onto the land or seafloor, they chill quickly to form basalts (Figure 4.9). If crystals are allowed to form slowly in such a mafic magma, they may accumulate and be preserved as gabbro (Figure 4.8) and/or as coarse-grained ultramafic rocks.

Crystals that settle out of a cooling magma cannot have chemical reactions with the remaining magma. Because this crystallization removes a specific fraction of the elements from the magma, the process is called *fractional crystallization*. This re-

58 EXERCISE FOUR

moval of some elements changes the magma composition, leaving in the magma a different combination of elements to form the next crystals as cooling proceeds. Intermediate and felsic magmas/rocks can be derived in this manner.

HEATING UP—THE SEQUENCE OF MELTING

The sequence of crystallization is very generally reversed when rocks are heated. Earth materials melt at different temperatures as they are heated. An analogy is a plastic tray of ice cubes, heated in an oven. The ice cubes would melt long before the plastic tray would melt—i.e., the ice cubes melt at a much lower temperature. As rocks are heated, the different mineral crystals and mineraloids that compose them also melt at different temperatures.

Therefore, at a given temperature, it is possible to have rocks that are partly molten and partly solid. This phenomenon is known as *partial melting*.

Just as Bowen's Reaction Series (Figure 4.2) can be used to predict sequences of crystallization, it also can be used in reverse to predict the sequence of melting for mineral crystals in a rock that is undergoing heating. Mineral crystals formed at low temperatures also melt at low temperatures; mineral crystals formed at high temperatures also melt at high temperatures.

Partial melting is another process by which magmas of more than one composition can be derived. As rocks undergo partial melting, the early-formed (low-temperature) magma may rise (due to convection) or otherwise separate from the solid portion of the rocks to produce a body of felsic magma. At higher temperatures, however, the

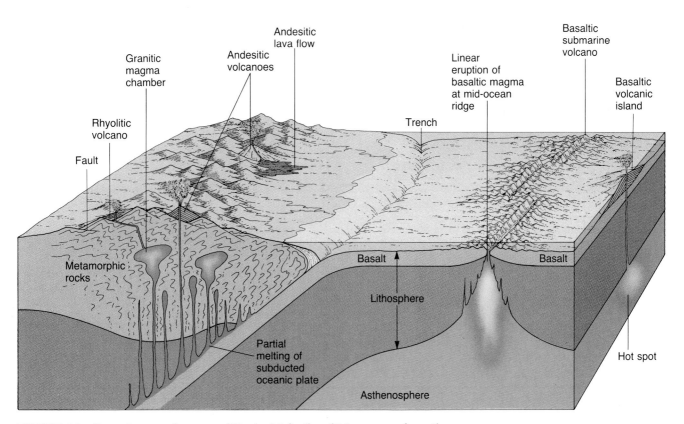

FIGURE 4.3 Some igneous features of Earth. Mafic (basaltic) magmas from the asthenosphere commonly erupt onto the seafloor along *mid-ocean ridges* and above isolated *hot spots* such as the Hawaiian Islands. Basaltic eruptions at mid-ocean ridges gradually force the older basalt rock to move laterally until it subsides into trenches beneath the continents. Partial melting of the subducted basalt commonly produces magmas that are intermediate (dioritic) to felsic (granitic). Partial melting also produces andesitic and rhyolitic eruptions. (Mount Saint Helens in Washington State is an andesitic volcano.) This model of *seafloor spreading* may explain the phenomena known as *continental drift* and *plate tectonics,* as examined in Exercises One, Seventeen, and Eighteen.

remaining portions of the rocks may melt to produce a higher-temperature magma of intermediate composition.

QUESTIONS

Examine Figures 4.4–4.19, then proceed to the following questions.

1. What is the color index for the granite sample in Figure 4.4?

2. Determine the color index for the rock in Figure 4.6.

3. How did the rock in Figure 4.18 get its texture?

4. How did the rock in Figure 4.10 get its texture?

5. At what approximate temperature did the rock in Figure 4.4 form, according to Bowen's Reaction Series?
   a. Describe the process of how this rock could have formed, starting with a high-temperature magma from the asthenosphere.
   b. Describe the chemistry and lowest melting temperature of a magma that is formed by melting light-colored sediments.
   c. Could a granite ultimately form from such a magma? How?

6. Obtain a set of igneous rocks from your instructor. For each rock:
   a. List the minerals present and estimate the percentage of each (phaneritic or pegmatitic rocks).
   b. Describe the texture(s).
   c. Determine the rock's name.

ADDITIONAL QUESTIONS

7. How might the rock in Figure 4.19 have formed? Be sure to consider temperature, chemistry, crystallization, and texture.

8. Examine Figure 4.7.
   a. Suggest a process by which this rock could have formed without involving fractional crystallization or cooling of a high-temperature magma.
   b. Where could such a process originate and end in Figure 4.3?

9. Olivine and plagioclase crystallize simultaneously, according to Bowen's Reaction Series (Figure 4.2). Suggest a process by which the peridotite in Figure 4.12 may have formed.

FIGURE 4.4 Granite is an intrusive, phaneritic igneous rock. It has a low color index (light color) and is composed chiefly of quartz and feldspar mineral crystals (see Figure 2.1). Ferromagnesian mineral crystals in granites generally include biotite and amphibole (hornblende). This sample contains pink microcline, white plagioclase, gray quartz, and biotite mica. Granites rich in potassium feldspar appear pink like this one, whereas those poor in K-spar appear gray or white.

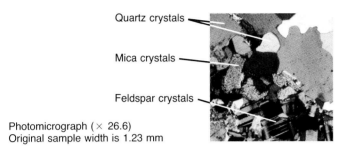

Quartz crystals

Mica crystals

Feldspar crystals

Photomicrograph (× 26.6)
Original sample width is 1.23 mm

FIGURE 4.5 Rhyolite is an aphanitic igneous rock that is the extrusive equivalent of a granite. It is usually light gray, when rich in light-colored feldspars and quartz. Some rhyolites resemble andesite (see Figure 4.7), so their identification should be finalized where possible by microscopic examination to verify the predominance of quartz and feldspar mineral crystals. (Also see Figure 4.11.)

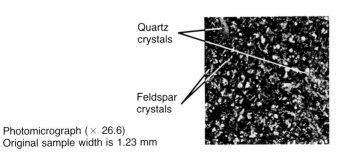

Quartz
crystals

Feldspar
crystals

Photomicrograph (× 26.6)
Original sample width is 1.23 mm

FIGURE 4.6 Diorite is an intrusive, phaneritic igneous rock that has an intermediate color index and is composed chiefly of plagioclase feldspar and ferromagnesian mineral crystals (see Figure 4.1). The ferromagnesian mineral crystals are chiefly amphibole (hornblende). Quartz is only rarely present and only in small amounts (<5%).

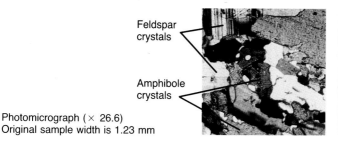

Feldspar crystals

Amphibole crystals

Photomicrograph (× 26.6)
Original sample width is 1.23 mm

FIGURE 4.7 Andesite is an aphanitic igneous rock that is the extrusive equivalent of diorite. It is usually medium-to-dark gray. Some andesites resemble rhyolite, so their identification is best finalized by microscopic examination to verify the predominance of plagioclase feldspar and ferromagnesian mineral crystals. This sample has a porphyritic-aphanitic texture, because it contains phenocrysts of amphibole and feldspar. (Also see Figure 4.10.)

Amphibole phenocryst

Groundmass of feldspar and ferromagnesian mineral crystals

Feldspar phenocrysts

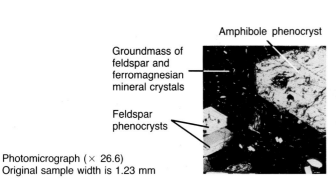

Photomicrograph (× 26.6)
Original sample width is 1.23 mm

FIGURE 4.8 Gabbro is an intrusive, phaneritic igneous rock having a high color index (dark) and composed chiefly of ferromagnesian and plagioclase feldspar mineral crystals. The ferromagnesian mineral crystals usually are pyroxene (e.g., augite). Quartz is absent. Gabbros composed only of plagioclase feldspar and pyroxene mineral crystals of about 1–2 mm diameter are commonly called *diabase*.

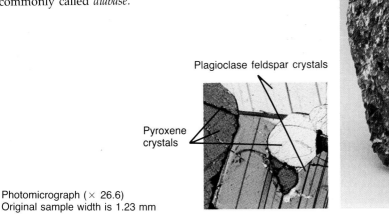

Plagioclase feldspar crystals

Pyroxene crystals

Photomicrograph (× 26.6)
Original sample width is 1.23 mm

FIGURE 4.9 Basalt is an aphanitic igneous rock that is the extrusive equivalent of gabbro, so it is dark gray to black. This sample has a vesicular texture. Microscopic examination of basalts reveals that they are composed chiefly of plagioclase and ferromagnesian mineral crystals. The ferromagnesian mineral crystals generally are pyroxene, but they also may include olivine or magnetite. Glass also may be visible between mineral crystals. Basalt forms the floors of modern oceans (beneath the mud and sand) and is the most abundant aphanitic igneous rock on Earth.

Ferromagnesian mineral crystals

Plagioclase feldspar crystals

Glass

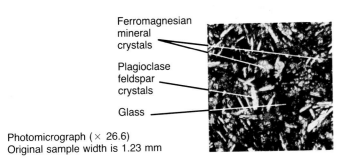

Photomicrograph (× 26.6)
Original sample width is 1.23 mm

FIGURE 4.10 Porphyritic andesite. This hand sample is mainly aphanitic and medium-gray, so it is an andesite. The specimen also contains phenocrysts (the larger black crystals) of the ferromagnesian mineral hornblende. The phenocrysts are isolated from one another—they "float" within the aphanitic groundmass (matrix). Therefore, this sample of andesite has a phaneritic-aphanitic texture, plus hornblende phenocrysts. Specifically, the rock is a "porphyritic hornblende andesite."

FIGURE 4.11 Porphyritic trachyte. This hand sample is aphanitic. Microscopic examination reveals that the groundmass (matrix) consists chiefly of mineral crystals of potassium feldspar, few mineral crystals of plagioclase and ferromagnesians, and no quartz. Therefore, the groundmass is like a rhyolite, except that it lacks quartz mineral crystals, so the rock is called a *trachyte* (see Figure 4.1). There also are large phenocrysts of potassium feldspar, so the rock's overall texture is porphyritic-aphanitic.

FIGURE 4.12 Peridotite is an intrusive, phaneritic igneous rock having a very high color index (>95%). It is composed essentially of ferromagnesian mineral crystals. The specimen shown is a peridotite composed of olivine mineral crystals; such a peridotite also is called *dunite*. Similarly, a peridotite composed of pyroxene mineral crystals is called *pyroxenite*.

FIGURE 4.13 Scoria is an extrusive igneous rock with a high color index and abundant adjacent vesicles. It can form from the cooling of lava flows that are dense and frothy (bubbly, like whipped egg whites), as in the sample shown. Scoria also can develop from the cooling of gas-charged lava that is explosively ejected from volcanoes, forming scoriaceous volcanic cinders.

FIGURE 4.14 Obsidian is an extrusive igneous rock composed of dark glass (volcanic glass). It forms when lava is cooled very suddenly, or quenched. Such a glassy texture is formally known as a *hyaline texture*. Some obsidian contains phenocrysts of feldspar that are visible in hand samples; such texture is called *porphyritic-hyaline*. Some obsidian also contains microscopic plagioclase feldspar crystals, which impart a glittery reflectiveness; gemstone manufacturers call this "golden-sheen" obsidian.

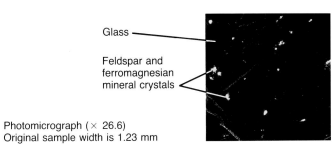

Glass

Feldspar and ferromagnesian mineral crystals

Photomicrograph (× 26.6)
Original sample width is 1.23 mm

FIGURE 4.15 Volcanic bombs are a type of pyroclast. They are aphanitic, commonly vesicular, cooled masses of lava that were violently ejected from volcanoes and then solidified while in the air. As such, many volcanic bombs have the shape of falling raindrops, as in the sample shown. (Actually they are cooled "lavadrops"!)

10 cm

FIGURE 4.16 Tuff is an extrusive, pyroclastic igneous rock composed chiefly of volcanic ash fragments of less than 2 mm diameter. Tuff also has a dull, earthy appearance, as in the sample shown. This sample also contains a few large brown pyroclasts.

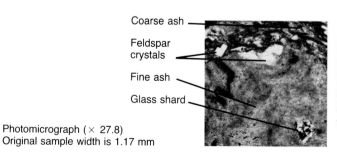

Coarse ash

Feldspar crystals

Fine ash

Glass shard

Photomicrograph (× 27.8)
Original sample width is 1.17 mm

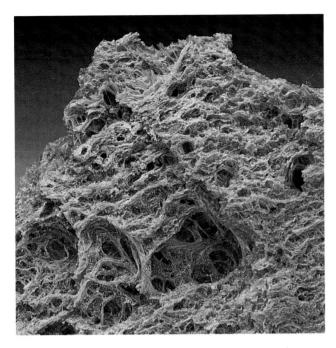

FIGURE 4.17 Pumice is an extrusive igneous rock, generally white to dark gray, having very abundant adjacent vesicles. In these properties, pumice is similar to scoria (Figure 4.13). However, pumice is less dense than scoria. Its density is so low that it floats on water!

FIGURE 4.18 Volcanic breccia is an extrusive igneous rock composed chiefly of pyroclastic fragments of more than 2 mm diameter. These clasts may include volcanic bombs (Figure 4.15) and volcanic cinders. The clasts in this sample are angular pieces of obsidian.

FIGURE 4.19 Granite-pegmatite. Pegmatite is an intrusive, phaneritic igneous rock composed of mineral crystals larger than 1 cm in diameter. The sample shown is a pegmatite having mineral crystals chiefly of gray quartz and white feldspar, so it is a granite-pegmatite. However, there also are diorite-pegmatites and gabbro-pegmatites (see Figure 4.1).

EXERCISE FIVE
Sedimentary Processes and Rocks

Pamela J. W. Gore
Dekalb College

Patricia A. Weisse
Harold E. Andrews
James R. Besancon
Margaret D. Thompson
Wellesley College

PURPOSE

This exercise introduces you to sedimentary processes and sedimentary environments, plus sedimentary rock textures, structures, and classification.

MATERIALS

Hand lens, metric ruler for grain-size measurement, pencil, eraser, and samples of sedimentary rocks provided by your instructor.

INTRODUCTION

Sedimentary rocks form by any of these processes: (1) *compaction* of sediments (loose or fragmented materials), (2) *cementation* of sediments, and/or (3) direct formation of *crystal aggregates* during evaporation of water. For example, sand (a sediment) can be compacted until it is pressure-hardened into sandstone (a sedimentary rock). Alternatively, sand grains can be cemented together by the growth of microscopic calcite crystals in the pore spaces (void spaces among the grains), which also produces sandstone. Examples resulting from the third process are rock salt and rock gypsum. They are sedimentary rocks formed entirely by the direct *precipi-*

tation of crystals (separation from a solution) during the evaporation of ocean water.

SEDIMENT

Sediment is any loose or fragmented material. Loose sand, shells, leaves, and mud are examples of sediment. All sediment has a **source** (place of origin). Here it was produced by the life cycles of plants or animals (shells, leaves, logs), or by **chemical weathering** of rocks (chemical disintegration and decomposition), or by **physical weathering** of rocks (mechanical breakdown).

All sediment has a **provenance**, which is the geographic place or region from which its components were derived. The particular rocks or other materials that are weathered are called **parent materials.** Sediment also is commonly **eroded** (physically removed) and **transported** (carried to other locations) from its provenance by water, ice, or wind.

The transportation process naturally separates different densities and sizes of sediments from one another, a phenomenon called **sorting.** Poorly sorted sediments are composed of many different sizes and/or densities of grains mixed together. Well-sorted sediments, however, are composed of grains that are of similar size and/or density.

Well-sorted sediments usually are composed of *well-rounded* grains, because the grains have been abraded (worn down) and rounded during transportation. Conversely, poorly sorted sediments usually are *angular* (have sharp corners), because of the lack of abrasion during transportation. *Roundness* is the sharpness of corners on a grain of sediment, viewed in profile (side view). Terms used by sedimentologists to describe roundness are well-rounded, subrounded, subangular, and angular.

Grain size usually is expressed in **Wentworth classes,** named after C. K. Wentworth, an American geologist who devised the scale in 1922. Here are the Wentworth grain-size classes commonly used by sedimentologists in describing sediments:

gravel   includes grains larger than 2 mm diameter (granules, pebbles, cobbles, boulders).

sand   includes grains from 1/16 mm to 2 mm diameter (in decimal form, 0.0625 mm to 2.000 mm).

silt   includes grains from 1/256 mm to 1/16 mm diameter (in decimal form, 0.0039 mm to 0.0625 mm).

clay   includes grains less than 1/256 mm diameter (in decimal form, 0.0039 mm).

SEDIMENTARY STRUCTURES

A variety of structures occur in sedimentary rocks. Most of these structures form as the sediments are being transported and deposited. The most obvious is **stratification** (layering of sediments). Most layers of sediment, or **strata** (plural of *stratum,* a single layer), accumulate in nearly horizontal sheets (Figures 5.1, 5.2, 5.3). Strata less than 1 cm thick are

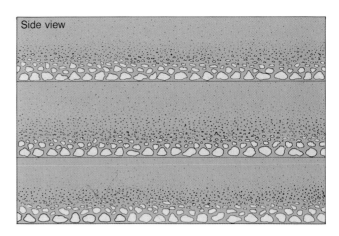

FIGURE 5.2   Graded stratification. Schematic vertical profile of a deposit of horizontal strata that are internally graded. Each stratum is internally graded from coarse (at the base) to fine (at the top).

called **laminations;** strata 1 cm or more thick are called **beds.**

Surfaces between strata are called **bedding planes.** These represent surfaces of exposure that occurred between sedimentary depositional events. To illustrate, imagine a series of storms, each of which causes sediment to be deposited in puddles. Each storm is a sedimentary depositional event. Between storms, deposition stops, and the sediment surfaces in the puddles (bedding plane surfaces) become exposed to the action of water in the puddles, or to the action of weathering as dry surfaces after puddles evaporate.

Most strata are deposited in nearly horizontal sheets. However, some stratification is inclined, and is referred to as **cross-stratification** or **cross-bedding.** For example, sediment transported in a single direction by water or air currents commonly forms **asymmetrical ripple marks** (Figure 5.4) or **dunes** (Figures 11.5 and 11.6). Transportation of sediments by bidirectional current or by very gentle waves commonly forms **symmetrical ripple marks** (Figures 5.5 and 5.6). Both types of structures are internally cross-stratified (Figures 5.4, 5.5, 5.7).

Individual strata also may be **graded** (Figure 5.2). Normally, graded beds are sorted from coarse at the bottom to fine at the top. This feature is caused when sediment-laden currents suddenly slow as they enter a standing body of water, or as current flow terminates.

Tool marks may form on bedding planes when objects such as shells, sticks, pebbles, or bones slide, roll, or bounce along a surface. Tool

FIGURE 5.1   Horizontal stratification. Schematic vertical profile (cutaway side view) of a deposit of horizontal strata.

FIGURE 5.3 Laminated beach sand, viewed in vertical profile. Note pen for size (15 cm or 6 in. long). The light-colored laminations are mainly quartz sand. Dark laminations are mainly magnetite and tourmaline sand, collectively called "heavy minerals" because their specific gravities are greater than those of light-colored minerals like the quartz. (Photo by P. J. W. Gore)

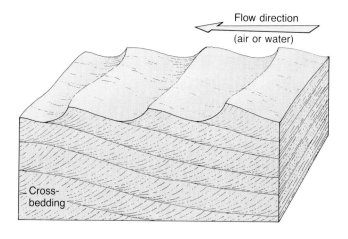

FIGURE 5.4 Asymmetrical ripple marks. Note their internal cross-stratification and the record they provide of the flow direction. They also are called "current" ripple marks, because water (or wind) currents make these ripples (or larger dunes) as they transport sedimentary grains in a single direction. This occurs either along the bottom of a water body or along the surfaces of sand dunes (see Figure 11.5).

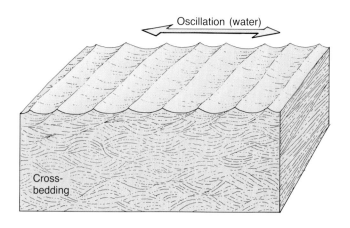

FIGURE 5.5 Symmetrical ripple marks. Note their internal cross-stratification and the record they provide of the bidirectional flow of water. Symmetrical ripple marks also are called "oscillatory" ripple marks because they can be caused by wave oscillations that gently reach the bottom of a water body.

FIGURE 5.6 Well-developed symmetrical (or oscillatory) ripple marks on a bedding surface. This rock formed in eastern Kansas about 290 million years ago. The original sedimentary grains that compose these ripple marks are fossil shells that have been naturally cemented together by calcite to form rock. Note pencil for size (14 cm or 5½ in. long). (Photo by R. Busch)

FIGURE 5.7 Large-scale cross-stratification that developed with sand-sized grains of quartz in a shallow sea. The sand was naturally cemented by calcite after it was deposited during the Mississippian Period about 340 million years ago in central Pennsylvania. These cross-strata now are preserved in a rock body called the Loyalhanna Member of the Mauch Chunk Formation. (Photo by R. Busch)

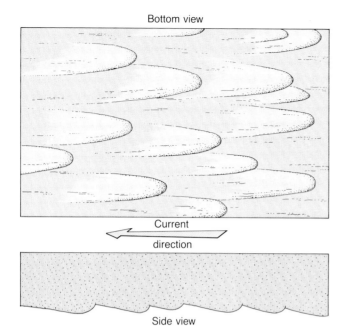

Bottom view

Current direction

Side view

FIGURE 5.8 Flute casts. Flutes are V-shaped or scoop-shaped depressions that are winnowed by water or wind currents. Flute casts form when the flutes fill with sediment. Note orientation of flute casts relative to actual current direction.

marks appear as holes or linear drag marks. **Flutes** are scoop-shaped or V-shaped depressions scoured into a surface by the erosional, winnowing action of currents. Natural casts of flutes are called **flute casts.** Flutes and flute casts indicate current direction, because they flare out (widen) and become shallower in the down-current direction (Figures 5.8 and 5.9).

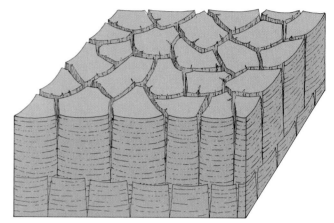

FIGURE 5.10 Mud cracks. The mud is stratified, with well-developed desiccation (drying) cracks. Note that the cracks between mud-crack polygons widen upward. This is due to shrinking of the mud as it dries.

FIGURE 5.9 Flute casts preserved on an ancient bedding surface. Also visible are casts of tool marks, indicating where ocean currents dragged objects along the ancient seafloor while they were winnowing the flutes. This occurred during the Ordovician Period (450 million years ago) in eastern New York state. Note hammer for size (about 38 cm or 15 in. long). (Photo by E. J. Anderson)

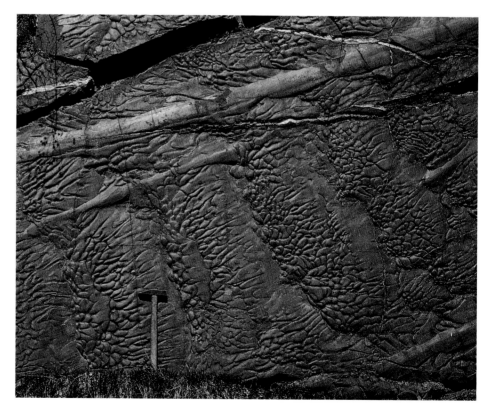

Many sedimentary rocks also contain structures that formed shortly after deposition of the sediments that compose them. For example, **desiccation cracks** often form while moist deposits of mud dry and shrink (Figures 5.10 and 5.12), and **raindrop impressions** or hailstone imprints may form on terrestrial (land) surfaces (Figure 5.11). Animals make tracks, trails, and burrows (Figures 5.13 and 5.15), which also can be preserved in sedimentary rocks (Figures 5.14, 5.15, 5.16). Such traces of former life are called **trace fossils.**

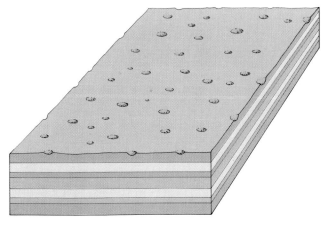

FIGURE 5.11 Raindrop impressions in the top bedding plane of stratified mud.

FIGURE 5.12 Mud cracks from the Silurian Period (410 million years ago), preserved in limestone in western Maryland. Field of view is 46 cm (18 in.) wide. (Photo by E. J. Anderson)

SEDIMENTARY ENVIRONMENTS

Sediments are deposited in many different environments. A variety of these environments are illustrated in Figure 5.17. They have been studied in great detail, so for each type we know the characteristic sediments, sedimentary structures, and **fossils** (any evidence of prehistoric life). We will examine some of these environments in more detail in later exercises. The information gained from grain characteristics, sedimentary structures, and fossils can be used to infer what ancient environments—**paleoenvironments**—were like in comparison to modern ones.

CLASTIC SEDIMENTS AND DETRITAL ROCKS

A **clast** is any mechanically transported fragment of a parent material. Therefore, **clastic sediment** is composed chiefly of mechanically transported fragments broken from some type of whole parent material (e.g., rocks, logs, animal shells). Because some sedimentary rocks are composed chiefly of clastic sediment, geologists informally classify them as **clastic rocks.**

Some clastic rocks are named for the particular type of clasts they contain. **Pyroclastic rocks** contain mostly clasts ejected from volcanoes (cin-

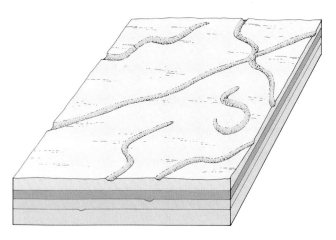 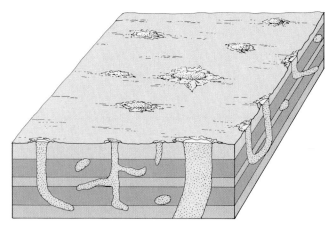

FIGURE 5.13 Trails and burrows in horizontal strata. Compare horizontal trails that lie within a single stratum and vertical/oblique trails that burrow through the stratification.

FIGURE 5.14 Bedding plane surface in limestone of Pennsylvanian age (290 million years old) in southeastern Kansas. Note the variety of trace fossils and coin for scale. (Photo by R. Busch)

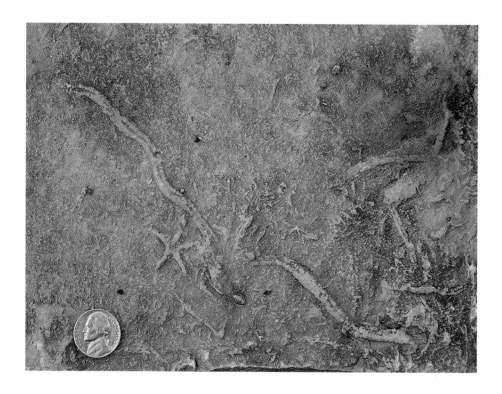

ders, ash, and volcanic bombs like that in Figure 4.15). These materials collectively are called *pyroclastics*. **Bioclastic rocks** contain mostly clasts derived from animals (bones, shells) and plants (trees). **Siliciclastic rocks** are composed of *siliciclasts*. These are either fragments of silicate minerals (like quartz, feldspar, mica) or rock-fragment clasts weathered from rocks composed of silicate minerals.

Most clastic sediment is mixed with chemically disintegrated portions of preexisting rocks, and with untransported fragments of preexisting

rocks, to form **detrital sediment.** Therefore, detrital sediment, or *detritus*, includes:

1. Microscopic clay minerals (formed chiefly from chemical disintegration of feldspars and micas).
2. Euhedral mineral crystals freshly weathered from nearby rock exposures (called *mineral grains*).
3. Abraded mineral crystals transported from distant sources (also called *mineral grains*).
4. Fragments (transported or untransported) of existing rocks (called *rock fragments*).

FIGURE 5.15 Animal tracks, now and then. A. Fresh dog print made on desiccation-cracked, muddy intertidal surface on St. Catherines Island, Georgia. B. Three-toed track made by a small dinosaur about 215 million years ago on desiccation-cracked bedding plane in Triassic-age shale from southeastern Pennsylvania. (Photos by R. Busch)

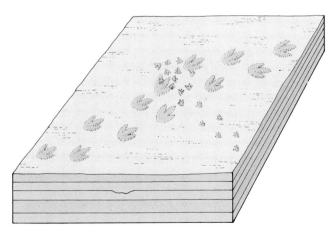

FIGURE 5.16 Dinosaur tracks on a plane bedding surface.

Rocks formed from detrital sediments are called **detrital sedimentary rocks.** These include *inorganic* detrital rocks (described in Figure 5.18) and *organic* detrital rocks formed of broken and unbro- ken shells or plant material (described in Figure 5.19).

CHEMICAL AND BIOCHEMICAL SEDIMENTARY ROCKS

Chemical sedimentary rocks are crystalline sedimentary rocks. They form by precipitation of inorganic materials from water (generally aragonite, calcite, halite, gypsum, or opal/chert). Chemical limestone forms from chemical precipitation of aragonite or calcite; rock salt from halite; and rock gypsum from gypsum. Chert develops by precipitation of fibrous varieties of quartz or by chemical alteration of opal.

Biochemical sedimentary rocks are the result of organic processes. They include rocky materials made of plant fragments (peat, coal) or resins (amber). They also include skeletal limestone (limestone made of animal shells, or skeletons).

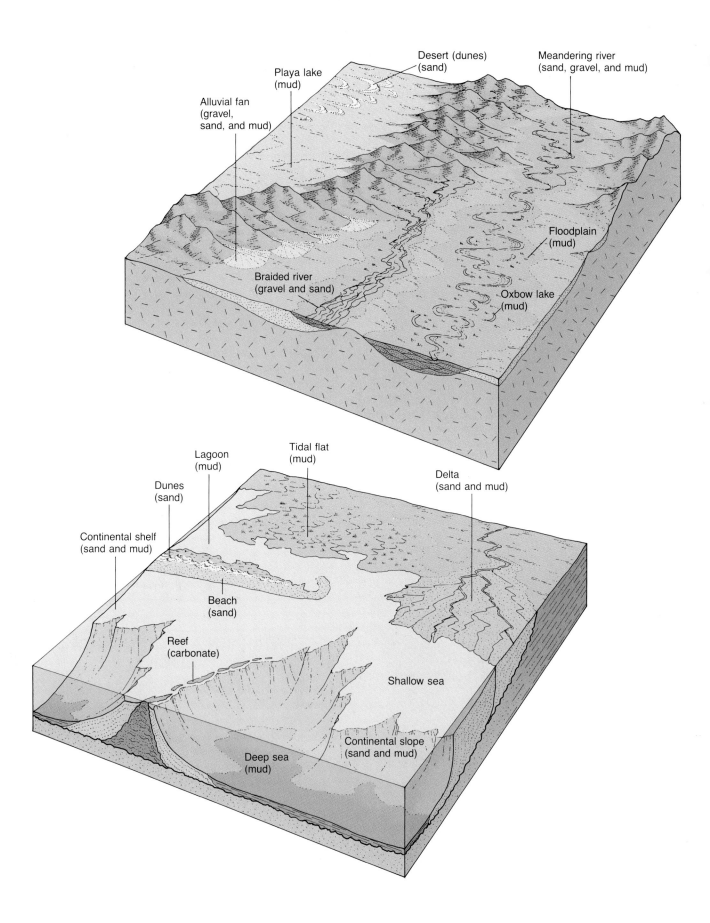

FIGURE 5.17 (Opposite page) The range of environments in which sediments accumulate. In each environment, specific physical processes form characteristic sedimentary structures and sediments. Each environment also supports particular plants and animals. These bio-agents disrupt sediments and contribute sedimentary grains (bones, shells, plant fragments) that may become fossilized.

FIGURE 5.18 Classification of sedimentary rocks: inorganic detrital.

Composition	Grain-size Class and Diameter		Comments	Name	
Mainly quartz, feldspar, rock fragments, and clay minerals	gravel (> 2mm)		rounded grains	CONGLOMERATE	
			angular grains	BRECCIA	
	sand (0.0625–2.00, or 1/16–2, mm)		mostly quartz grains	QUARTZ SANDSTONE	SANDSTONE
			mostly feldspar grains	ARKOSE	
			mostly rock fragments	LITHIC SANDSTONE	
			mixed with much silt and clay	WACKE	
	mud	silt (0.0039–0.0625, or 1/256–1/16, mm)	nonfissile (compact)	SILTSTONE	MUDSTONE
			fissile (splits easily)	SHALE	
		clay (< 0.0039, or 1/256, mm)	nonfissile (compact)	CLAYSTONE	
			fissile (splits easily)	SHALE	

SEDIMENTARY ROCK IDENTIFICATION

Use this procedure to identify sedimentary rocks:

1. Use Figures 5.18 and 5.19 to determine if the rock is:
   a. an inorganic detrital rock (Figure 5.18), or
   b. a chemical sedimentary rock (Figure 5.19), or
   c. a biochemical sedimentary rock (Figure 5.19).
2. In Figure 5.18, first determine the *grain-size class.* Then use the *comments* to determine the rock name.
3. In Figure 5.19, first determine the *composition* of the rock. Then use *comments* and *grain size* to determine the rock name.

Some sedimentary rocks are illustrated in Figures 5.20 through 5.35. Review them before you proceed.

QUESTIONS

1. The photograph in Figure 5.3 was taken by a person standing on an ocean beach and looking landward. Realize that this is a freshly excavated vertical section of beach sand, and not sandstone.
   a. Imagine how the bedding planes of these laminations are oriented. If you walked oceanward, would they be horizontal or inclined? Explain.
   b. Explain a coastal process that could produce the segregation of the light-colored and dark-colored mineral grains.
   c. What freshly buried items would you expect to find in this modern sandy beach deposit which could be found by future geologists after this sand has turned to sandstone?

2. Examine Figures 5.4 and 5.5.
   a. Which type of ripple marks would you expect to see on the bed of a river? Why?
   b. Which type would you expect to find on the floor of a standing body of water, such as a lake? Why?

3. Examine Figure 5.6.
   a. Suggest a paleoenvironment where these ripple marks may have formed.
   b. What other information would you look for at the location to test your idea?

4. The cross-stratification in Figure 5.7 is inclined in two different directions. This is called bimodal cross-stratification.
   a. How could this form?
   b. Suggest a modern environment (from Figure 5.17) where such a marine deposit could form.

5. The flow direction of prehistoric currents, or paleocurrents, is indicated by sedimentary structures like the flute casts in Figure 5.9. From what direction did the currents flow that formed these flute casts (from the right or left)?

6. Examine Figure 5.10.
   a. Suggest a rule for using desiccation cracks to determine which-way-is-up in a sequence of strata.
   b. Could desiccation cracks form in deposits of sand? Explain.

7. Imagine that you just found the rock in Figure 5.14.
   a. What paleoenvironment is represented by this sample? (Refer to Figure 5.17 for some possibilities.)
   b. What is your evidence for this?

Composition	Comments		Grain-size	Name	
Mainly calcium carbonate, $CaCO_3$	shells or shell fragments (i.e., skeletal grains) well cemented to form dense rock		gravel (> 2 mm)	CALCIRUDITE	SKELETAL LIMESTONE
			sand (0.0625–2 mm)	CALCARENITE	
			silt (0.0039–0.0625 mm)	CALCISILTITE	
			clay (< 0.0039 mm)	MICRITE	
	shells or shell fragments (i.e., skeletal grains) poorly cemented to form porous, earthy rock		gravel (> 2 mm)	COQUINA	
			sand (0.0625–2 mm)	CALCARENITE	
			silt and clay (< 0.0625 mm)	CHALK	
	spherical grains with concentric laminations		< 2 mm	OOLITIC LIMESTONE	
	crystals fomed as inorganic chemical precipitates		coarse-grained (> 2 mm) to fine-grained (0.0039 mm)	CRYSTALLINE LIMESTONE	CHEMICAL LIMESTONE
			very fine grained (< 0.0039 mm)	MICRITE	
Mainly dolomite, $CaMg(CO_3)_2$	commonly altered from limestone		all sizes	DOLOSTONE	
Mainly varieties of quartz, SIO_2 (chalcedony, flint, chert, opal, jasper, etc.)	layers, lenses, nodules		microcrystalline or amorphous	CHERT	
Mainly halite, NaCl	crystals formed as inorganic chemical precipitates		all sizes	ROCK SALT	
Mainly gypsum, $CaSO_4 \cdot 2H_2O$	crystals formed as inorganic chemical precipitates		all sizes	ROCK GYPSUM	
Mainly plant fragments	brown and porous		all sizes	PEAT	
	black and nonporous		all sizes or dense with conchoidal fracture	BITUMINOUS COAL	

FIGURE 5.19 Classification of sedimentary rocks: chemical and biochemical.

FIGURE 5.20 Clastic shell gravel that accumulated on a modern beach of Crane Key, Florida. Also visible are blades of the sea grass *Thalassia*. Except for the plant debris, all sediment on this island consists of shells or shell clasts that are gravel-to-clay sized. Note pen for size (11 cm or 4 in. long). (Photo by R. Busch)

8. Imagine that you just found the rock in Figure 5.15 (right side).
    a. Suggest a paleoenvironment that is represented by the sample, and explain your reasoning.
    b. What other evidence would you look for to support your hypothesis?

9. Examine the dinosaur footprints in Figure 5.16. Imagine that you found a rock exposure with such a bedding plane surface. What biologic activity would you infer to have occurred there?

10. Obtain a set of sedimentary rocks from your instructor. For each sample:
    a. Name any structures present.
    b. Identify the type(s) of mineral grains or mineral crystals that compose the rock, and give their sizes.
    c. Describe how the rock and its structures (if present) formed.
    d. Name the rock.

FIGURE 5.21 Coquina, a poorly cemented, porous, skeletal limestone composed chiefly of whole shells or shell clasts (commonly both). This sample is from mainland Florida, where it formed by poor cementation of a shell gravel like that in Figure 5.20.

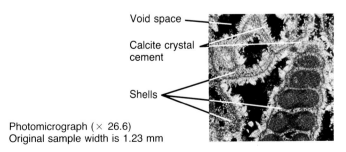

Void space
Calcite crystal cement
Shells

Photomicrograph (× 26.6)
Original sample width is 1.23 mm

FIGURE 5.22 Dense skeletal limestone. This well-cemented specimen is more dense and less porous than the coquina in Figure 5.21. Note the shells and shell clasts.

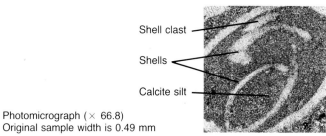

Shell clast

Shells

Calcite silt

Photomicrograph (× 66.8)
Original sample width is 0.49 mm

FIGURE 5.23 A chemical limestone called *travertine.* Note its layers of intergrown calcite crystals, precipitated from water that flowed over the walls of a cave (thus giving rise to its alternate name, flowstone). Travertine also forms around the edges of evaporating ponds or springs, but it generally is less dense than cave travertine and is called *tufa.*

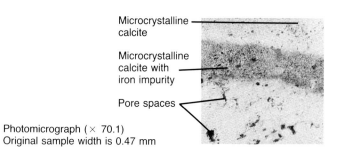

Microcrystalline calcite

Microcrystalline calcite with iron impurity

Pore spaces

Photomicrograph (× 70.1)
Original sample width is 0.47 mm

FIGURE 5.24 Gypsum, a hydrous calcium sulfate which commonly occurs as beds of rock gypsum in sedimentary rocks. Gypsum is an *evaporite* mineral, meaning that it precipitates from evaporating brines (very salty waters). Gypsum precipitates from ocean water after about 80% of the water has evaporated. Halite (Figure 5.26) precipitates when about 90% of the water has evaporated.

ADDITIONAL QUESTIONS

11. Refer to Figure 5.36. Place checks in appropriate boxes to indicate environments where the listed sedimentary structure may form. (It may be helpful to refer to Figure 5.17).
12. Consider the weathering (both chemical decomposition and mechanical breakdown) of a freshly exposed granite body to produce detrital sediment. Describe the chemical and physical changes that will occur, and characterize the sediment, from its source (the granite body) to a quartz sand beach 200 miles away.
13. Based upon your reasoning in the last question, describe the origin of the sediments that formed the rocks in:
    a. Figure 5.32
    b. Figure 5.29
    c. Figure 5.28
    d. Figure 5.34

FIGURE 5.25 Chert, a fibrous variety of quartz common in sedimentary rocks as nodules or beds. Because silica is rare in ocean water (about 12–14 parts per million), chert does not form in significant amounts from evaporation of ocean water. Instead, it occurs where silica has been concentrated in animal shells, plant cells, or groundwater. Siliceous parts of organisms can dissolve and re-form as chert, or chert can form inorganically from silica-rich groundwater. This piece of a chert nodule formed in the Threemile Limestone near Manhattan, Kansas during the Permian Period (270 million years ago). (Photo by R. Busch)

FIGURE 5.26 Rock salt, a chemical sedimentary rock consisting of intergrown crystals of the mineral halite (table salt). Halite is an evaporite mineral that precipitates when about 90% of a body of ocean water has evaporated (compare Figure 5.24). This sample formed in Michigan near the end of the Silurian Period (about 415 million years ago) when an ocean arm was closed off and the water evaporated. Its orange-brown color is due to an impurity, iron.

FIGURE 5.27 Sandstone. This sample could be called "ferruginous quartz sandstone" because it is composed of sand-size quartz grains that have been cemented with limonite. Limonite is a ferruginous (iron-bearing) mineral, a hydrous iron oxide that gives the rock its rusty-brown color (see Figure 2.24). The limonite forms from water percolating through the sand and sandstone. Alternating wet and dry conditions produce bands of limonite called liesegang bands.

Liesegang band of limonite cement

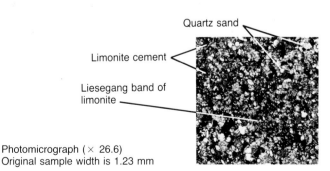

Quartz sand

Limonite cement

Liesegang band of limonite

Photomicrograph (× 26.6)
Original sample width is 1.23 mm

FIGURE 5.28 Sandstone. This sample could be called "calcareous quartz sandstone" because it is composed of sand-size quartz grains that have been cemented with calcite. A minor amount of hematite cement gives the rock its pinkish color.

Quartz sand

Calcite cement

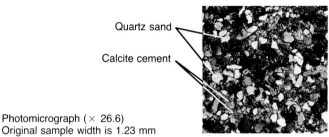

Photomicrograph ($\times$ 26.6)
Original sample width is 1.23 mm

FIGURE 5.29 Conglomerate is a detrital sedimentary rock composed chiefly of rounded gravel (grains larger than sand) that is poorly sorted. The gravel in this sample has been cemented with hematite (see Figure 2.7), which gives the rock its red-to-brown color.

FIGURE 5.30 Breccia, a detrital sedimentary rock composed chiefly of angular gravel (grains larger than sand) that is poorly sorted. This sample is a limestone breccia, because it consists of angular fragments of limestone cemented with calcite. Some of the calcite cement is brown due to a minor iron impurity.

FIGURE 5.31 Shale, a detrital sedimentary rock composed of mud-sized grains, making it a type of mudstone. Shale also has a characteristic fissility (splitting) that is developed along bedding plane surfaces. This sample bears a fossil on a bedding plane. It is a trilobite, a marine creature related to modern crayfish and horseshoe crabs. Trilobites lived only during the Paleozoic Era and are extinct.

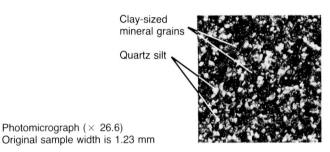

Clay-sized mineral grains

Quartz silt

Photomicrograph (× 26.6)
Original sample width is 1.23 mm

FIGURE 5.32 Arkose is sandstone (a detrital sedimentary rock) composed chiefly of feldspar grains derived from preexisting rocks. The feldspar grains in this specimen are potassium feldspar, because they are pink (see Figure 2.21). Some gray or white quartz grains also are present.

FIGURE 5.33 Siltstone is a detrital sedimentary rock composed of silt-sized grains. It generally is more compact and less fissile than shale. This sample contains a fossil leaf.

FIGURE 5.34 Claystone is mudstone (a detrital sedimentary rock) composed of clay-sized grains. It usually lacks fissility. Most claystones contain abundant grains of "clay minerals." These are mica-like aluminum silicate minerals that commonly form from the chemical disintegration of feldspars and micas. Some claystone also is cemented with calcite, and can be termed "calcareous claystone." The sample shown contains a leaf from a tree that grew in North Dakota about 63 million years ago (Paleocene Epoch).

FIGURE 5.35 Bituminous coal, a biochemical sedimentary rock composed chiefly of compacted plants and plant fragments. Bituminous coal also is called "soft coal" because you can easily break it apart with your hands. Note the original stratification visible in this sample.

FIGURE 5.36 Some sedimentary environments and the sedimentary structures that they contain.

Sedimentary structure	River, stream	Shallow sea	Beach	Dry lake bottom	Sand dunes (wind)	Deep sea	Tidal flat
Asymmetrical ripple marks							
Symmetrical ripple marks							
Cross-bedding							
Mud cracks							
Raindrop prints							
Lamination							
Graded bedding							
Flute marks							
Tool marks							
Tracks							
Trails							
Burrows							

EXERCISE SIX
Metamorphic Processes and Rocks

Patricia A. Weisse
Harold E. Andrews
James R. Besancon
Margaret D. Thompson
Wellesley College

PURPOSE

This exercise introduces you to metamorphic processes, rock textures, mineralogical changes, and rock classification.

MATERIALS

Hand lens, metric ruler, mineral identification materials of your choice, pencil, paper, and samples of metamorphic rocks provided by your instructor.

INTRODUCTION

Metamorphic rocks are those that have been altered physically and/or chemically. The agents of these changes include intense heat, intense pressure, and/or the chemical action of hot *fluids* (flowing substances, including both liquids and gases). (The word "metamorphic" means *of changed form*.)

Because every metamorphic rock is a changed rock, each has a *precursor*: the rock type that existed prior to metamorphism. Precursors for metamorphic rocks can be any of the three basic types: igneous rock, sedimentary rock, or even metamorphic rocks (i.e., metamorphic rocks can be metamorphosed again).

SCALES OF METAMORPHISM

There are two main scales at which metamorphic processes occur: contact and regional.

Contact metamorphism occurs locally, adjacent to igneous intrusions (Figure 6.1, lower right corner). It also occurs along fractures that are in contact with hot fluids (gases or liquids). The intensity of contact metamorphism is greatest at the contact between host rock and intrusive magma or hot gases (metamorphosing fluids). The intensity then decreases rapidly over a short distance from the magma or gases. Thus, zones of contact metamorphism are narrow.

Regional metamorphism occurs over very large areas, such as mountain ranges (Figure 6.1). Regional metamorphism results from (1) major igneous intrusions that form and cool over long periods (thousands to millions of years); (2) the extreme pressure and heat associated with deep burial or tectonic movements of rock; or (3) very widespread migration of hot fluids throughout a region. The latter process involves condensation of gases to form liquids, and precipitation of crystals. Such alteration by hot, watery fluids is called **hydrothermal metamorphism.**

You should know that the distinction between contact and regional metamorphism often is blurred. Contact metamorphism may be caused by

FIGURE 6.1 Hypothetical vertical section through a mountain range that contains a very large granite intrusion (lower right). The cross section illustrates both contact and regional metamorphic effects of the heat and pressure caused by the intrusion. Compare the broad, regional metamorphic changes to the narrow zone of *contact metamorphism* adjacent to the intrusion.

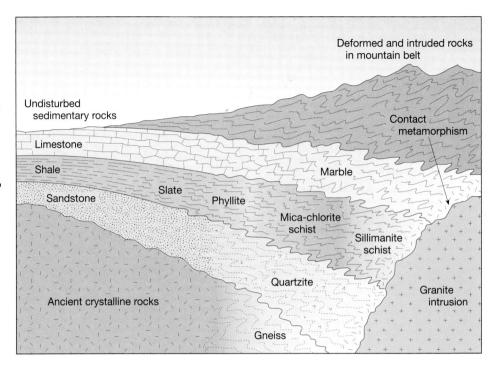

small igneous intrusions, or by the local effects of hydrothermal fluids from some distance away that are traveling along fractures or other voids. Regional metamorphism may be caused by large intrusions, the action of abundant and widespread hydrothermal fluids associated with large intrusions, and/or tectonism. One kind of metamorphism replaces another, so that rocks undergo both regional and contact metamorphism. Most major intrusions are preceded by contact metamorphism and followed by regional metamorphism.

PLATE TECTONICS AND METAMORPHISM

Recall the process of seafloor spreading, which forces large plates of Earth's thin lithosphere to move about relative to one another, like pieces in a global jigsaw puzzle (see Figure 1.13, plate tectonics features). These plates move toward, beside, or away from one another. This causes large-scale deformation of the plates, called **plate tectonism.**

Seafloor spreading and plate tectonism account for several Earth phenomena: (1) crustal melting in subduction zones (see Figure 4.3, showing igneous features); (2) emplacement of magma under large regions; (3) widespread zones of pressure compaction and folding, due to lateral motions; and (4) widespread hydrothermal activity

zones associated with crustal weakness or intrusion of magma. Therefore, seafloor spreading and plate tectonism play a major role in the development of metamorphic rocks on Earth.

For example, during the Permian Period, over 250 million years ago, the North American and Eurasian plates collided (see map, Figure 1.14). This caused Appalachian Mountain sediments in eastern North America to become highly folded and otherwise pressure-compacted, like an accordion. The enormous pressure caused preexisting rocks to become metamorphosed, shown schematically in Figure 6.1. Shales metamorphosed into slates, phyllites, and schists. Sandstones metamorphosed into quartzites, and limestones into marbles. Where bituminous coals existed, they metamorphosed into anthracite coal. Beneath the sedimentary strata, ancient crystalline rocks metamorphosed into gneisses.

Subsequent separation (rifting) of the North American and Eurasian plates began during the Triassic Period (213–248 million years ago). This rifting allowed hot fluids to rise through the metamorphic rocks along fractures from Earth's mantle. Thus, much hydrothermal metamorphism occurred following the plate-collision pressure metamorphism.

Of course, plate separation has continued to the present day, and has led to development of the present Atlantic Ocean basin. No tectonic activity

FIGURE 6.2 (Opposite page) Some minerals commonly found in metamorphic rocks, in addition to those considered in Exercise Two. (Photos by R. Busch)

A. Staurolite.
   Fe-Al silicate, in long prisms;
   H = 7, brown, S.G. = 3.7–3.8;
   Indicates intermediate-to-high-grade
   metamorphism.

B. Actinolite.
   Calcium Mg-Al silicate in long prisms; H = 5–6;
   S.G. = 3.0–3.2; Indicates low to intermediate
   grade of metamorphism (also in some
   igneous rocks).

C. Kyanite.
   Al silicate, in blades;
   H = 5 and 7, gray-blue, S.G. = 3.6–3.7;
   Indicates intermediate-to-high-grade
   metamorphism.

D. Sillimanite.
   Al silicate, in needles;
   H = 6–7, white to brown, S.G. = 3.2;
   Indicates high-grade metamorphism.

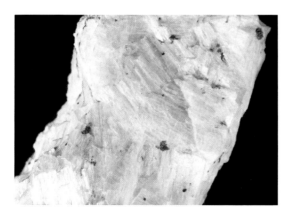

E. Wollastonite.
   Ca silicate, fibrous or massive;
   H = 4.5–5, S.G. = 2.8–2.9;
   Slight reaction to HCl;
   Indicates contact metamorphism in
   carbonate rocks.

F. Tremolite.
   Hydrous Ca silicate, fibrous;
   H = 5–6, S.G. = 2.9–3.2;
   No reaction to HCl;
   Indicates contact metamorphism in
   carbonate rocks.

is presently in action in eastern North America. The metamorphic rocks in this region presently are being exposed at Earth's surface by the surficial processes of weathering and erosion.

MINERAL CHANGES DURING METAMORPHISM

You may encounter some minerals during this laboratory exercise that were not included in Exercise Two. These additional minerals appear in Figure 6.2.

The effects of pressure, heat, and fluids during metamorphism cause mineralogical changes in rocks (Figure 6.3). The most common change is **recrystallization**—small crystals of one mineral will slowly convert to fewer, larger crystals of the same mineral, without melting of the rock. For example, microscopic muscovite crystals in a *slate* (Figure 6.4) can recrystallize to larger (although essentially microscopic) muscovite crystals in *phyllite* (Figure 6.5), and to even larger (easily visible to the unaided eye) muscovite crystals in *schist* (Figure 6.6). These changes indicate an increasing grade of metamorphism (bottom of Figure 6.3).

Mineralogy also may change due to **neomorphism.** In this process, minerals not only recrystallize, but also form different minerals from the same chemical elements. For example, shales composed mainly of clay minerals, quartz grains, and feldspar grains may neomorphose to a metamorphic rock composed mainly of muscovite and garnets (Figure 6.7).

Mineralogy also may change due to **metasomatism.** In this process, elements are added or lost, causing new minerals to form. The new minerals include only some of the precursor elements, plus new ones from hydrothermal fluids. (Metasomatism is an effect of hydrothermal metamorphism; migrating hydrothermal fluids make available new elements for crystal growth and exchange.) **Skarn** is a metamorphic rock for which the precursor rock was limestone, but as a metasomatic product, skarn also contains many unusual silicate, carbonate, and sulfide minerals.

Metasomatism occurs only in open systems, where elements can be gained or lost. On the other hand, recrystallization and neomorphism can occur in closed systems, where essentially no elements are gained or lost.

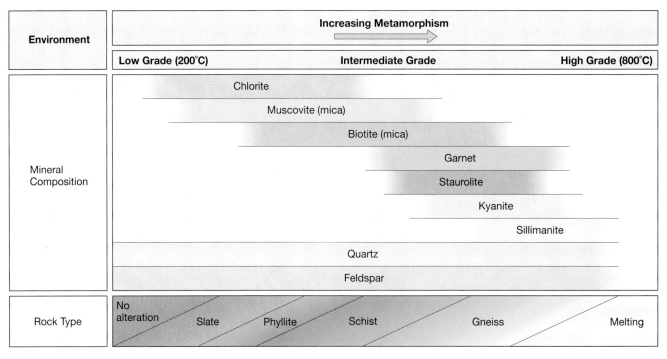

FIGURE 6.3 The typical transition in mineralogy (neomorphism) that can result from progressive metamorphism of shale. (After Lutgens, F. K., and Tarbuck, E. J., 1989, *Essentials of Geology,* 3d ed., Fig. 5.13, p. 116, Columbus: Macmillan Publishing Company)

FIGURE 6.4 Slate is a foliated metamorphic rock having very fine grains (microscopic). It is formed by low-grade metamorphism of mudstones (shales, claystones). The foliations are planar and parallel, so the rock breaks into thin, planar sheets. This type of foliation resembles cleavage in minerals, so it is called *slaty cleavage* or slaty rock cleavage.

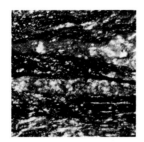

Photomicrograph (× 27.8)
Original sample width is 1.17 mm

METAMORPHIC TEXTURES

There are two main metamorphic rock textures, foliated and nonfoliated.

Foliated textures exhibit foliations, which are parallel planes of platy (flat) minerals (mostly micas) that have been realigned due to pressure and recrystallization. (Some elongated minerals, such as tourmaline and hornblende, also are foliated, for a different reason: their crystalline growth has a preferred orientation due to directed pressure.) The common types of foliated texture are:

- **slaty cleavage** a nearly perfect, planar, parallel foliation of very fine-grained platy minerals (mainly micas). Slaty cleavage commonly is developed in slate (Figure 6.4), a product of low-grade metamorphism (Figure 6.3).
- **phyllitic texture** a parallel, but wavy, foliation of fine-grained platy minerals (mainly micas and chlorite), exhibiting a shiny or glossy luster. Phyllitic texture is best developed in phyllite (Figure 6.5), a product of relatively low-grade metamorphism (Figure 6.3).
- **schistosity** a parallel-to-subparallel foliation of medium-to-coarse-grained platy minerals (mainly micas and chlorite). It is commonly developed in schists (Figures 6.6, 6.7, and 6.8), which are products of intermediate-to-high grades of metamorphism (Figure 6.3).
- **gneissic texture** a parallel-to-subparallel foliation of medium-to-coarse-grained platy minerals, in alternating layers of different composition (dominated by different minerals). This texture is well developed in gneiss (Figure 6.9). Gneisses are

thus often distinctly banded. Ferromagnesian minerals usually form the dark bands, and quartz, feldspars, or carbonate minerals usually form the light bands. Most gneisses are the

FIGURE 6.5 Phyllite is a foliated metamorphic rock having fine-to-medium grains (barely visible to the unaided eye). Phyllites have a silvery reflection and a wrinkled appearance (*phyllitic texture*). They form by the low-grade metamorphism of mudstones (shales, claystones) or slate. The grade of metamorphism is between the low grade that produces slate and the intermediate grade that produces schist (Figure 6.3).

FIGURE 6.6 Schist is a foliated metamorphic rock having medium-to-coarse grains (easily visible). It is formed by recrystallization that accompanies intermediate-grade metamorphism of mudstone, slate, or phyllite. The subparallel alignment of medium-to-coarse-grained platy minerals (usually micas) is called *schistosity*. This gives the rock a shiny luster.

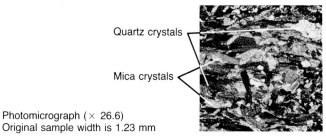

Quartz crystals

Mica crystals

Photomicrograph (× 26.6)
Original sample width is 1.23 mm

FIGURE 6.7 Garnet schist. This sample is composed chiefly of coarse-grained muscovite minerals that are aligned to form schistosity. However, there is a large *porphyroblast* of garnet, so the rock has a porphyroblastic texture. The specimen also can be called "garnet muscovite schist." The presence of schistosity, large muscovite crystals, and garnet crystals indicates intermediate-grade metamorphism.

FIGURE 6.8 Chlorite schist. This medium-grained sample is chiefly composed of the green platy mineral, chlorite. Pyrite porphyroblasts (brassy cubes) give this rock a "porphyroblastic schistosity" like the rock in Figure 6.7. The specimen also can be called "pyrite chlorite schist."

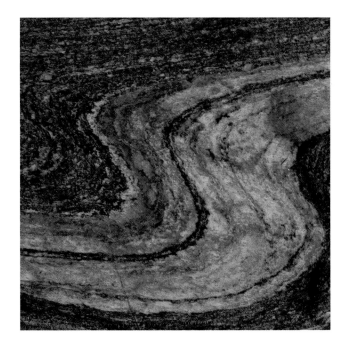

FIGURE 6.9 Folded gneiss. Gneiss is a foliated metamorphic rock having distinct layers or lenses of contrasting mineralogy. Generally, light-colored layers are rich in quartz and feldspars, alternating with dark layers rich in mica and hornblende or tourmaline. This characteristic texture is called *gneissic texture*. Gneisses represent intermediate-to-high-grade metamorphism of granite, diorite, schist, shale, and other rocks. The high grade of metamorphism allowed this gneiss to bend (fold) easily, just as iron bends more easily when heated.

product of intermediate-to-high-grade metamorphism (Figure 6.3).

Nonfoliated textures lack parallel layers of platy minerals. However, they may exhibit stretched fossils or other grains (Figure 6.15). Nonfoliated metamorphic rocks typically are composed of stubby, interlocking mineral grains. All are about the same size (equigranular) due to metamorphic crystallization or recrystallization. Note the examples of marble (Figure 6.10) and quartzite (Figures 6.11 and 6.12), both of which have equigranular, nonfoliated textures.

Some metamorphic rocks contain large crystals, called *porphyroblasts,* set in a finer-grained groundmass (Figure 6.7). This *porphyroblastic texture* may be present in foliated or nonfoliated metamorphic rocks. It is analogous to phenocrysts in igneous porphyries (Figures 4.10, 4.11). Other common features of metamorphic rocks are **folds** (bends) or **crenulations** (parallel sets of very tiny folds up to 1 cm long).

CLASSIFICATION OF METAMORPHIC ROCKS

You can classify common metamorphic rocks, using Figure 6.16 for foliated samples and Figure 6.17 for nonfoliated samples. The foliated rocks can be further classified on the basis of their specific textures and mineralogy (e.g., biotite schist versus garnet

FIGURE 6.10 Marble is a nonfoliated metamorphic rock composed of tightly interlocking grains of calcite. It forms due to intermediate-to-high-grade metamorphism of limestone or dolostone. Compare this densely packed mineral crystal arrangement (note photomicrograph) with the mineral crystal arrangement in travertine (Figure 5.23) and the clastic grains in unmetamorphosed coquina (Figure 5.21).

Calcite crystals

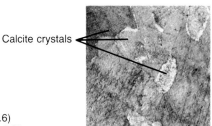

Photomicrograph ($\times$ 26.6)
Original sample width is 1.23 mm

FIGURE 6.11 Quartzite is a nonfoliated metamorphic rock composed chiefly of fused quartz grains. Compare the fused quartz grains of this sample (photomicrograph) with the sedimentary fabric of sandstone, a precursor of quartzite (photomicrographs in Figures 5.27 and 5.28).

Quartz sand grains

Photomicrograph (× 26.6)
Original sample width is 1.23 mm

schist). The nonfoliated rocks can also be qualified with mineralogical denotations (e.g., graphite marble).

QUESTIONS

1. Besides the heat and pressure effects of the granite intrusion in Figure 6.1, list and explain what other metamorphic processes should have affected the cross section of rocks depicted there.

2. Was the rock in Figure 6.12 deformed after the tourmaline crystal formed? How can you tell?

3. Examine the rock in Figure 6.18, and do the following:
   a. Describe its texture(s).
   b. Determine the name of the rock.
   c. Name a likely precursor for the rock (refer to Figure 6.17).
   d. Note whether the rock represents a low, intermediate, or high grade of metamorphism (refer to Figures 6.3, 6.16, 6.17).

4. Examine the rock in Figure 6.19, and do the same directives as listed for Question 3.

5. Examine the rock in Figure 6.20, and do the same directives as listed in Question 3.

6. Examine the rock in Figure 6.21, which is called migmatite. How would such a rock form?

7. How does the rock in Figure 6.21 relate to the subduction zone diagram in Figure 4.3?

8. Obtain a set of metamorphic rocks from your instructor. For each rock sample, do the following:
   a. Describe its texture(s).
   b. Identify minerals of the groundmass, if their size is sufficient to permit identification.
   c. Identify porphyroblasts, if present.
   d. Determine the name of the rock.
   e. Name a likely precursor for the rock (refer to Figure 6.17).
   f. Note whether the rock represents a low, intermediate, or high grade of metamorphism (refer to Figures 6.3, 6.16, 6.17).

ADDITIONAL QUESTIONS

9. Is it likely that nonfoliated metamorphic rocks could be crenulated? Explain.

10. Would a thick sequence of folded metamorphic rocks in a mountain range tend to be foliated or nonfoliated? Would all of the rocks have to be only one way or the other? Explain.

11. If the metamorphic rock in Figure 6.13 were subjected to an even higher grade of metamorphism, then what might it become?

FIGURE 6.12 Tourmaline quartzite. This quartzite is very coarse grained and contains large crystals of tourmaline. Tourmaline is a very complex silicate mineral that forms striated prisms having 3, 6, or 9 sides and a conchoidal fracture. It is a common mineral in metamorphic rocks of all grades.

FIGURE 6.14 Serpentinite is a metamorphic rock composed chiefly of serpentine, which gives the rock its green color. Serpentinites commonly contain minor amounts of talc, magnetite, and chlorite. They form by the low-to-intermediate-grade metamorphism of peridotite (Figure 4.12). This sample contains some fibrous serpentine called *asbestos*.

FIGURE 6.13 Anthracite coal, also known as "hard coal," cannot easily be broken apart like its precursor, bituminous or "soft" coal (see Figure 5.35). Anthracite has a homogeneous texture and breaks along glossy conchoidal fractures. It is formed by low-to-intermediate-grade metamorphism of bituminous coal.

|← —————— 34 cm —————— →|

FIGURE 6.15 Stretched-pebble metaconglomerate. During metamorphism, this sample was naturally heated so much that individual grains softened. As the softened rock was stretched, the grains became elongated. Compare this sample to the unmetamorphosed conglomerate in Figure 5.29.

Crystal Size	Rock Names		Comments
Microscopic, very fine grained	SLATE		Slaty cleavage well developed
Fine-grained	PHYLLITE		Phyllitic texture well developed; silky, shiny luster
Coarse-grained, macroscopic, mostly micaceous minerals or prismatic crystals; often with porphyroblasts	SCHIST	MUSCOVITE SCHIST CHLORITE SCHIST BIOTITE SCHIST TOURMALINE SCHIST GARNET SCHIST STAUROLITE SCHIST KYANITE SCHIST SILLIMANITE SCHIST AMPHIBOLE SCHIST	Types of schist recognized on the basis of mineral content
Coarse-grained; mostly nonmicaceous minerals	GNEISS		Well-developed color banding due to alternating layers of different minerals

(Left margin: arrow labeled "Increasing Grade of Metamorphism" pointing downward)

FIGURE 6.16 Classification of common *foliated* metamorphic rocks.

Precursor Rock	Metamorphic Rock	Comments
QUARTZ SANDSTONE	QUARTZITE	Composed of interlocking quartz grains
CONGLOMERATE	STRETCHED-PEBBLE CONGLOMERATE	Original pebbles distinguishable, but strongly deformed
BASALT or GABBRO	GREENSTONE	Composed of epidote and chlorite; green
	AMPHIBOLITE	Composed of amphibole and plagioclase; coarse-grained
	HORNFELS	Composed of pyroxene and plagioclase; fine-grained
SILTSTONE	HORNFELS	Composed of quartz and plagioclase; fine-grained
LIMESTONE/ DOLOSTONE	MARBLE	Composed of interlocking calcite or dolomite grains
	SKARN	Composed of calcite and added minerals; multicolored
PERIDOTITE (ULTRAMAFIC ROCKS)	SERPENTINITE	Composed chiefly of serpentine; greens
	SOAPSTONE	Composed chiefly of talc; soapy feel
BITUMINOUS COAL	ANTHRACITE COAL	Bright, hard coal; breaks with conchoidal fracture
ANTHRACITE COAL	GRAPHITE	Soft, dark gray, with greasy feel

FIGURE 6.17 Classification of common *nonfoliated* metamorphic rocks.

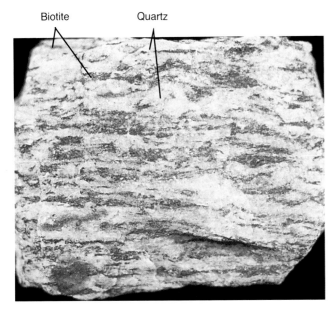

Biotite   Quartz

FIGURE 6.18 Sample of metamorphic rock for Question 3. (Photo by R. Busch)

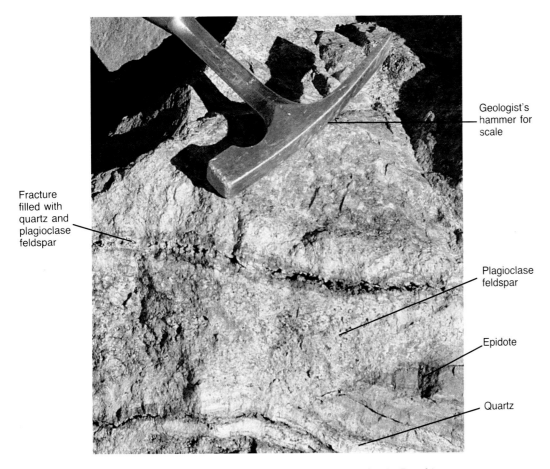

Geologist's hammer for scale

Fracture filled with quartz and plagioclase feldspar

Plagioclase feldspar

Epidote

Quartz

FIGURE 6.19 Sample of metamorphic rock for Question 4. (Photo by R. Busch)

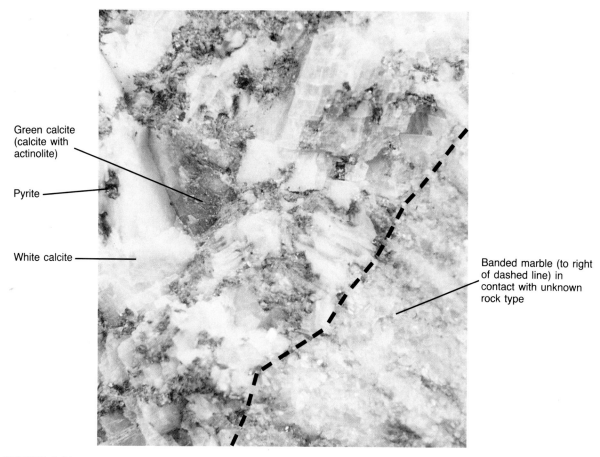

Green calcite
(calcite with
actinolite)

Pyrite

White calcite

Banded marble (to right
of dashed line) in
contact with unknown
rock type

FIGURE 6.20   Sample of metamorphic rock for Question 5. (Photo by R. Busch)

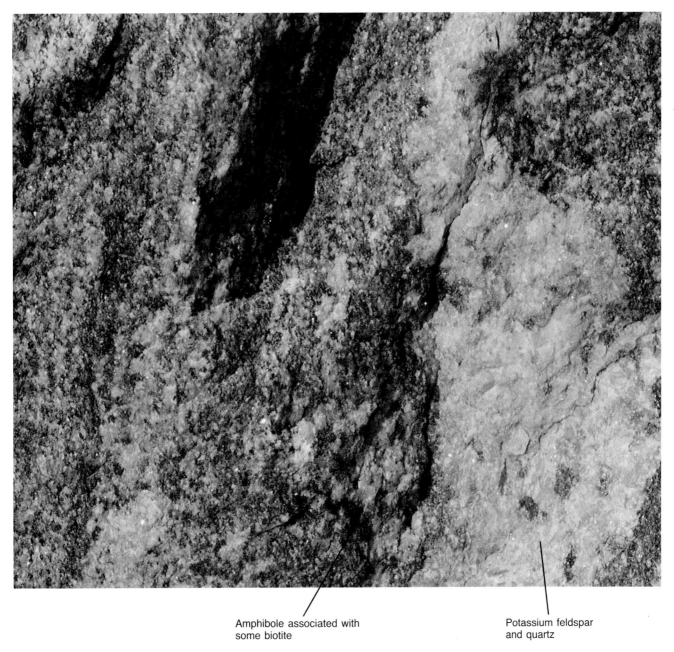

Amphibole associated with
some biotite

Potassium feldspar
and quartz

FIGURE 6.21 Migmatite for consideration in Question 6. (Photo by R. Busch)

EXERCISE SEVEN

Topographic Maps and Aerial Photographs

Charles G. Higgins
University of California at Davis

John R. Wagner
Clemson University

Evelyn M. Vandendolder
Arizona Geological Survey

James R. Wilson
Weber State College

PURPOSE

The first part of this exercise develops your proficiency in reading and interpreting topographic maps. You will learn how to draw contour lines, based on points of known elevation. You also will learn how to construct topographic profiles. The second part acquaints you with aerial photographs and how they are valuable in geological studies.

MATERIALS

Topographic quadrangle map (provided by your instructor), millimeter ruler, pencil and eraser, protractor, pocket stereoscope, calculator.

INTRODUCTION

In 1937, American aviator Amelia Earhart and her navigator Fred Noonan attempted to make the first round-the-world flight. But two-thirds of the way around the globe, they disappeared in the South Pacific Ocean. Earhart and Noonan were trying to reach tiny Howland Island, a mere speck of land just north of the equator, when they vanished. It appears that their flight plan gave the wrong coordinates for the island.

Earhart's flight plan listed the island's coordinates as 0°49' north latitude, 176°43' west longi-

tude. But the actual coordinates are 0°48' north latitude, 176°38' west longitude (Barker, V., *New Haven Register*, Dec. 21, 1986:A48). In the open ocean, with nothing else to guide them, and limited fuel, such a miss was fatal. Investigators who researched their disappearance thought that Earhart and Noonan were on course and would certainly have reached Howland Island—had they been given the correct coordinates. Thus, their demise probably was due to a mapmaker's mistake, or to the flight planner's inability to correctly read a map.

Earhart's story illustrates how important accurate maps are. It demonstrates that mapping errors, or errors in map use, can have drastic effects on the outcome of any endeavor that relies on maps for basic information (data). Your ability to construct maps, to read them, and to interpret them is essential for conducting many geologic studies. Geologists generally use aerial photographs in combination with maps to confirm the accuracy of map information and to provide additional information not given on maps.

TOPOGRAPHIC MAPS

A **topographic map** is a two-dimensional (flat) representation of a three-dimensional land surface. It shows the three-dimensional information (relief or height variation) by using *contour lines* to represent elevations of hills and valleys. (These are the brown lines in Figure 7.6.) This vertical information is the distinguishing feature of a topographic map. A topographic map differs from the more familiar *planimetric* map, such as a highway map, because a planimetric map does not show relief.

Most topographic maps also depict many features common to planimetric maps, such as water bodies, vegetation, roads, buildings, political boundaries, and placenames. Topographic maps are a valuable tool in geological and engineering studies. They also are used by hikers, hunters, campers, and anyone who needs to know the three-dimensional aspect of land surfaces.

TOPOGRAPHIC QUADRANGLES

Most United States topographic maps are published by the U.S. Geological Survey. Although some topographic maps cover areas defined by political boundaries (like a state, county, or city), most topographic maps depict rectangular sections of the surface, called quadrangles. A **quadrangle** is a section of the Earth's surface that is bounded by lines of **latitude** at the top (north) and bottom (south) and by lines of **longitude** on the left (west) and right (east)—see Figures 7.1, 7.2.

Quadrangle maps are published in several sizes, but two are most common: 15-minute quadrangle maps and 7½-minute quadrangle maps. The numbers refer to the amount of area that the maps depict, in degrees of latitude and longitude. A *15-minute topographic map* represents an area that measures 15 minutes of latitude × 15 minutes of longitude. A *7½-minute topographic map* represents an

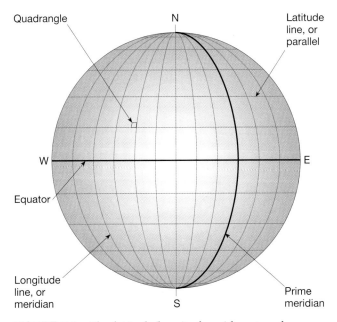

FIGURE 7.1 The latitude/longitude grid system for Earth, showing a quadrangle.

LATITUDE AND LONGITUDE	
	1. Latitude lines, or *parallels,* are parallel to the Equator and measure distances north and south of the Equator.
	2. Longitude lines, or *meridians,* pass through the North and South Poles. They measure distances east and west of the Prime Meridian, which passes through Greenwich, England.
	3. Any point on the Earth's surface can be represented as an intersection of a line of latitude and a line of longitude.
	4. Since all of North America is north of the Equator and west of the Prime Meridian, all latitudes in the continental United States are north and all longitudes are west.
	5. Latitude and longitude are expressed in degrees, minutes, and seconds.

1 degree (°) = 60 minutes (')
1 minute = 60 seconds (")
360° makes a complete circle.

FIGURE 7.2 Latitude and longitude.

area that measures 7½ minutes of latitude × 7½ minutes of longitude. Each 15-minute map can be divided into four 7½-minute maps.

Because longitude lines (lines running north-south) form the left and right boundaries of a topographic map, *true geographic north* is always at the top of the map. Unfortunately, magnetic compasses are not attracted to true geographic north (the North Pole). Instead, they are attracted to the *magnetic north pole,* currently located northwest of Hudson Bay in Northern Canada, about 700 km (450 mi) from the true North Pole.

The angle formed between the direction of true geographic north and magnetic north is the **magnetic declination.** The magnetic pole migrates very slowly, so the declination is exact only for the year listed on the map. Tables are available from which you can calculate the correct declination for any quadrangle and year. On topographic maps, magnetic declination for a specific year usually is shown in the margin.

COMPASS BEARINGS

A **bearing** is the *direction* from one point to another. If expressed in degrees east or west of true north or south, it is called a "quadrant bearing." Or it may be expressed in degrees between 0 and 360, called an "azimuth bearing," where north is 0° (or 360°), east is 90°, south is 180°, and west is 270°.

Refer to Figure 7.3. Suppose you need to determine the bearing (direction) from one point on a map (*A*) to another (*B*). First, draw a line (very lightly in pencil, so that it can be erased) through the two points. Make sure the line also intersects the edge of the map, either left (west) or right (east). For example, in both parts of Figure 7.3, a line was drawn through points *A* and *B* so that it also intersects the east edge of the map.

Next, orient a protractor so that its 0° and 180° marks are on the edge of the map, with the 0° end toward geographic north. Place the origin of the protractor at the point where your line *A–B* intersects the edge of the map. You can now read the bearing from the protractor. For example, in Figure 7.3, the protractor is oriented as just mentioned, and you can read a bearing of 43° east of north. We express this as "North 43° East" or N43°E.

You also can use a compass to read bearings, as shown in Figure 7.3 (right). Ignore the compass needle and use the compass as if it were a circular protractor. Some compasses are graduated in degrees 0–360, in which case you read a bearing as an azimuth from 0–360°.

Note that we described the bearing as "North 43° East," because it is the bearing of a direction pointing northeast. This bearing could also be read as an azimuth of 43°. If you were to determine the opposite bearing, from *B* to *A*, the bearing would be pointing southwest and would be read as "South 43° West," or as an azimuth of 223°.

PUBLIC LAND SURVEY SYSTEM

The **U.S. Public Land Survey System (PLS)** was initiated in the late 1700s. All but the original thirteen states, and a few states derived from them, are covered by this system. Other exceptions occur in the southwestern United States, where land surveys may be based upon Spanish land grants, and in areas of rugged terrain that were never surveyed.

The PLS scheme is shown in Figure 7.4. It was established in each state by surveying **principal meridians,** which are north-south lines, and **base lines,** which are east-west lines (Figure 7.4, part A). Once the initial principal meridian and base lines were established, additional parallels and meridians were surveyed with 24-mile lengths along their southern, eastern, and western boundaries. Further subdivision created a grid of nearly 16 square areas, where each "square" was 6 miles on a side (part B in Figure 7.4).

Squares along each north-south strip of the grid are called **townships** and are numbered relative to the base line (Township 1 North, Township 2 North, etc.). Squares along each east-west strip of the grid are **ranges** and are numbered relative to the principal meridian (Range 1 West, Range 2 West, etc.). This often is called the "township-and-range" system.

The squares created by the intersection of townships and ranges are used as political subdivisions in some states. These squares are called "townships" and often are given placenames. Each township square is divided into 36 small squares, each having an area of almost 1 square mile (640 acres). These squares are called **sections.**

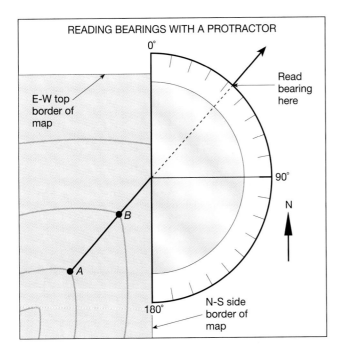

READING BEARINGS WITH A PROTRACTOR

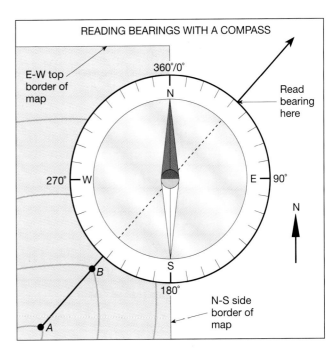

READING BEARINGS WITH A COMPASS

FIGURE 7.3 Examples of how to read bearings. See text for discussion.

Sections are numbered from 1 to 36, beginning in the upper right corner (Figure 7.4, part B). Sometimes these are shown on topographic quadrangle maps (Figure 7.5, red grid). Any point can be located precisely within a section by dividing the section into quarters (labeled NW, NE, SW, SE). Each of these quarters can itself be subdivided into quarters and labeled (Figure 7.4).

SCALE

Maps are scale models, like toy cars or boats. To make a model of anything, you first must establish a model scale. This is the proportion by which you will reduce the real object to the model size. For example, if you make a ¼-scale model of a 16-foot car, your model would be 4 feet long. The scale of model-to-object is 4:16, which reduces to 1:4. A house floorplan, which really is a map of a house, commonly is drawn so that a foot on the plan equals 30 or 40 feet of real house, or a **ratio scale** of 1:30 or 1:40.

Topographic maps model the surface of the Earth, often large portions of it, so the **ratio scale** must be much greater, like 1:24,000. This also can be expressed as a fraction (1/24,000), indicating that

the portion of the Earth represented has been reduced to 1/24,000 of the actual size.

Using such a **fractional scale** means that any unit (inch, centimeter, foot, etc.) on the map represents 24,000 of the same units (inches, centimeters, feet) on Earth's surface. For example, 1 cm on the map represents 24,000 cm on the ground; your thumb width on the map represents 24,000 thumb widths on the ground; or any unit you wish to use. Other common map scales are 1:62,500 and 1:250,000. Figure 7.6 shows how maps at different fractional scales show the same locality, but present different amounts of detail and area.

Drawing a map at 1:24,000 scale provides a very useful amount of detail. But knowing that 1 inch on the map = 24,000 inches on the ground is not very convenient, because no one measures big distances in inches! However, if you divide the 24,000 inches by 12 to get 2000 feet, the scale suddenly becomes useful: 1 inch on the map = 2000 feet on the ground. This is a **verbal scale.**

Another example: On a map with a scale of 1:63,360, 1 inch = 63,360 inches, again not meaningful in daily use. But 63,360 inches is a mile. So, if we say that "1 inch = 1 mile," the scale becomes very meaningful. A standard 1:62,650 map is very close to this scale, so we commonly say that "one

A. Township and range grid

B. A township contains 36 sections

C. Sections are further subdivided

inch equals approximately one mile" on such a map. Note that these verbal scales may be approximate, for their sole purpose is to increase the convenience of using a map.

Finally, a **graphic scale** (or *bar scale*) is printed in the lower margin of topographic maps. It usually includes three scales, showing miles, feet, and kilometers. Some topographic maps add a fourth scale, showing meters.

MAP SYMBOLS

On topographic maps, the map symbols provide remarkably detailed information about both natural and cultural features. You can use Figure 7.7 to identify every feature shown on a topographic map.

Additional information is presented in the margins of these maps, most importantly the revision date. Because people constantly change the cultural features on Earth's surface, and because Earth's surface itself occasionally changes rapidly from events such as landslides and floods, the maps must be updated. This is done by **photorevision.** Aerial photographs are used to discover changes on the surface, and the changes are overprinted on the maps in a stand-out color like purple or red.

CONTOUR LINES

Topographic maps are scaled-down models of Earth's three-dimensional surface, printed on two-dimensional pieces of paper. You have seen how length and width are easily reduced from the real world to the map. The third dimension, height (or elevation), is shown using **contour lines.** A contour line connects all points on the map that have the same elevation above sea level. Please examine Figure 7.8 to see how a topographic map is drawn.

A contour line acts as an imaginary boundary, separating areas above that elevation from areas below it (Figure 7.9). Note that, to get from a point below the contour to a point above it, you must cross the contour line.

Look at the top map in Figure 7.6. Note the heavier brown contour line, labeled *400*, that rings Maytown. This heavier line is an **index contour,** labeled with the elevation (400 feet above sea level). Index contours are your starting point in interpreting a topographic map. For example, if you wanted to know how high both of Maytown's cemeteries are ("Cem" on map), both are on the 400-foot contour line, so both are 400 feet above sea level.

On this particular map, contours have been drawn to show each 20-foot difference in elevation. Thus, the light brown line to the left of the 400-

FIGURE 7.4   (Opposite page) Example of the U.S. Public Land Survey System (PLS).

A. Township and range grid. The starting points are the *principal meridian* of longitude and a *base line* that is surveyed perpendicular to it. *Township* strips of land run parallel to the base line and are numbered north and south of it (T1N, T1S, etc.). *Range* strips of land run parallel to the principal meridian and are numbered east and west of it (R1E, R1W, etc.). Each intersection of a township strip with a range strip forms a square, called a *township.*

B. Each township is 6 miles long by 6 miles wide, so it contains 36 square miles. Each square mile is a numbered *section.*

C. Sections are further subdivided into blocks. For example, point **X** is located in the southeast corner, of the southwest ¼, of the southeast ¼, of section 11, of the township designated Township 1 South, Range 2 West. This is written in a shorthand: SE¼, SW¼, SE¼, sec. 11, T1S, R2W.

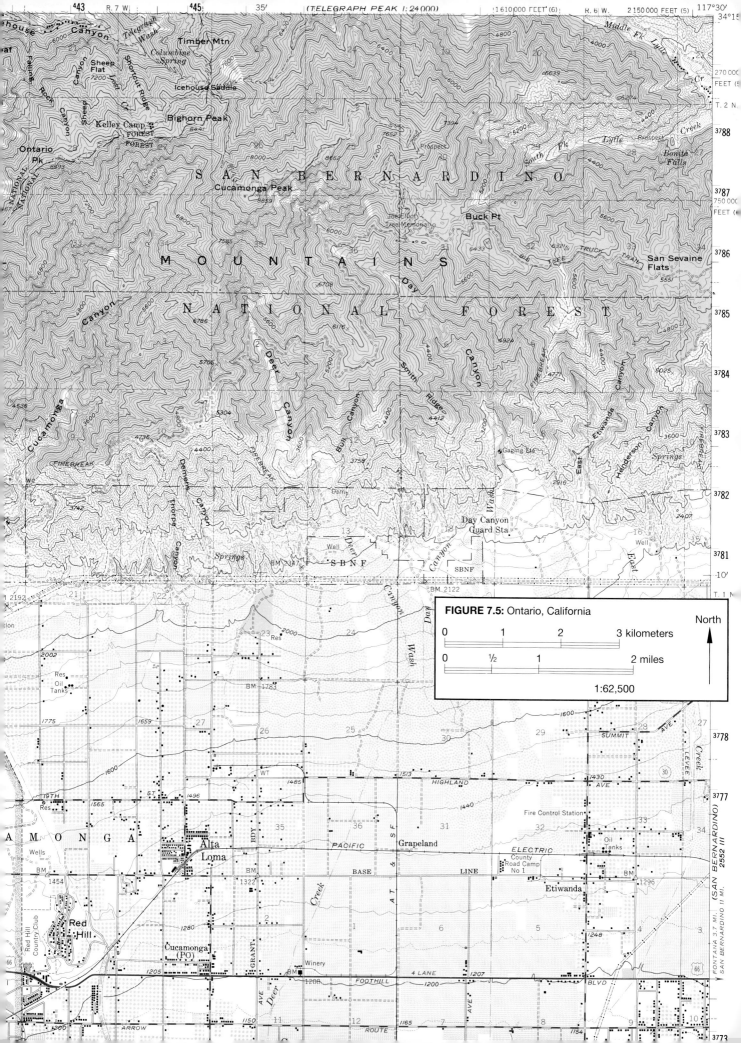

FIGURE 7.5: Ontario, California

| 0 | 1 | 2 | 3 kilometers |

| 0 | ½ | 1 | 2 miles |

1:62,500

North

FIGURE 7.5 (Opposite page) Portion of the Ontario, California topographic quadrangle map. Note dashed red lines, which portray the Public Land Survey (PLS) grid.

FIGURE 7.6 A locality in southeastern Pennsylvania shown at three different scales. Note the striking difference in level of detail at the different scales and the differences in the amount of area depicted.

1:24,000 scale, 1 inch = 2000 feet. Area shown = approximately 1 square mile.

1:62,500 scale, 1 inch = approximately 1 mile. Area shown = approximately 6¼ square miles.

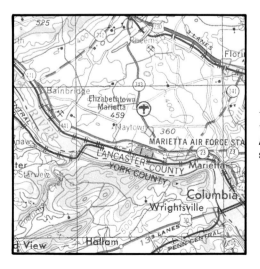

1:250,000 scale, 1 inch = approximately 4 miles. Area shown = approximately 100 square miles.

FIGURE 7.7 TOPOGRAPHIC MAP SYMBOLS

VARIATIONS WILL BE FOUND ON OLDER MAPS

Primary highway, hard surface . . . .

Secondary highway, hard surface . . . .

Light-duty road, hard or improved surface . . . .

Unimproved road . . . .

Road under construction, alinement known . . . .

Proposed road . . . .

Dual highway, dividing strip 25 feet or less . . . .

Dual highway, dividing strip exceeding 25 feet . . . .

Trail . . . .

Railroad: single track and multiple track . . . .

Railroads in juxtaposition . . . .

Narrow gage: single track and multiple track . . . .

Railroad in street and carline . . . .

Bridge: road and railroad . . . .

Drawbridge: road and railroad . . . .

Footbridge . . . .

Tunnel: road and railroad . . . .

Overpass and underpass . . . .

Small masonry or concrete dam . . . .

Dam with lock . . . .

Dam with road . . . .

Canal with lock . . . .

Buildings (dwelling, place of employment, etc.) . . . .

School, church, and cemetery . . . .

Buildings (barn, warehouse, etc.) . . . .

Power transmission line with located metal tower . . . . . .

Telephone line, pipeline, etc. (labeled as to type) . . . . . .

Wells other than water (labeled as to type) . . . . oOil . . . . oGas

Tanks: oil, water, etc. (labeled only if water) . . . . ● ● ● ⊘Water

Located or landmark object; windmill . . . . o

Open pit, mine, or quarry; prospect . . . . ✕ x

Shaft and tunnel entrance . . . . ▪ . . . . Y

Horizontal and vertical control station:

Tablet, spirit level elevation . . . . BM △ 5653

Other recoverable mark, spirit level elevation . . . . △ 5455

Horizontal control station: tablet, vertical angle elevation VABM △ 9519

Any recoverable mark, vertical angle or checked elevation △ 3775

Vertical control station: tablet, spirit level elevation . . . . BM ✕ 957

Other recoverable mark, spirit level elevation . . . . ✕ 954

Spot elevation . . . . ✕ 7369   ✕ 7369

Water elevation 670   670

Boundaries: National . . . .

State . . . .

County, parish, municipio . . . .

Civil township, precinct, town, barrio . . . .

Incorporated city, village, town, hamlet . . . .

Reservation, National or State . . . .

Small park, cemetery, airport, etc. . . . .

Land grant . . . .

Township or range line, United States land survey . . . . . .

Township or range line, approximate location . . . .

Section line, United States land survey . . . .

Section line, approximate location . . . .

Township line, not United States land survey . . . .

Section line, not United States land survey . . . .

Found corner: section and closing . . . .

Boundary monument: land grant and other . . . . □

Fence or field line . . . .

Index contour		Intermediate contour . .
Supplementary contour		Depression contours . . .
Fill		Cut . . . .
Levee		Levee with road . . . . . .
Mine dump		Wash . . . .
Tailings		Tailings pond . . . .
Shifting sand or dunes		Intricate surface . . . . .
Sand area		Gravel beach . . . .

Perennial streams		Intermittent streams . .
Elevated aqueduct		Aqueduct tunnel . . . . .
Water well and spring . .		Glacier . . . .
Small rapids		Small falls . . . .
Large rapids		Large falls . . . .
Intermittent lake		Dry lake bed . . . .
Foreshore flat		Rock or coral reef . . . .
Sounding, depth curve .	10	Piling or dolphin . . . . .
Exposed wreck		Sunken wreck . . . .
Rock, bare or awash; dangerous to navigation		✱

Marsh (swamp)		Submerged marsh . . . .
Wooded marsh		Mangrove . . . .
Woods or brushwood . .		Orchard . . . .
Vineyard		Scrub . . . .
Land subject to controlled inundation		Urban area . . . .

FIGURE 7.7 (Opposite page) Symbols used on topographic quadrangle maps produced by the U.S. Geological Survey.

FIGURE 7.8 How topographic maps are constructed. A contour is a line drawn where any plane (like *B* or *C*) intersects the land surface. Where the plane of the water (*A*) intersects the island, it forms the 0-foot contour line. Here, elevation = 0, because it is sea level. Where the 50-foot-higher plane *B* intersects the land surface, it forms the 50-foot contour line. Where the 100-foot-high plane *C* intersects the land surface, it forms the 100-foot contour line. *D* is the resulting topographic map of the island. It was made using the contours in 50-foot increments above mean sea level.

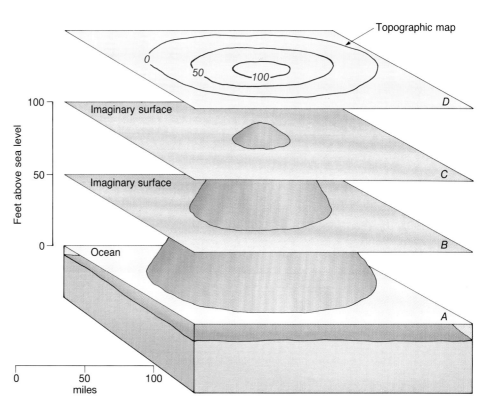

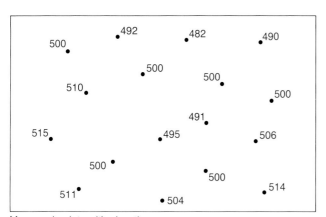

Measured points with elevations

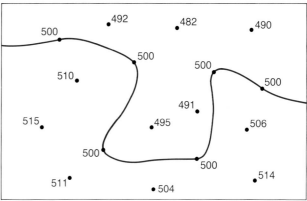

Same points with 500-foot contour

FIGURE 7.9 Construction of a contour line from points of known elevation.

foot line represents all points that are 380 feet above sea level; the line to the left of it represents 360 feet elevation; and so on. This 20-foot elevation difference between lines is the **contour interval.** The contour interval is specified on every map; 20 feet is very common, but you will see maps with contour intervals of 5 feet, 10 feet, 40 feet, and others.

All contour lines are multiples of the contour interval. Examples: if a map uses a 10-foot contour interval, the contour lines might represent 0, 10, 20, 30, 40 feet, and so on. For a 50-foot contour interval, the contour lines might represent 0, 50, 100, 150 feet, and so on. Most maps use the smallest contour interval that will allow easy readability and provide as much detail as possible.

Figure 7.10 is a handy reference for the rules of interpreting contour lines.

READING ELEVATIONS

If a point lies on an index contour, you simply read its elevation from that line. If the point lies on an unnumbered contour line, then its elevation can be determined by counting up or down from the nearest index contour. For example, if the nearest index contour is 300 feet, and your point of interest is on the fourth contour line *above* it, and the contour interval is 20 feet, then you simply count up by 20s from the index contour: 320, 340, 360, 380. The point is 380 feet above sea level. (Or, if the point is three contour lines *below* the index contour, you count down: 280, 260, 240; the point is 240 feet above sea level.)

If a point lies between two contour lines, then you must estimate its elevation. For example, on a map with a 20-foot contour interval, a point might

---

RULES FOR CONTOUR LINES

1. Every point on a *contour line* is of the exact same elevation; that is, contour lines connect points of equal elevation.

2. Contour lines always separate points of higher elevation (uphill) from points of lower elevation (downhill). You must determine which direction on the map is higher and which is lower, relative to the contour line in question, by checking adjacent elevations.

3. Contour lines always close to form an irregular circle; but, sometimes part of a contour line extends beyond the mapped area, so that you cannot see the entire circle formed.

4. The elevation between any two adjacent contour lines of different elevation on a topographic map is the *contour interval.* Often every fifth contour line is heavier, so that you can count by five-times the contour interval. These heavier contour lines are known as *index contours,* because they generally have elevations printed on them.

5. Contour lines never cross one another, except for one rare case: where an overhanging cliff is present. In such a case, the hidden contours are dashed.

6. Contour lines can merge to form a single contour line only where there is a vertical cliff.

7. Evenly spaced contour lines of different elevation represent a uniform slope.

8. The closer the contour lines are to one another, the steeper the slope. In other words, the steeper the slope, the closer the contour lines.

9. A concentric series of closed contours represents a hill:

10. *Depression contours* have hachure marks on the downhill side and represent a closed depression:

11. Contour lines form a V pattern when crossing streams. The apex of the V always points upstream (uphill):

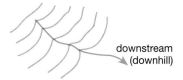

downstream (downhill)

12. Contour lines that occur on opposite sides of a valley always occur in pairs.

13. Topographic maps published by the U.S. Geological Survey are contoured in feet or meters referenced to sea level.

FIGURE 7.10 Rules for contour lines.

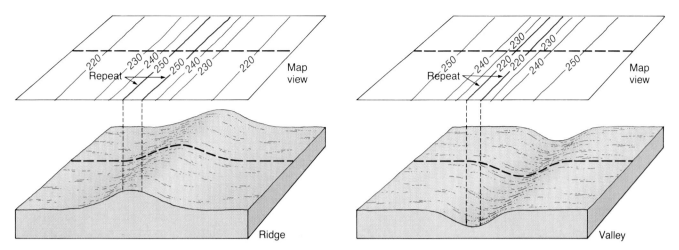

FIGURE 7.11 Contour lines repeat on opposite sides of sloping features like ridges and valleys. For example, in the ridge illustration, if you walked the dashed line from right to left, you would cross the 230-foot contour, go over the top of the ridge, and cross the 230-foot contour again as you walked down the other side.

lie between the 340 and 360 foot contours, so you know it is between 340 and 360 feet above sea level.

Figure 7.11 shows how topographic contour lines represent ridge crests and valley bottoms. Ridges and valleys are roughly symmetrical, so individual contour lines repeat on each side. To visualize this, picture yourself walking along an imaginary trail across the ridge or valley (dashed lines in figure). Every time you go uphill or down-

hill, you cross contours. Then, when you traverse the other side, you recross the contours that you previously crossed. Figure 7.12 shows a similar situation in depressions or hollows.

Relief is the difference in elevation between two points on a map. *Local relief* refers to adjacent hills and valleys; it can be determined from contours. *Total relief* is the difference in elevation between the highest and lowest points on the map. The highest point is the top of the highest hill or

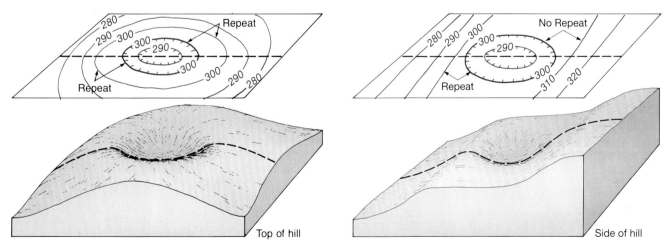

FIGURE 7.12 Contour lines repeat on opposite sides of depressions *except* when the depression is on a steep slope.

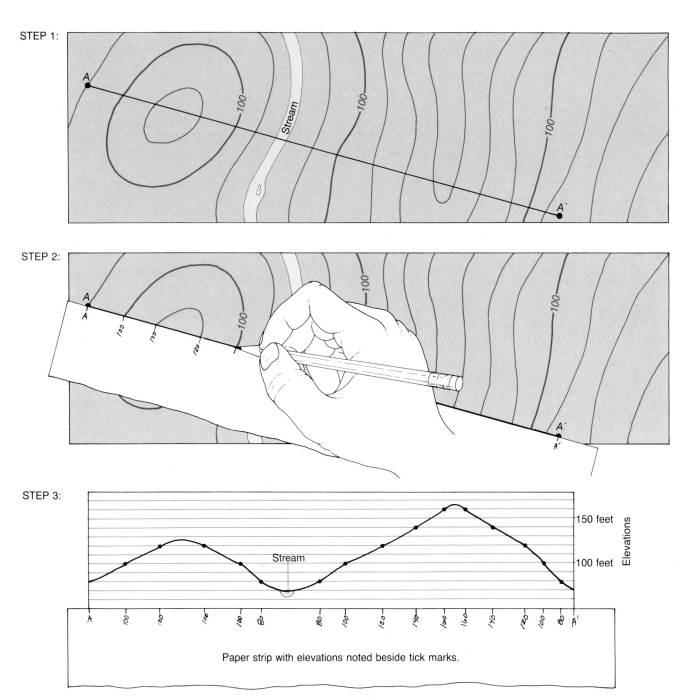

STEP 1:

STEP 2:

STEP 3:

150 feet

100 feet

Elevations

Stream

Paper strip with elevations noted beside tick marks.

FIGURE 7.13 Topographic profile construction. Shown are a topographic map and a profile constructed along line segment *A–A'*. To construct the profile, the edge of a piece of paper was placed along *A–A'* on the topographic map. A tick mark was then placed on the edge of the paper at each point where a contour line intersected the edge of the paper. The elevation represented by each contour line was noted on its corresponding tick mark. Next, the edge of the paper was placed along the bottom line of the profile, and the profile was graduated for elevations along its right margin. Finally, a black dot was placed on the profile above each tick mark, at the elevation noted on the tick mark. The black dots then were connected with a line to complete the profile.

mountain; the lowest point is generally where the major stream of the area leaves the map, or a coastline.

Elevations of specific points on topographic maps (tops of peaks, bridges, survey points, etc.) sometimes are indicated directly on the maps beside the symbols indicated for that purpose in Figure 7.7. The notation "BM" denotes a **benchmark,** a permanent marker (usually a metal plate) placed by the U.S. Geological Survey or Bureau of Land Management at the point indicated on the map. Elevations usually are given. For example, look at the middle map in Figure 7.6. At top center is "BM 463," indicating that this point was measured to be exactly 463 feet above sea level at the time of the survey. Note several other benchmarks on this map.

TOPOGRAPHIC PROFILES

A topographic map provides an overhead (aerial) view of an area, depicting features and relief by means of its symbols and contour lines. Occasionally a more pictorial representation is useful. A **topographic profile** is a cross section that shows the elevations and slopes along a given line (Figure 7.13). Topographic profiles are easily made, using the following steps and Figure 7.13:

1. On the map, draw a **line of section** along which the profile is to be constructed. Label the section line *A–A'*. Be sure that the line intersects all of the features (ridges, valleys, streams, etc.) that you wish the profile to show.
2. On a strip of paper placed along section line *A–A'*, make tick marks at each place where a contour line intersects the section line, and note the elevation at the tick marks. Also note the location and elevation of points *A* and *A'* and any streams crossed.
3. Draw the profile. To do so:
    a. On a separate sheet of paper, draw a series of equally spaced parallel lines that are the same length as the line of section (graph paper can be used). Each horizontal line on this sheet represents a *constant elevation,* and therefore corresponds to a contour line. The total number of horizontal lines that you need, and their elevations, depends on the total relief along the line of section, and on whether you make the space between the lines equal to the contour interval, or to multiples of it (vertical exaggeration, which will be discussed shortly). Label your lines so that

the highest and lowest elevations along the line of section will be within the grid.
    b. Then, take the strip of paper you marked in step 2, and place it along the base of your profile. Mark a dot on the grid above it for each elevation. Smoothly connect these dots to complete the topographic profile. (This line should not make angular bends or "bounce off" of a horizontal grid line. Make it a smoothly curving line that reflects the relief of the land surface along the line of section.)

The vertical scale of your profile will vary greatly, depending on how you draw the grid. It almost certainly will be larger than the horizontal scale of the map. In Figure 7.16, for example, the grid has been drawn so that 1 inch represents the distance between the 700-foot and 800-foot elevation lines. The vertical scale is, therefore, 1 inch = 100 feet or 1 inch = 1200 inches (1:1200). This is quite different from the horizontal scale of 1:24,000.

This difference causes an exaggeration in the vertical dimension. Such exaggeration almost always is necessary to construct a readable profile, for without vertical exaggeration, the profile might be so shallow that only the highest peaks would be visible. The **vertical exaggeration** can be calculated by dividing the fractional vertical scale (1/1200) by the fractional horizontal scale (1/24,000), giving a value of 20 in this example. This number (sometimes written 20×) indicates that the relief shown on the profile is 20 times greater than the true relief. This makes the slopes on the profile 20 times steeper than the corresponding real slopes on the ground.

QUESTIONS

1. On Figure 7.14, mark each contour line with its proper elevation, using a contour interval of 40 meters.

2. On Figure 7.15, construct and label contour lines, using a contour interval of 10 meters. Draw contours for lines having elevations in even 10s of meters—e.g., 90 meters, 100 meters, etc.

3. On Figure 7.16, construct a topographic profile along *A–A'* using the grid provided. What is the vertical exaggeration of your profile?

Refer to the quadrangle map provided by your instructor, and answer the following questions. *(Do not mark the map.)*

4. What parallel (latitude line) marks the northern boundary of the quadrangle?

5. What parallel marks the southern boundary of the quadrangle?

6. What meridian (longitude line) marks the eastern boundary of the quadrangle?

7. What meridian marks the western boundary of the quadrangle?

8. What is the distance (in degrees, minutes, and seconds) from the southern to the northern boundary of the quadrangle?

9. What is the distance (in degrees, minutes, and seconds) from the western to the eastern boundary of the quadrangle?

10. Is this a 7½-minute quadrangle or a 15-minute quadrangle?

11. What is the latitude of the exact center of the quadrangle?

12. What is the longitude of the exact center of the quadrangle?

13. What is the magnetic declination of this quadrangle?

14. In what year was the magnetic declination measured?

15. In what year was the map originally published?

16. What is the fractional scale of this quadrangle?

17. How can this scale be expressed as a verbal scale in miles? In kilometers?

18. Two inches on this quadrangle map represent how many feet on the ground? How many miles? How many kilometers?

19. Measure the length of the northern boundary of the quadrangle map in inches. What is the real distance of this boundary in feet? In miles? In kilometers?

20. What is the area of this quadrangle in square miles (area = length × width)?

21. What is the name of this quadrangle?

22. What is the contour interval?

23. What is the name of the quadrangle map directly adjacent to the south?

24. What is the name of the quadrangle map directly adjacent to the northeast?

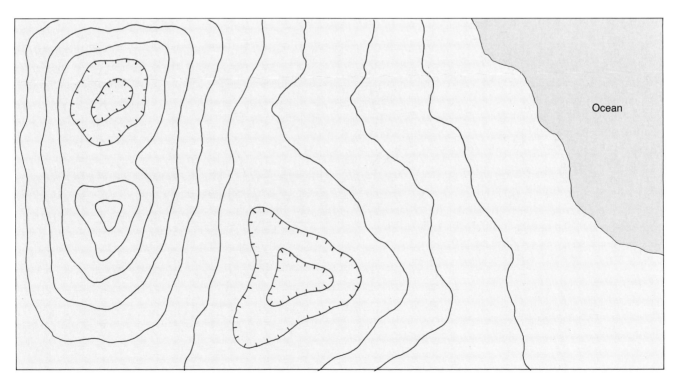

Ocean

FIGURE 7.14 Contour problem. On this map, mark each contour line with its proper elevation above sea level. Use a contour interval of 40 meters.

FIGURE 7.15 Contour problem. Construct all contour lines on the map. Use a contour interval of 10 meters. Draw contours only for lines having elevations in even 10s of meters—e.g., 90 m, 100 m, and so on.

125 •	112 •	100 •	78 •	90 •	106 •	117 •
130 •	115 •	103 •	84 •	110 •	111 •	119 •
133 •	122 •	110 •	98 •	107 •	116 •	130 •
140 •	125 •	118 •	110 •	113 •	123 •	134 •

1:24,000

Contour interval 20 ft

800 ft

700 ft

FIGURE 7.16 Topographic profile problem. Construct a topographic profile for line *A–A'*. Then, calculate the vertical exaggeration of the profile.

25. What color indicates these features?
    a. water
    b. vegetation (mainly forests)
    c. contour lines
    d. buildings

26. Was this map ever photorevised? If so, when?

27. What is the elevation of the highest point on the quadrangle?

28. What is the elevation of the lowest point on the quadrangle?

29. What is the total relief within the quadrangle?

Refer to Figure 7.5 and answer the following questions.

30. What natural feature is located in the SW¼, NE¼, sec. 13, T1N, R7W?

31. To the right of center on the map, find the Day Canyon Guard Station. About a mile north is a gaging station. Use the PLS system to describe the location of the gaging station.

32. Use the PLS numbering system to describe the location of Bighorn Peak in the northwestern corner of the map. What is the exact elevation of Bighorn Peak?

33. What is the distance in miles from the railroad intersection in Grapeland (sec. 31, T1N, R6W) to the Day Canyon Guard Station (sec. 17, T1N, R6W)?

34. What is the length in miles of the permanent stream in Day Canyon, south of the Joe Elliot Tree Memorial (measured along the stream course)?

35. In what general direction does the stream in Day Canyon flow?

36. What is the difference in elevation from the beginning of the stream in Day Canyon to the point where it becomes an intermittent stream?

37. What is the contour interval of this map?

38. What is the exact elevation of Cucamonga Peak?

39. What is the total relief on this map area?

40. Identify the three forms of vegetation shown by the green patterns in sec. 29, T1N, R6W.

41. In what general direction does the stream flow in Sheep Canyon (northwest corner of the map)? How can you tell?

42. What is the elevation of the benchmark on the southern boundary of sec. 33, T1N, R6W?

AERIAL PHOTOGRAPHS

Aerial photographs are pictures of Earth taken from airplanes, generally with large single-lens cameras that make 9 × 9-inch negatives. Most of these photographs are black and white, but color pictures sometimes are available. The photographs may be large scale or small scale, depending on the elevation at which they were taken, on the focal length of the camera lens, and on whether the pictures have been enlarged or reduced from the negatives.

Air photographs can be taken straight down from the plane, termed **vertical,** or they may be taken at an angle to the vertical, termed **oblique.** Oblique views help reveal geological features and landforms; however, vertical air photographs are even more useful in geological studies. The photographs used in this exercise are verticals (Figure 7.18).

Vertical air photos are taken in a series during a flight, so that the images form a continuous view of the area below. They are taken so that approximately 60% image overlap occurs between any two adjacent photos. The view is straight down at the very center of each picture (called the **center point** or **principal point**), but all other portions of the landscape are viewed at an angle that becomes increasingly oblique away from the center of the picture.

The **scale** of any photographic image cannot be uniform, because it differs with the distance of the camera lens from the ground. Thus, in photos of flat terrain, the scale is largest at the center of the photo, where the ground is closest to the camera lens, and decreases away from the center. Also, hilltops and other high points, which are closer to the camera lens, are shown at larger scales than are valley bottoms and other low places.

Air photos commonly are overlapped to form a **stereogram,** or **stereopair.** When viewed through a viewer called a **stereoscope,** the image appears three-dimensional. This view is startling, dramatic, and reveals surprises about the terrain, as you shall see shortly. Stereoscopes can be of many types, but the most commonly used variety is a **pocket stereoscope** (Figure 7.17).

Air photos can be black-and-white or color images. They may be taken with or without special lenses that filter out certain kinds of light rays. Most black-and-white photos are unfiltered, but most color photos are filtered to emphasize infrared light waves. Infrared indicates how much heat

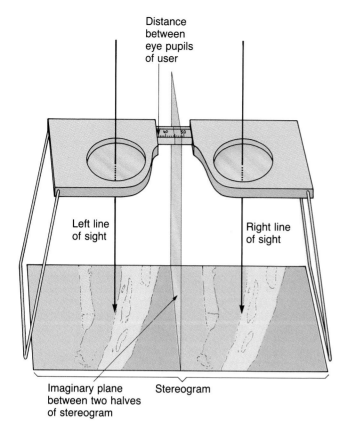

Distance
between
eye pupils
of user

Left line
of sight

Right line
of sight

Imaginary plane
between two halves
of stereogram

Stereogram

FIGURE 7.17 Use of pocket stereoscope. First, have a partner measure the distance between the pupils of your eyes, in millimeters. Set this distance on the stereoscope. Then, position the stereoscope so that your lines of sight are aimed at a common point on each half of the stereogram, or a stereopair. As you look through the stereoscope, move it around slightly until the image "pops" into three dimensions. Be patient during this first attempt, so that your eyes can focus correctly.

a surface is radiating. Different types of plants, animals, rocks, or soil may appear identical on black-and-white photos, or on unfiltered, true-color photos. But on color-infrared photos, these same features often appear in distinctly different colors. Other information also can be obtained from color-infrared photos, such as water temperature, ground temperature, and heat loss from buildings.

QUESTIONS

Figure 7.18 shows parts of three overlapping vertical air photos. They have been cropped (trimmed) and mounted in sequence. The view is of Garibaldi Provincial Park, in British Columbia, Canada. All three pictures show a dark volcanic cinder cone bulging out into Garibaldi Lake from the edge of Mount Price. Each photo shows it from a different overhead viewpoint. These landscape features are depicted by contours on the topographic map in Figure 7.19.

The center point of each photo is marked with a circled **X**. In the right-hand photo (BC 866:50), the center point is in the lake. In the middle photo (BC 866:49), it is near the cinder cone. In the left-hand photo (BC 866:48), it is near the left edge. By locating these center points on the map and connecting them with straight lines, you can see the **flight line,** or route flown by the photographing aircraft.

Locating the centers of these photos on the topographic map (Figure 7.19) is not easy, because the map and the photos show different types of features. However, you can plot the centers fairly accurately by referring to recognizable topographic features such as stream valleys and angles in the lake shore.

Now, answer these questions about the air photos and map.

43. Notice how the image of the cinder cone is distorted when you compare the three successive pictures. Not only is the base of the cone different in each picture, but the round patch of snow in the central crater appears to shift position relative to the base. In which photo does the image of the cone appear to be least distorted? Why?

The same varying-perspective view that distorts features in air photos also makes it possible to view them **stereoscopically.** Thus, when any two overlapping photos in a sequence are placed side by side and viewed with the stereoscope, you see the overlap area as a vertically exaggerated three-dimensional image of the landscape. (With practice, you can train your eyes to do this without a stereoscope.)

44. The scale of the original negatives of the Garibaldi Lake photos is approximately 1:31,680, or 1 inch = ½ mile. However, the pictures reproduced here have been reduced in size. Can you calculate their scale by measuring corresponding distances on the photos and on the topographic map, setting these distances as a ratio, and then multiplying the map scale by this ratio? What is the nominal scale thus derived? (You must write "nominal scale," because the actual scale differs with elevation and

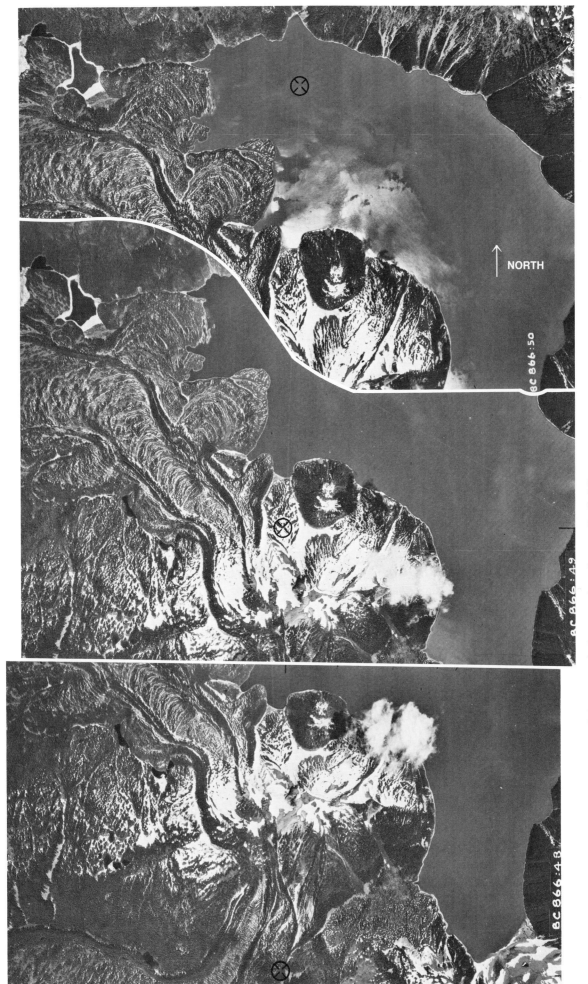

FIGURE 7.18 Stereogram composed of three aerial photographs taken at Garibaldi Lake and vicinity, British Columbia, on July 13, 1949. (Photos BC 866:48–50, reproduced courtesy of Surveys and Resource Mapping Branch, Ministry of Environment, Government of British Columbia, Canada)

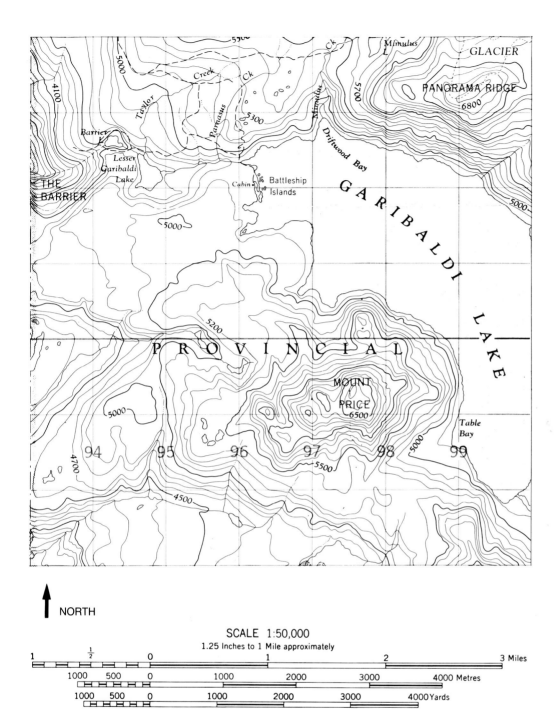

↑ NORTH

SCALE 1:50,000
1.25 Inches to 1 Mile approximately

1   ½   0   1   2   3 Miles

1000   500   0   1000   2000   3000   4000 Metres

1000   500   0   1000   2000   3000   4000 Yards

FIGURE 7.19 Portion of the Cheakamus River, East, topographic quadrangle, British Columbia, on July 13, 1949, the same time at which the stereogram in Figure 7.18 was made. (Reproduced courtesy of Surveys and Resource Mapping Branch, Ministry of Environment, Government of British Columbia, Canada)

distance from the camera lens, as mentioned above.)

45. Photograph BC 866:48 shows two broad pathways that sweep down the slopes of Mount Price from a point near the summit. One trends down to the south and west and the other to the north and west. Both are bordered by narrow ridges. What are these features? Of what rock type are they probably formed?

46. On the map and stereogram, examine both sides of the outlet channel where Garibaldi Lake overflows into Lesser Garibaldi Lake, near the northwest corner of BC 866:50. Is the rock that forms the slopes on the north side of the outlet channel the same or different from that on the south side? Name two features in the photos that lead you to this interpretation.

47. Note that water seems to be flowing into, but not out of, Lesser Garibaldi Lake. Where do you think the water goes that flows into this lake? Why?

48. Lakes, and the basins they occupy, can be formed in many ways. On the basis of these photos, how do you think Garibaldi Lake formed?

49. On Figure 7.20, fill in the chart by writing *good* or *poor* in each box.

Task	Topographic map	Stereoscopic aerial photographs
Determining precise elevations		
Determining extent of vegetation cover		
Determining extent of snow/ice cover		
Measuring angles of slopes		
Examining terrain in great detail		
Precisely describing the location of a feature on the Earth's surface		
Identifying local rock or soil types		
Constructing a topographic profile		
Preventing oneself from getting lost on a hike		

FIGURE 7.20 Comparing the usefulness of topographic maps and aerial photo stereopairs.

EXERCISE EIGHT
Groundwater Processes and Use

Gary D. McKenzie
Ohio State University

Richard N. Strom
University of South Florida, Tampa

James R. Wilson
Weber State College

PURPOSE

The first part of this exercise helps you understand the topographic features and groundwater movements associated with *karst topography*. It shows how you can recognize and understand karst features using water-table contour maps. The second part shows how removal of groundwater can cause *subsidence*, or sinking, of the land.

MATERIALS

Pencils, eraser, calculator.

INTRODUCTION

Water that seeps into the ground is pulled downward by the force of gravity through void spaces in the soil and bedrock. As this process continues, the water reaches a zone below the land surface where all void spaces are completely saturated with water. This zone is called the **saturated zone,** and its upper surface is the **water table.** Water in the saturated zone is called **groundwater.**

The volume of void space in sediment or bedrock is termed **porosity.** The larger the voids, and the greater their number, the higher is the porosity. If void spaces in the sediment or bedrock are interconnected, then water can migrate through

them, and they are said to be **permeable.** Permeable rock units make good **aquifers,** or rock strata that conduct water; examples are sandstones and limestones. Impermeable sediments or rocks that conduct water poorly are called **confining beds;** examples are clays and most shales.

KARST TOPOGRAPHY

The term **karst** describes a distinctive topography that indicates dissolution of underlying soluble rock, generally limestone (Figure 8.1). The limestone dissolves because rainwater is mildly acidic. The rainwater soaks into the ground to form acidic groundwater, which dissolves the limestone. Rainwater may contain several acids, but the most common is carbonic acid (H_2CO_3). It results when water (H_2O) and carbon dioxide (CO_2) in the air combine. Carbonic acid in rainwater dissolves the calcite in limestone by this reaction:

$$CaCO_3 + H_2CO_3 = Ca^{+2} + 2HCO_3^{-1}$$

calcite — carbonic acid — calcium ions dissolved in groundwater — bicarbonate ions dissolved in groundwater

A typical karst topography has these features, shown in Figure 8.1:

121

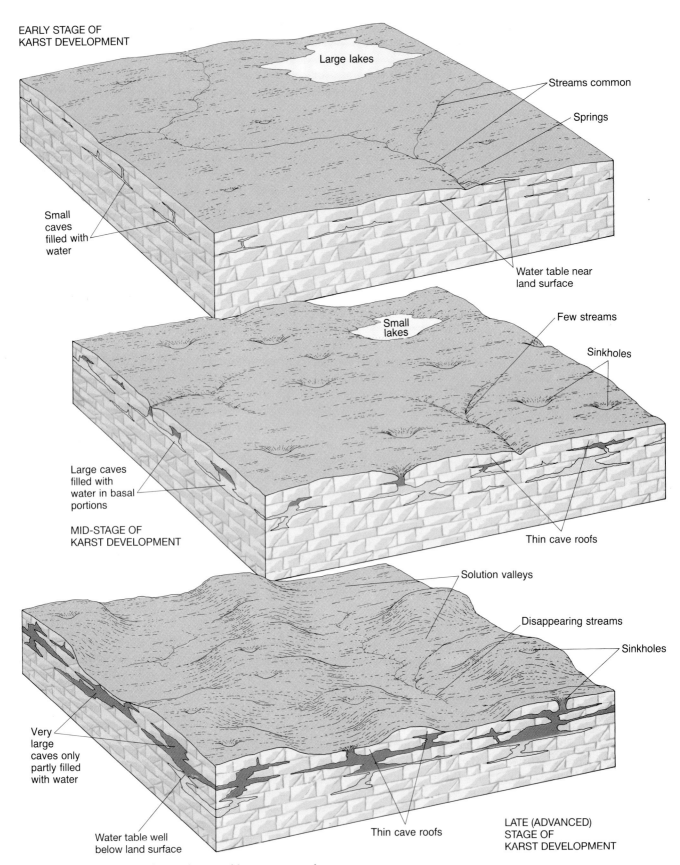

FIGURE 8.1 Stages in the evolution of karst topography.

EARLY STAGE OF
KARST DEVELOPMENT

Large lakes

Streams common

Springs

Small
caves
filled with
water

Water table near
land surface

Small
lakes

Few streams

Sinkholes

Large caves
filled with
water in basal
portions

MID-STAGE OF
KARST DEVELOPMENT

Thin cave roofs

Solution valleys

Disappearing streams

Sinkholes

Very
large
caves only
partly filled
with water

Water table well
below land surface

Thin cave roofs

LATE (ADVANCED)
STAGE OF
KARST DEVELOPMENT

sinkholes surface depressions formed by the collapse of caves or other large underground void spaces.

solution valleys valleylike depressions formed by a linear series of adjacent sinkholes.

springs places where water issues from the ground (bedrock).

disappearing streams streams that terminate abruptly by seeping into the ground.

Much of the drainage in karst areas occurs underground, rather than by surface runoff. Lakes or ponds commonly form where water fills the sinkholes. Drainage generally occurs through networks of large underground cavities called **caves.**

Caves in karst areas often have **stalactites,** icicle-like masses of calcite (chemical limestone) that hang from cave ceilings. They form because calcite precipitates from water droplets as they drip from the ceiling. The broken end of a stalactite is shown in Figure 5.23. Water dripping onto the cave floor also can precipitate calcite and form more stout **stalagmites.** A stalactite and stalagmite can grow together to form a **column.**

Figures 8.4 and 8.5 show the features just described in the northern part of Tampa, Florida. Notice that most of the lakes occupy closed depressions. They are indicated on the map with hachured contour lines (contours with small tick marks that point inward, indicating a depression). These depressions intersect the water table and the subjacent limestone bedrock, as shown in Figure 8.6. By noting the elevations of water surfaces in the lakes, you can determine the slope of the water table and the direction of flow in the shallow sand aquifer.

LAND SUBSIDENCE

Land subsidence caused by human withdrawal of groundwater is a serious problem in many places. For example, in the heart of Mexico City, the land surface has gradually subsided up to 25 feet. At the northern end of California's Santa Clara Valley, 17 square miles of land have subsided below the highest tide level in San Francisco Bay, and now must be protected by earthworks. Other centers of subsidence include Houston, Tokyo, Venice, and Las Vegas. With increasing withdrawal of groundwater and more intensive use of the land surface, we can expect the problem of subsidence to become more widespread.

Subsidence induced by withdrawal of groundwater commonly occurs in areas underlain by stream-deposited (alluvial) sand and gravel that is interbedded with lake-deposited (lacustrine) clays and silts. The sand-and-gravel beds are aquifers, and the clay beds are confining beds.

In Figure 8.7, the water in the lower aquifer ("sand and gravel") is confined between impermeable beds of clay and silt, and is under pressure from its own weight. Thus, water in wells drilled to this aquifer will rise to the water-pressure surface. Such wells are termed **artesian wells.** The upper aquifer ("sand") contains water that is not under pressure. In wells drilled to this aquifer, the groundwater would stand at the level of the water table.

Land subsidence is related to the compressibility of water-saturated sediments. Pumping of wells not only removes water from the system, but also reduces the hydrostatic pressure and lowers the water-pressure surface (Figure 8.8). This results in compaction of the aquifer and in gradual lowering of the ground surface. This process can be reversed if the water pressure is increased, usually by replenishing (or **recharging**) the aquifer with water. This may cause the aquifer to return approximately to its original form, but the confining beds, once compacted, will not expand to their earlier thicknesses.

The Santa Clara Valley (Figure 8.9) was one of the first areas in the United States where land subsidence due to groundwater overdraft was recognized. The Santa Clara Valley is a large structural trough filled with an over-1500-foot thickness of alluvium. Sand-and-gravel aquifers predominate near the valley margins, but the major part of the alluvium is fine grained. Below a depth of 200 feet, the groundwater is confined by layers of clay, except near the margins.

Initially, wells as far south as Santa Clara were artesian, because the water-pressure surface was above the land surface. However, pumping them for irrigation lowered the water-pressure surface 150–200 feet by 1965. This decline was not continuous; natural recharge of the aquifer occurred between 1938 and 1947, in part because of controlled infiltration from surface reservoirs. As of 1971, the subsidence had been stopped due to a reversal of the water-level decline.

Most wells tapping the artesian system are 500–1000 feet deep, although a few reach 1200 feet. Well yields in the valley are 500–1500 gallons per minute (gpm), which is very high.

FIGURE 8.2 Looking east toward the Arkansas River from Vap's Pass, Oklahoma (15 miles northeast of Ponca City). Note the widespread exposures of Fort Riley Limestone bedrock and natural vegetation. (Photo by R. Busch)

QUESTIONS ON KARST

1. In Figure 8.2, notice the pattern along which plants have grown. What does this indicate about how water travels through bedrock in this part of Oklahoma?

2. If you had to drill a water well in Figure 8.2, how would you pick the site where you would get the most water? Explain your answer.

3. In Figure 8.3, what are the long icicle-like rock formations called?

4. How is Figure 8.3 related to Figure 8.2?

5. On Figure 8.5, mark the elevations of water levels in the lakes (obtain this information from Figure 8.4). The elevations of Lake Magdalene and some lakes beyond the boundaries of the topographic map already are marked for you.

6. Contour the water-table surface (use a 5-foot contour interval). Draw only lines representing whole 5s (40, 45, and so on). Do this in the same manner that you contoured land surfaces in Exercise Seven.

7. The flow of shallow groundwater is at right angles to the contour lines. Use three or four long arrows to indicate the direction of shallow groundwater flow in this part of Tampa. The southeastern part of Figure 8.4 shows numerous closed depressions, but only tiny lakes. What does this indicate concerning the level of the water table in that region?

In Figure 8.6, you can see how several deeper sinkholes in the area connect directly with the underlying Floridan Aquifer (limestone).

8. Note the Poinsettia Sinks in Figure 8.5. Find them on the topographic map, Figure 8.4. Note their closely spaced hachured contour lines. Now, find the cluster of five similar sinkholes, about 2 inches away, just west of the WHBO radio tower. Mark their locations on Figure 8.5 with asterisks (*). These are called the Blue Sinks.
   a. What is the elevation of the water table in the sinkholes at Blue Sinks?
   b. On Figure 8.4, note the stream and valley just west of Blue Sinks. This is a fairly typical disappearing stream. On Figure 8.5,

trace its approximate course. In what direction does the water flow? Draw an arrowhead on one end of the stream to indicate its flow direction. How does this compare to the general slope of the water table?
   c. Where is the streamwater going?

9. In March, 1958, fluorescent dye was injected into the northernmost of the Blue Sinks. It was detected 28 hours later in Sulphur Springs, on the Hillsborough River to the south (see Figure 8.5). Calculate the approximate velocity of flow in this portion of the Floridan Aquifer:
   a. in feet per hour
   b. in miles per hour
   c. in meters per hour
   d. in kilometers per hour

The velocities you just calculated are quite high, even for the Floridan Aquifer. But this portion of Tampa seems to be riddled with solution channels and caves in the underlying limestone. Sulphur Springs has an average discharge of approximately 44 cubic feet per second (cfs), and its maximum recorded discharge was 165 cfs (it once was a famous spa).

10. During recent years the discharge at Sulphur Springs has decreased. Water quality has worsened substantially.
    a. Examine the human-made structures on Figure 8.4. Note especially those in red, indicating new structures. Why has the discharge of Sulphur Springs decreased in recent years?
    b. Why has the water quality decreased in recent years?

11. Imagine you are selling homeowner's insurance in the portion of the Sulphur Springs quadrangle shown in Figure 8.4. List all the potential groundwater-related hazards to homes and homeowners in the area.

QUESTIONS ON LAND SUBSIDENCE

12. On Figure 8.12, solid contour lines show land surface elevation. Dashed lines represent the water-pressure surface (potentiometric surface)

FIGURE 8.3 (Opposite page) Part of the roof in Cave of the Winds, formed in Paleozoic limestones near Manitou Springs, Colorado. (Photo by R. Busch)

FIGURE 8.4: Sulfur Springs, Florida

North

| 0 | .5 | 1 kilometer |
| 0 | ¼ | ½ | 1 mile |

Contour interval = 5 ft.   1:24,000

of a confined aquifer. This is the height to which water will rise in a well that is drilled into the aquifer.

   a. Find and connect the points on Figure 8.12 where the two sets of contour lines have the same elevation.

   b. Shade in the area on the same figure where wells would flow at the land surface without having to be pumped (i.e., where wells would be artesian).

13. Label on Figure 8.7: **A** for artesian, or confined, aquifer; **CB** for confining bed; **WPS** for water-pressure surface (or potentiometric surface, which equals the water table for an artesian system); and **WTA** for water-table aquifer.

14. On Figure 8.7, draw two wells (vertical lines) at points where you would obtain a good water supply (1) from an artesian aquifer (label it **AW** for artesian well), and (2) from a water-table aquifer (label it **WTW**).

15. Would the water in your artesian well (**AW**) flow from the well naturally, without pumping? Explain.

   Refer to Figures 8.9, 8.10, and 8.11 while answering these questions:

16. Where are the areas of greatest subsidence in the Santa Clara Valley?

17. What was the total subsidence at San Jose (Figure 8.10) from 1934 to 1967 (inclusive)?

18. What was the average annual rate of subsidence for this period in feet per year?

19. At what places in the Santa Clara Valley would subsidence cause the most problems?

20. Would you expect much subsidence to occur in the darker shaded areas of Figure 8.9? Explain.

21. By 1960, the total subsidence at San Jose had reached 9.0 feet (Figure 8.10). What was the average annual rate of subsidence (in feet per year) for the seven-year period from 1960 through 1967?

22. Refer to Figure 8.11. What was the level of the water in the San Jose well in:

   a. 1915?

   b. 1967?

23. During what period would this well have been a flowing artesian well?

24. How can you explain the minor fluctuations in the hydrograph?

25. What might explain the upward trend in the potentiometric surface shown in the hydrograph between 1938 and 1944?

ADDITIONAL QUESTIONS

26. Using the data for a nearby benchmark in San Jose (in Figure 8.10), plot on Figure 8.11 the decline of the land surface. (Use the scale on the right side of Figure 8.11 to plot this subsidence.)

27. In Figure 8.11, the slope of a line joining the level of the land surface in 1915 with subsidence that had occurred by 1967 gives the average rate of subsidence for that period. How did the rate of subsidence occurring between 1935 and 1948 differ from earlier rates?

28. Explain the probable cause of the subsidence rate change noted in the previous question.

29. Subsidence was arrested by 1971. What measures might have been taken to accomplish this?

FIGURE 8.4 (Opposite page) Portion of the Sulphur Springs, Florida topographic quadrangle map.

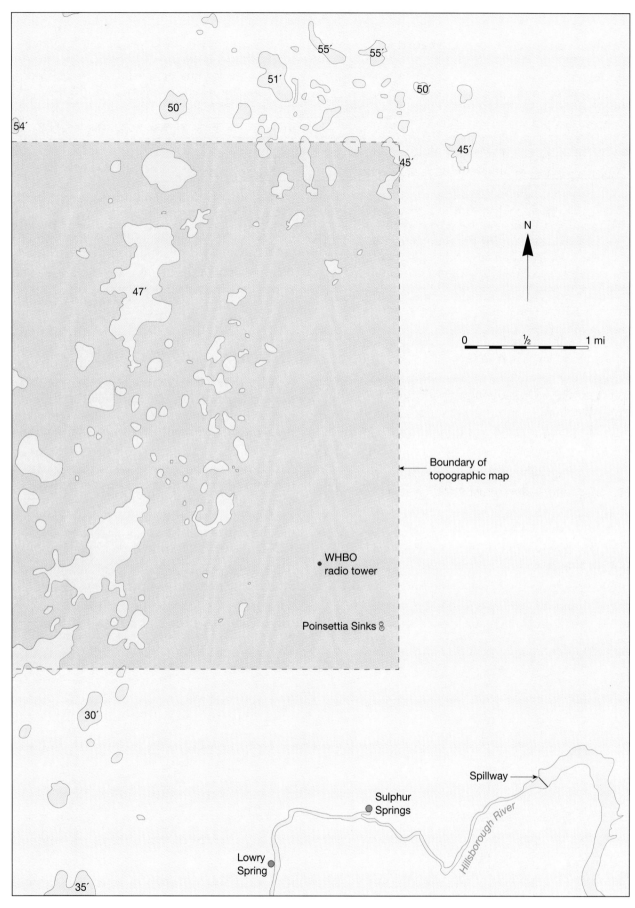

FIGURE 8.5 Sketch map of the area shown in Figure 8.4 and neighboring areas to the north, east, and south.

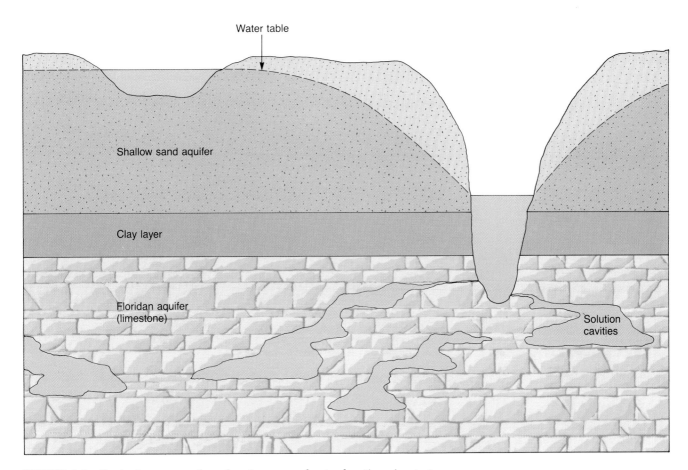

FIGURE 8.6 Geologic cross section showing groundwater locations in strata underlying the Tampa, Florida area.

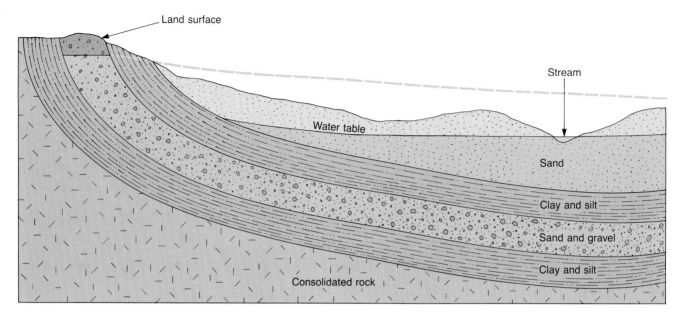

FIGURE 8.7 Geologic cross section illustrating water-table aquifer and confined aquifer. Vertical scale is exaggerated.

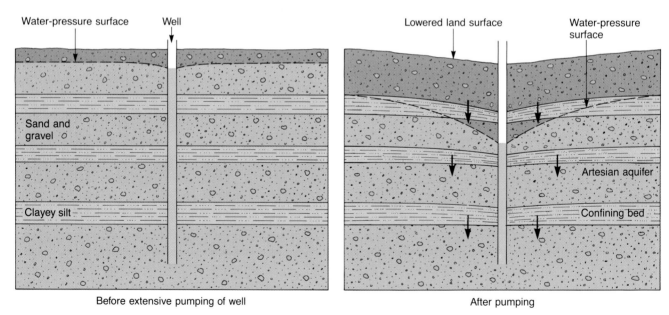

FIGURE 8.8 Before and after extensive pumping of a well. Note in the right-hand illustration the lowering of the water-pressure surface, compaction of confining beds between the aquifers, and resulting subsidence of land surface. Arrows indicate the direction of compaction caused by the downward force of gravity, after the opposing water pressure was reduced by excessive withdrawal (discharge) of groundwater from the well.

130 EXERCISE EIGHT

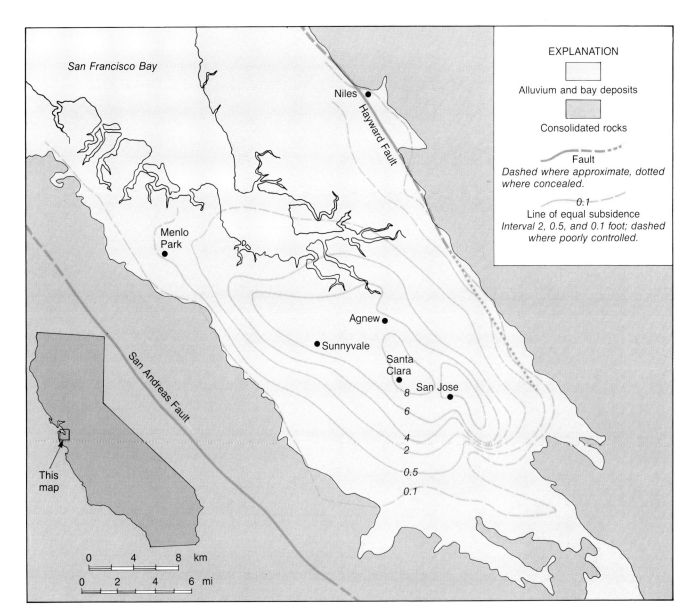

FIGURE 8.9 Land subsidence, 1934–1967, in the Santa Clara Valley, California. (Courtesy of U.S. Geological Survey)

Year	Subsidence (feet)
1912	0.0
1920	0.3
1934	4.6
1935	5.0
1936	5.0
1937	5.2
1940	5.5
1948	5.8
1955	8.0
1960	9.0
1963	11.0
1967	12.7

FIGURE 8.10 Subsidence at benchmark P7 in San Jose, California.

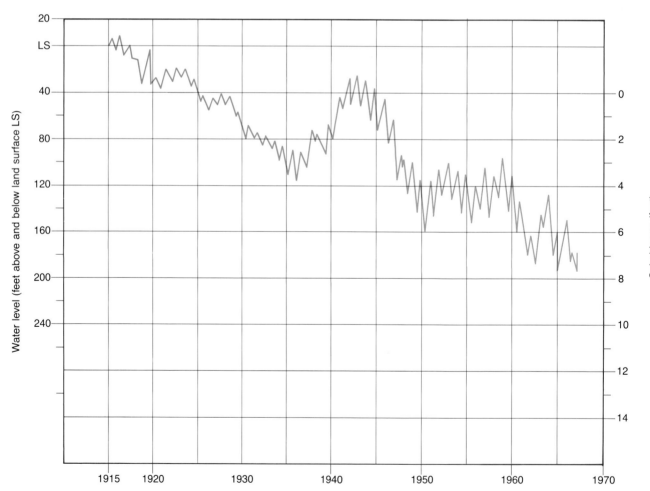

FIGURE 8.11 Hydrograph showing changes of water level in a well at San Jose, California.

FIGURE 8.12 Where will wells flow at the land surface without having to be pumped? Solid brown lines are topographic contour lines showing elevation of the land surface. Dashed blue lines represent the water-pressure surface (potentiometric surface) of a confined aquifer.

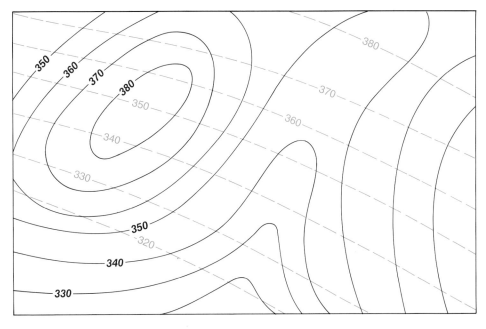

EXERCISE NINE

Surface Water Processes and Fluvial Landscapes

Richard W. Macomber
Long Island University, Brooklyn

PURPOSE

This exercise shows you how topographic maps and stereograms are used to understand streams: their valley shapes, channel configurations, drainage patterns, and the eroded landscapes they create.

MATERIALS

Pencil, eraser, ruler, calculator, 12-inch length of string, pocket stereoscope.

INTRODUCTION

Streams are the single most important agent of land erosion. They downcut into soil and bedrock, increase their length by headward erosion, increase their width by slope retreat of the valley walls, transport sediments, and deposit them. Deposited sediments are called **alluvium**. Alluvium is deposited in floodplains, point bars, channel bars, deltas, and alluvial fans. Therefore, stream processes, or **fluvial processes,** are among the most important agents that shape Earth's surface.

STREAM VALLEYS

Stream valleys form drainage networks that merge downslope until they ultimately form a single river valley. The total area drained by such a complete network is a **watershed,** or **drainage basin.**

The smallest valleys in a drainage basin occur at its highest elevations, or **headlands.** In the headlands, a stream's point of origin, or **head,** may be at a spring or at the start of narrow runoff channels developed during rainstorms. These channels deepen and erode uphill through time, a process called **headward erosion.** Headwater valleys merge into larger tributary valleys, and these eventually merge into a single large river valley. The end of such a valley is the **mouth** of the river, where it enters a lake, ocean, or dry basin.

The shape of a river valley varies with these factors:

gradient   the slope of the stream channel along a selected length of its course. Gradient generally is measured in *feet per mile.* For example, if a stream descends 20 feet over a distance of 40 miles, then its gradient is 20 feet/40 miles, or 0.5 foot/mile. You can estimate the gradient of a stream by studying the spacing of contours on a topographic map. Or, you can precisely calculate the exact gradient by measuring how much a stream descends along a measured segment of its course.

discharge the rate of stream flow at a given time and location. Discharge is measured in water volume per unit of time, commonly *cubic feet per second*.

load the amount of sediment that is transported by a stream.

Near the headwaters, most streams have relatively steep gradients, so the streams cut narrow-bottomed, V-shaped valleys. You can see this in Figure 9.1A and Figure 9.2A. Near the headwaters, most streams carry only a minor load.

Downstream, the gradient decreases, discharge increases, and valleys are wider (Figure 9.1B and C; Figure 9.2C and D). Here, the load of the stream may exceed the ability of the water to carry it and accumulate as sedimentary deposits along the river margins, or banks. **Floodplains** develop when alluvium accumulates landward of the river banks, during floods. Flooding also may erode the valley walls.

Still farther downstream, the gradient decreases even more as discharge and load increase. The stream valleys develop very wide, flat floodplains with sinuous channels. These channels may become highly sinuous, or **meandering** (Figures 9.1B and 9.2D). Erosion occurs on the outer edge of meanders, which are called **cutbanks.** At the same time, **point bar** deposits accumulate along the inner edge of meanders. Progressive erosion of cutbanks and deposition of point bars makes meanders "migrate" over time.

Channels may cut new paths during floods. This can cut off the outer edge of a meander, abandoning it to become a crescent-shaped **oxbow lake** (Figures 9.1B, 9.2D). When low gradient/high discharge streams become overloaded with sediment, they may form **braided stream** patterns. These consist of multiple channels with linear, underwater sandbars **(channel bars)** and islands (Figure 9.1C).

Some stream valleys have level surfaces that are higher than the present floodplain. These are remnants of older floodplains that have been dissected (cut by younger streams) and are called **stream terraces.** Sometimes several levels of stream terraces may be developed along a stream, resembling steps.

Where a stream enters a lake, ocean, or dry basin, its velocity decreases dramatically. The stream drops its sediment load, which accumulates as a triangular or fan-shaped deposit. Such a deposit in a lake or ocean is called a **delta.** A similar fan-shaped deposit of stream sediment also occurs where a steep-gradient stream abruptly enters a wide level plain, creating an **alluvial fan.**

STREAM DRAINAGE PATTERNS

Stream systems can have different branching patterns (Figure 9.3). Most common is the **dendritic** pattern, shaped like tree branches or a root system. Dendritic drainage is typical of stream systems that develop in regions underlain by relatively flat-lying or homogeneous rock.

Where sedimentary rocks have been bent into long folds and broken by faults (e.g., in mountain belts), the eroded edges of upturned resistant and nonresistant layers form parallel ridges and valleys. These control the branching of streams to produce a **trellis** drainage pattern.

Note the other drainage patterns in Figure 9.3.

STREAM-ERODED LANDSCAPES

Imagine an upland region, with few stream valleys. It becomes progressively dissected by new tributaries that form, lengthen, deepen, and develop branches of their own. Because this active erosion takes place along the valleys, remnants of the original upland tend to retain their original characteristics. However, as the erosion process continues, the upland is gradually transformed into a landscape of nothing but hills and valleys, sculptured by the streams. When the hills are finally eroded, broad lowlands form.

This process traditionally is thought of as an "erosion cycle" that includes three stages: *"youthful," "mature,"* and *"old age."* The youthful stage is characterized by deep, narrow channels that dissect limited portions of the uplands. By the old-age stage, mostly lowlands remain, with a few small hills and shallow, meandering stream valleys.

Although these terms are useful in a very general sense, they imply a misleading sense of time, and they overgeneralize the process. For example, some "youthful" stream-eroded landscapes actually are older than other landscapes labeled as being in "old age." Other factors—climate, discharge, bedrock type, and stream load—also are important in the stream-erosion process. So, you

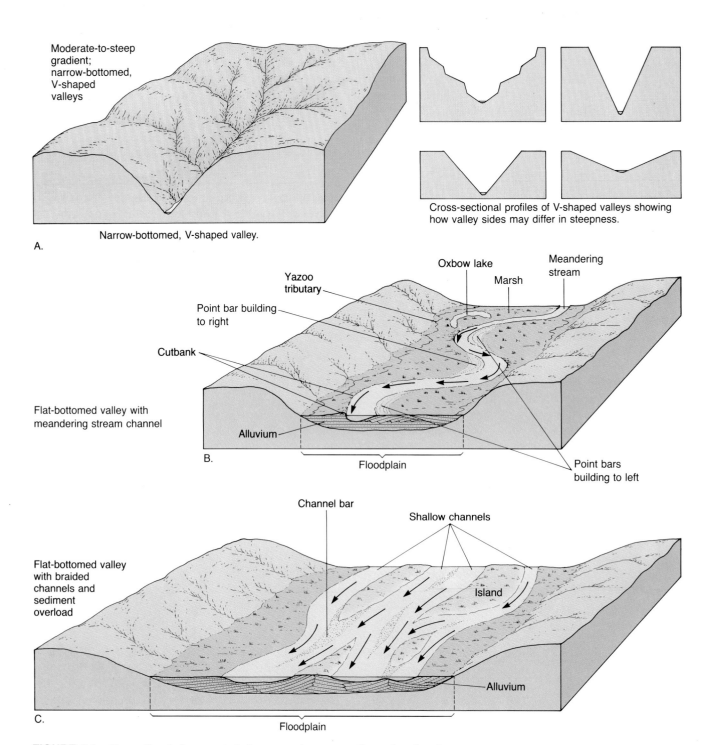

FIGURE 9.1 Generalized characteristic features of stream valleys that develop in response to variations in stream gradient, discharge, and load. Arrows indicate current flow in main stream channels.

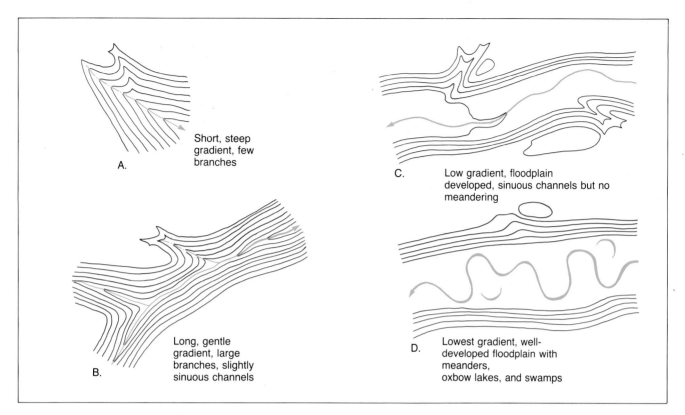

FIGURE 9.2 Examples of different stream valley types as they appear on topographic maps.

must consider all of these factors when studying a particular stream-eroded landscape.

A **divide** is the land between stream valleys. Divides may be either broad uplands or ridges. Thus, divides are the boundaries between drainage basins (they divide the drainage). In extensive uplands with widely spaced stream valleys, divides generally are poorly defined. Conversely, in remnant uplands with closely spaced stream valleys, divides generally are clearly defined by sharp ridges. Figure 9.4 displays examples as they appear on topographic maps.

QUESTIONS

Refer to the Renovo West, Pennsylvania quadrangle (Figure 9.5) for Questions 1–6. To measure the length of a stream on the map, it is helpful to fit a string on top of the stream. Then, pull the string straight, and compare its length to the graphic scale (in miles, kilometers, or feet).

1. Make a topographic profile along *A–A'*.
   a. How would you characterize the shapes of the stream valleys?
   b. Label the headlands.
   c. Label (with arrows) the points on your profile that represent divides.

2. What is the probable attitude of the layers of bedrock in this portion of the quadrangle? How can you tell?

3. Locate Summerson Run, a stream at the bottom center of the map.
   a. What is the gradient of this stream from the point where it crosses the 1400-foot contour line to the upslope start of the stream?
   b. What is the gradient of this stream from the point where it crosses the 1400-foot contour line to the point where it enters Kettle Creek at an elevation of 800 feet?
   c. What may be the cause of this abrupt change in stream gradient?

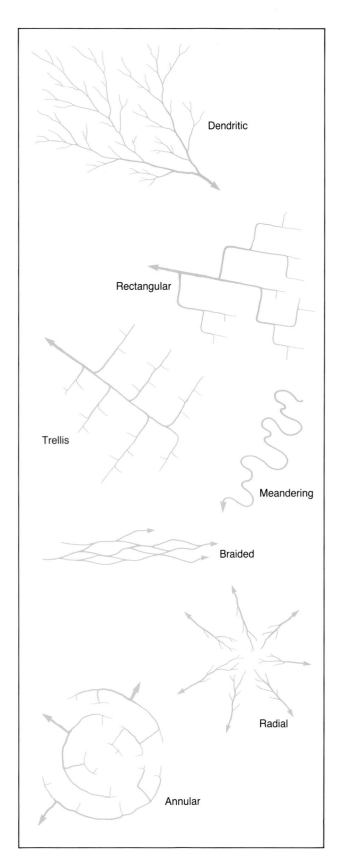

FIGURE 9.3 Examples of stream drainage patterns observed in map (aerial) view.

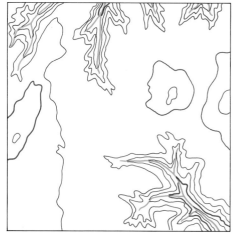

Few streams;
broad uplands (divides) between streams

Many streams;
hilly, narrow divides;
little or no upland left

Fewer streams;
no upland; narrow divides;
broad lowlands developing

FIGURE 9.4 Examples of some upland landscapes as they appear on topographic maps.

4. Compare the gradients, sinuosities, and development of floodplains for Summerson Run, Trout Run (crossed by section line *A–A'*), and Kettle Creek. Write a brief description of each in the manner of Figure 9.2.

5. Why are these three stream valleys so different, even though all are part of the same drainage system?

6. What type of stream drainage patterns (Figure 9.3) are developed in the Renovo West quadrangle?

Refer to the Voltaire, North Dakota quadrangle (Figures 9.6 and 9.7) for these questions:

7. This landscape is much younger than that around Renovo, Pennsylvania (Figure 9.5). It has been etched into a thick mantle of sand and gravel deposited here by glaciers and glacial meltwater only about 11,000–12,000 years ago. Nevertheless, note how well developed the meanders and floodplains of the Souris River are, relative to Kettle Creek in Figure 9.5. Based upon this information, what can you say about the use of the traditional concept of an "erosion cycle" involving youth, maturity, and old age?

8. Look at the flat valley bottoms like those of Kettle Creek (Figure 9.5) and the Souris River (Figures 9.6 and 9.7). Why are they called floodplains?

9. On Figures 9.6 and 9.7, note the swampy oxbow lakes and depressions (hachured contours on Figure 9.6) in the Souris River floodplain. These show that the river channel has changed course repeatedly. Explain how its course has changed at the oxbow just east of Westgaard Cemetery (northeast of map center, Figure 9.6).

10. Do the hachured contours and other oxbows of the Souris River Valley show that this same process has occurred elsewhere along the valley?

11. Where along the course of the Souris River might the same thing happen in the future, if the course of the channel is not controlled by engineers?

12. Imagine what the topographic profile looks like along *X–X'*. (Refer to the stereogram in Figure 9.7 to help you with this.) Notice the relatively flat areas of the profile, such as those in SW¼ sec. 33 and SE¼ sec. 4.

a. What are these features called?
b. How do they form?
c. Why are they of such different elevations?

13. In SE¼ sec. 3, a stream trends northeast-southeast. What is the name of this type of stream?

14. Notice the marsh in sec. 9 and the depression on which it is located. What was this depression before it became a marsh?

15. How might the discharge of the Souris River have changed over the past 12,000 years? Why?

16. How has this affected the width of the Souris River Valley and the load of the Souris River?

Some rivers are subject to large floods, either seasonal or periodic. In mountains, this flooding is due to snowmelt; in deserts it is caused by thunderstorms. During such times, rivers transport exceptionally large volumes of sediment. This causes characteristic features, two of which are braided (anastomosing) channels and alluvial fans. Both features are relatively common in arid mountainous regions, such as the Ennis, Montana area in Figures 9.8 and 9.9. Both features also can occur wherever conditions are right, even at construction sites! Refer to the Ennis, Montana quadrangle and photos for these questions:

17. What is the source of sediments that have accumulated on the Cedar Creek Alluvial Fan?

18. What is the approximate stream gradient of:
a. the main stream in the forested southeastern corner of the map?
b. most streams on the Cedar Creek Alluvial Fan?
c. the Madison River?

19. What drainage patterns (shown in Figure 9.3) are present on:
a. the forested southeastern corner of the map?
b. the Cedar Creek Alluvial Fan?
c. the valley of the Madison River (northwestern portion of map)?

20. How are the stream gradients and drainage patterns in Questions 18 and 19 related?

21. How did the Cedar Creek Alluvial Fan form?

Refer to the Waldron, Arkansas quadrangle (Figure 9.10) for these questions:

22. What type of drainage pattern (shown in Figure 9.3) is present in this area?

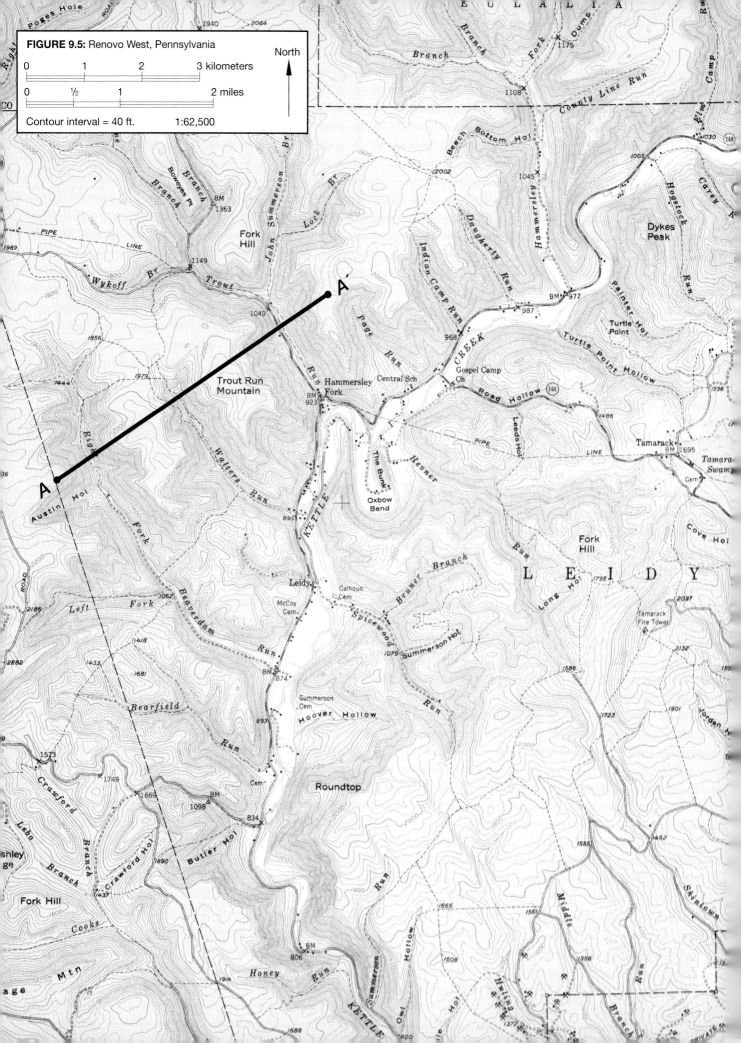

FIGURE 9.5: Renovo West, Pennsylvania

North

| 0 | 1 | 2 | 3 kilometers |

| 0 | ½ | 1 | 2 miles |

Contour interval = 40 ft.   1:62,500

23. The bedrock of this region is alternating layers of mudstone and quartz-rich sandstone.
    a. Which rock type probably forms the ridges? Explain your reasoning.
    b. Which rock type probably forms the valleys? Explain your reasoning.

24. Explain what may have caused this type of drainage pattern (Question 22) to develop here.

Refer to the Lake Scott, Kansas quadrangle (Figure 9.11) for the following questions:

25. Note that the upland surface of this area is not horizontal.
    a. In what general direction does the surface slope downward?
    b. What is the gradient of this surface?
    c. The bedrock of the headlands is overlain by alluvium that was deposited prior to dissection of the surface. It is the upper surface of this alluvium that has the attitude described in Questions 25a and 25b. What is the probable source area for the water and sediments that formed this alluvial deposit?
    d. What stream drainage pattern (shown in Figure 9.3) probably was associated with the deposition of this headland alluvium?

26. What drainage pattern currently is developed in this area?

27. What does this drainage pattern suggest about the attitude of bedrock layers in this area?

The Niagara River flows from Lake Erie to Lake Ontario (Figure 9.12). The gorge of the Niagara presents good evidence of the erosion of a caprock falls, Niagara Falls (Figure 9.13). The edge of the falls is composed of the resistant Lockport Dolomite. The retreat of the falls is due to undercutting of mudstones that support the Lockport Dolomite. Water cascading from the lip of the falls enters the plunge pool with tremendous force, and the turbulent water easily erodes the soft mudstones. With the erosion of the mudstones, the Lockport Dolomite collapses.

28. Geologic evidence indicates that the Niagara River began to cut its gorge about 11,000 years ago as the Laurentide Ice Sheet retreated from the area. It started at the Niagara Escarpment, Figure 9.12. Based on this geochronology and the length of the gorge, calculate the average rate of falls retreat in cm/year.

29. Name some factors that could cause the falls to retreat at a faster rate.

30. Name some factors that could cause the falls to retreat more slowly.

31. Niagara Falls is about 35 km north of Lake Erie, and it is retreating southward. If the falls were to continue its retreat at the average rate calculated in Question 28, how many years from now would the falls reach Lake Erie?

ADDITIONAL QUESTIONS

Regional uplift, change of climate, or other major factors may interrupt a drainage pattern and cause the development of a new one. For example, recall the Lake Scott, Kansas quadrangle (Figure 9.11), and the two different types of drainage that have existed there.

32. What probably caused the change in stream drainage and deposition that occurred in the Lake Scott quadrangle?

33. Return to the Renovo West, Pennsylvania quadrangle (Figure 9.5).
    a. Have drainage conditions changed in this quadrangle? (Hint: How can you explain the very steep-sided valleys of Kettle Creek and upland hills such as "The Bunk" at Oxbow Bend near the center of the map?)
    b. What has probably occurred to cause such steep-sided valleys to develop instead of gentle-sided valleys?

FIGURE 9.5 (Opposite page) Portion of the Renovo West, Pennsylvania topographic quadrangle map.

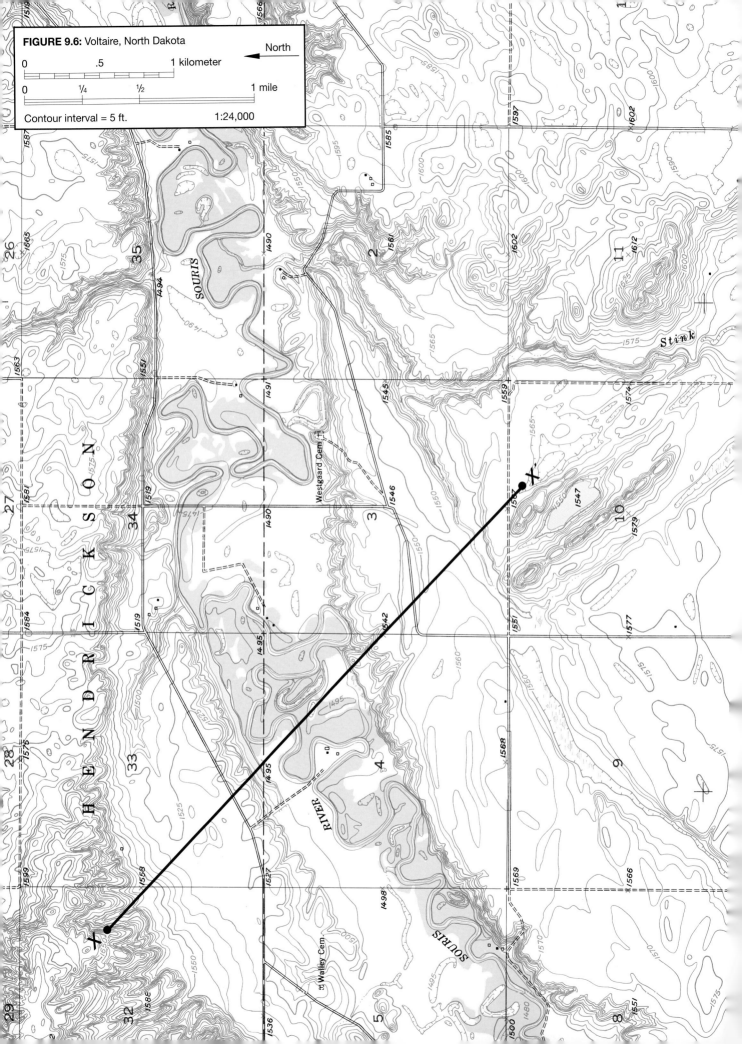

FIGURE 9.6: Voltaire, North Dakota

North

| 0 | .5 | 1 kilometer |

| 0 | 1/4 | 1/2 | 1 mile |

Contour interval = 5 ft.

1:24,000

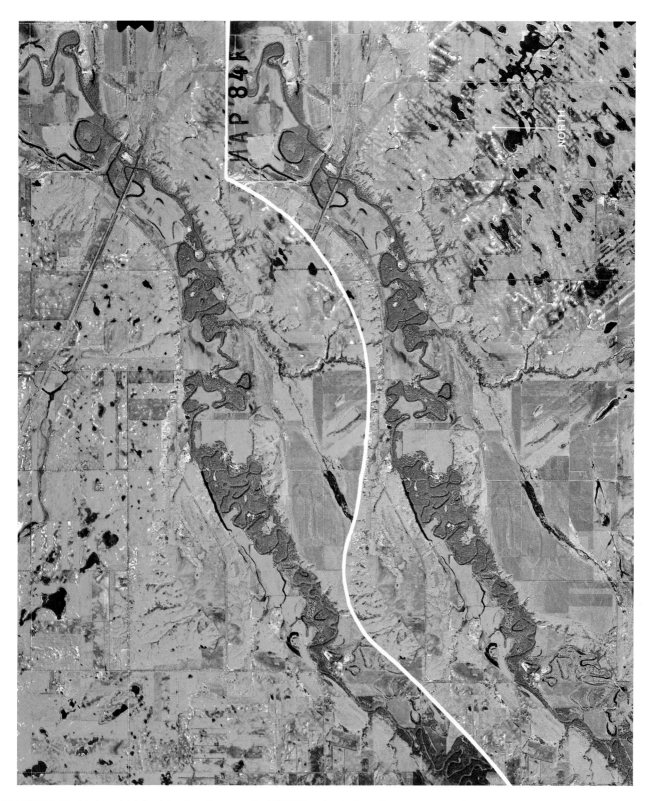

FIGURE 9.7 National high-altitude photograph (NHAP, color-infrared) stereogram of the Voltaire, North Dakota area. (USGS)

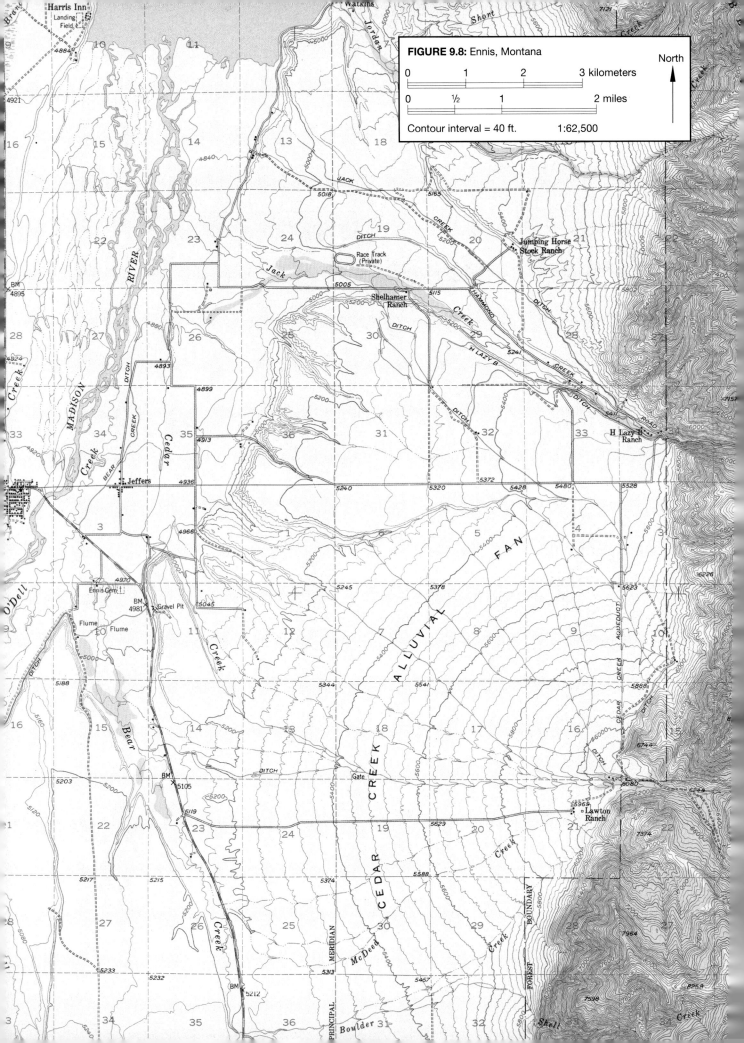

FIGURE 9.8: Ennis, Montana

North

| 0 | | 1 | | 2 | | 3 kilometers |

| 0 | | ½ | | 1 | | 2 miles |

Contour interval = 40 ft.   1:62,500

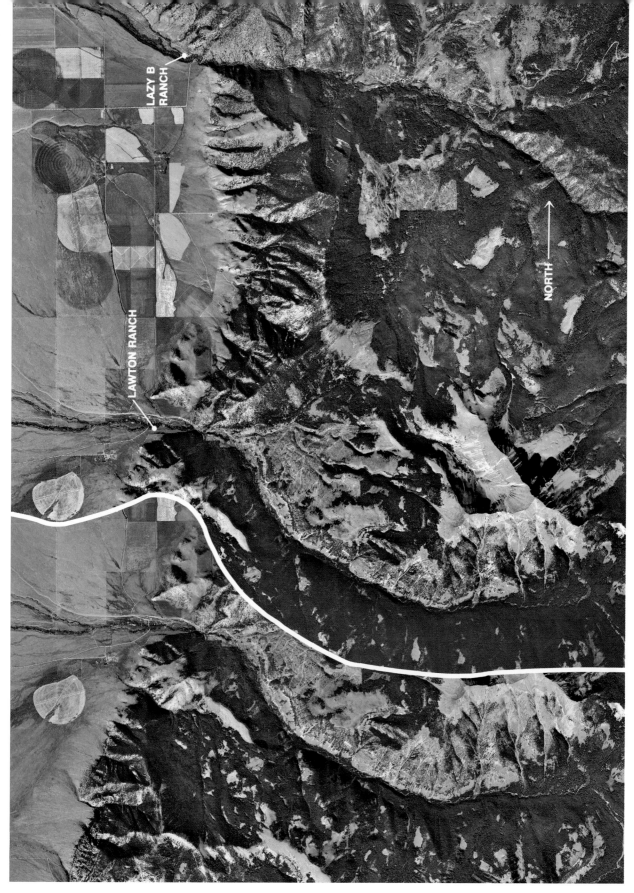

FIGURE 9.8 (Opposite page) Portion of the Ennis, Montana topographic quadrangle map.

FIGURE 9.9 National high-altitude photograph (NHAP, color-infrared) stereogram of a portion of the Ennis, Montana area. (USGS)

145

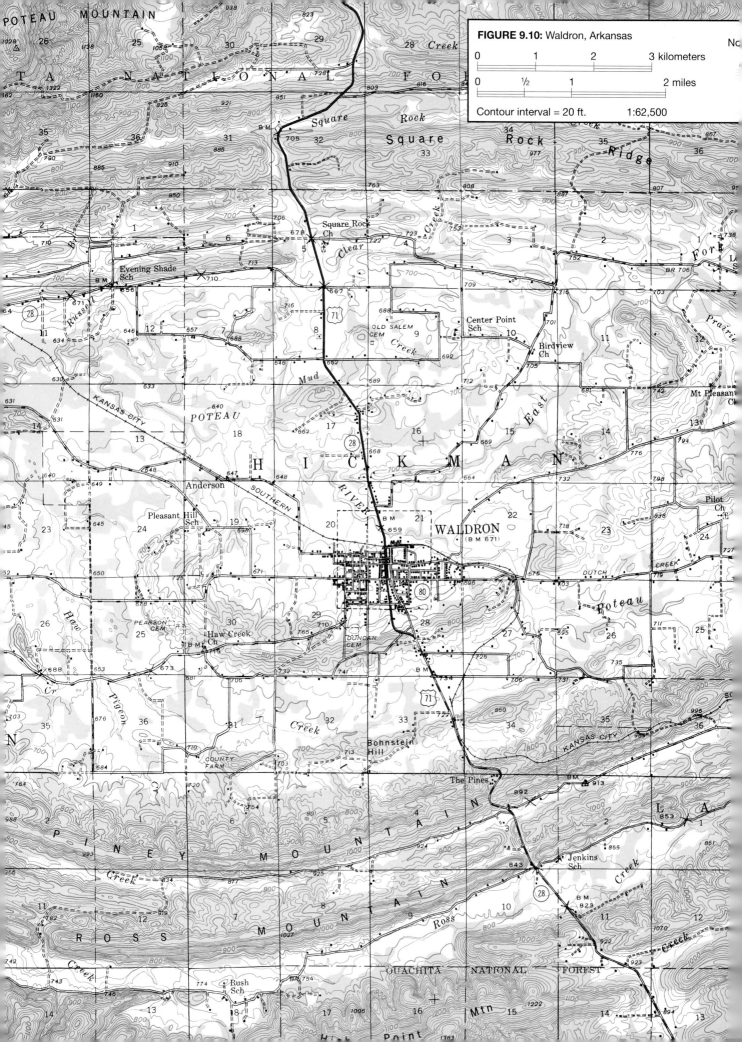

FIGURE 9.10: Waldron, Arkansas

| 0 | 1 | 2 | 3 kilometers |

| 0 | ½ | 1 | 2 miles |

Contour interval = 20 ft.   1:62,500

FIGURE 9.11: Lake Scott, Kansas

.5   1 kilometer

North

1/4   1/2   1 mile

Contour interval = 10 ft.   1:24,000

FIGURE 9.10 (Previous page) Portion of the Waldron, Arkansas topographic quadrangle map.

FIGURE 9.11 (Previous page) Portion of the Lake Scott, Kansas topographic quadrangle map.

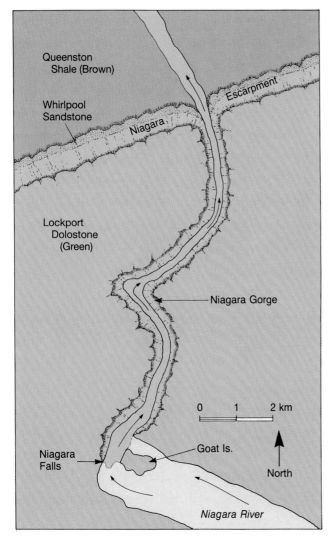

FIGURE 9.12 Map of the Niagara Gorge region of Canada and the United States.

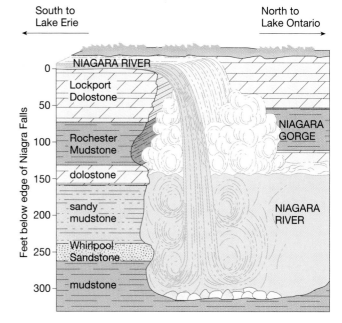

FIGURE 9.13 Schematic of Niagara Falls and geologic units of the Niagara escarpment.

EXERCISE TEN

Coastal Processes and Landforms

Cherukapalli E. Nehru
John A. Shimer
John C. Stewart
Brooklyn College (CUNY)

Donald W. Watson
Slippery Rock University

PURPOSE

This exercise shows you how to identify and interpret common shoreline features as they appear on topographic maps and aerial photographs.

MATERIALS

Pocket stereoscope, pencils, eraser, ruler.

INTRODUCTION

The shorelines of lakes and oceans are among the most rapidly changing parts of the Earth's surface. All coastlines are subject to erosion by wave attack. A coastline composed of loose sediments can be eroded easily and rapidly. A coastline composed of dense bedrock or plastic-like mud erodes much more slowly.

Several factors determine the characteristic landforms of shorelines: the shape of the shoreline, the composition of coastal substrates (rock, plastic mud, or loose sediment), the source and supply of sediments, the direction of longshore transport, and the effects of major storms.

Most coastlines also are affected by changes in mean (average) sea level:

- A *rising* sea level creates a **submergent coastline** that is receding, or *retrogradational*. Sea level rise is caused either by the water level actually rising (called **transgression**), or by the land subsiding.
- A *falling* sea level creates an **emergent coastline** that is building out into the water, or *progradational*. Sea level fall is caused either by the water level actually falling (called **regression**), or by the land rising.

Submergent coastlines may display some emergent features, and vice versa. For example, the Louisiana coastline is submergent, enough so that dikes and levees have been built to keep the ocean from drowning New Orleans. However, the Mississippi delta is progradational—building into the water—a feature of most emergent coastlines. It is progradational because of the great supply of sediment from the vast Mississippi drainage.

Thus, *sediment supply* is a major factor in determining whether a coastline is progradational or retrogradational, regardless of vertical changes of land level or water level. Sediment transport and the effects of major storms also are very important agents of shoreline change.

Figure 10.1 illustrates some features of *emergent* marine shorelines. These include well-developed deltas, beaches, and tidal flats/salt marshes.

Figure 10.2 illustrates some features of *submergent* marine shorelines. These include poorly developed deltas, beaches, and tidal flats/salt marshes. Such features are drowned by the rising sea level. Cliffs are cut into headlands and barrier islands are well developed, although exceptions can occur locally.

DEFINITIONS

Refer to Figures 10.1 and 10.2 for illustrations of these features:

barrier island   low, elongate sand ridge, above sea level; parallels the coast and is separated from the mainland by a lagoon, tidal flat, or salt marsh.

baymouth bar   a bar, or low submerged sand deposit, that crosses the mouth of a bay, sealing it off from the main body of water.

beach   a gently sloping deposit of sand or gravel along a shoreline.

berm crest   the highest and most landward edge of a beach; separates the foreshore (seaward) from the backshore (landward) parts of the coastline.

washover fan   fan-shaped deposit of sand or gravel transported and deposited landward of the beach during a storm or very high tide.

estuary   inlet of the sea, formed by the flooding of a river mouth due to sea level rise or land subsidence.

longshore current   water current in the surf zone (zone where waves break). It moves slowly parallel to shoreline, driven by waves caused by wind.

delta   a sediment deposit at the mouth of a river, where it enters an ocean or lake.

headland   projection of land that extends into an ocean or lake and generally has cliffs along its water boundary.

marine terrace   a wave-cut platform, bounded on its seaward side by a cliff, or steep slope.

spit   a sand bar extending from the end of a beach into the mouth of an adjacent bay.

stack   isolated pillarlike rocky island near a steep shoreline, created by wave erosion.

tidal flat   marshy or sandy area that is covered with water at high tide and exposed at low tide.

tied island   an island connected ("tied") to the mainland by a tombolo.

tombolo   a sand bar that connects a tied island to the mainland or to another island.

wave-cut cliff   seaward-facing cliff along a steep shoreline, produced by wave erosion and mass wasting.

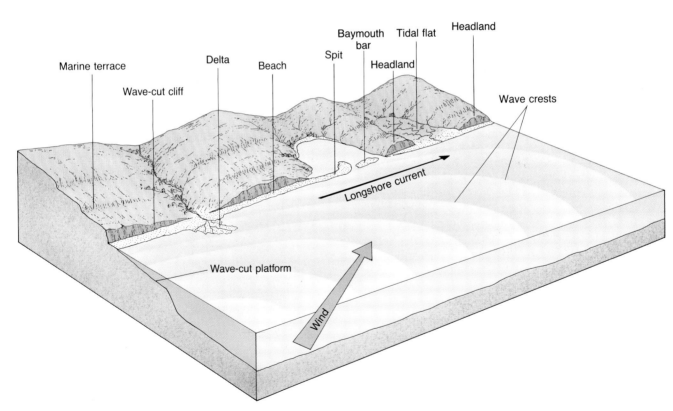

FIGURE 10.1 *Emergent* coastline features. An emergent coastline is caused by the land level rising, or the water level falling (regression), or both.

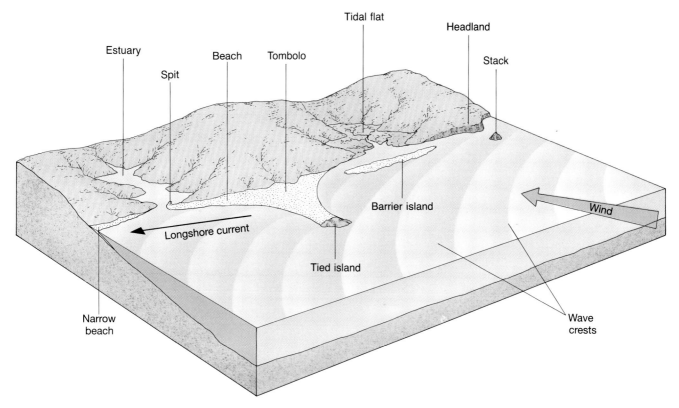

FIGURE 10.2 *Submergent* (drowning) coastline features. A submergent coastline is caused by the land level sinking, or the water level rising (transgression), or both.

wave-cut platform   a bench or shelf at sea level along a steep shore, formed by wave erosion.

QUESTIONS

Refer to the Kingston, Rhode Island quadrangle (Figure 10.3) for the following questions. Note that this area was recently glaciated, leaving behind deposits of sand and gravel. Some of these deposits formed streamlined hills like Green Hill (bottom center).

1. What type of feature is Green Hill Beach? What is it probably composed of?

2. What is the source of the material that makes up these beaches?

3. How was it transported?

4. Explain the origin of Green Hill Pond.

5. Carefully examine features of this shoreline. Is the longshore current transporting sediment east or west? What is the evidence for your answer?

6. One might assume that this coastline is emergent, because of the presence of well-developed baymouth bars. What is an alternative explanation for these well-developed baymouth bars that does not require vertical changes of the land level or sea level?

Refer to the Lynn, Massachusetts quadrangle (Figure 10.4) for these questions:

7. Examine the southwest corner of the map.
   a. What type of feature is the land area containing Revere Beach?
   b. Why does the Pines River flow northward behind Revere Beach?

8. Compare Green Hill Pond on the Kingston quadrangle (Figure 10.3) with the area behind Revere Beach.
   a. How are the two areas similar?
   b. How are the two areas different?

9. What is the probable direction of longshore transport along Revere Beach?

FIGURE 10.3   (Following page) Portion of the Kingston, Rhode Island topographic quadrangle map.

FIGURE 10.4   (Following page) Portion of the Lynn, Massachusetts topographic quadrangle map.

FIGURE 10.3: Kingston, Rhode Island

| 0 | .5 | 1 kilometer |

| 0 | 1/4 | 1/2 | 1 mile |

Contour interval = 10 ft.   1:24,000

North

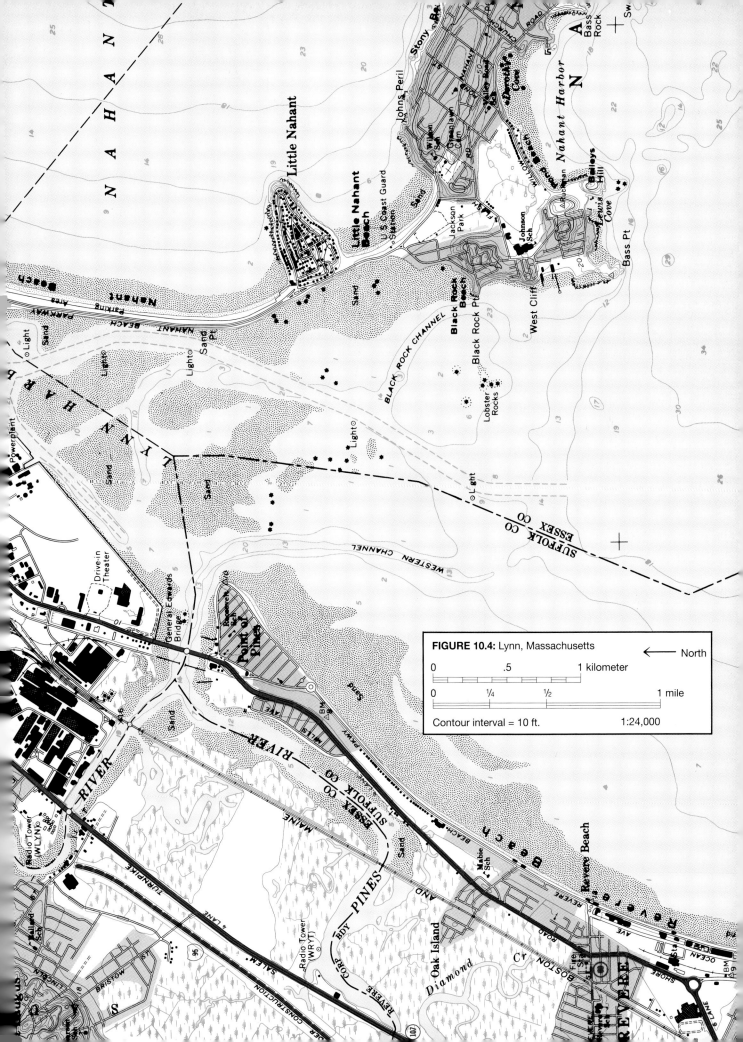

FIGURE 10.4: Lynn, Massachusetts

← North

0 .5 1 kilometer

0 ¼ ½ 1 mile

Contour interval = 10 ft.   1:24,000

10. What type of feature is Nahant Beach (northeast corner)?

11. How did Nahant Beach form?

12. What is the name of features like the landmass called Little Nahant at the south end of Nahant Beach?

Refer to the Boothbay, Maine quadrangle (Figures 10.5 and 10.6) for these questions:

13. What is the name for the type of bays shown on this map? How did they form?

14. What is the meaning of the stars and jagged black symbols along much of the shoreline in this quadrangle.

15. Why are there no spits or tombolos in this area? (Consider what is needed to form beach features.)

16. What is the name for features like Outer Heron Island and White Islands? How do such features form?

17. Is this a coastline of emergence or submergence? What is your evidence?

Refer to the Oceanside, California quadrangle (Figure 10.7) for these questions:

18. If you climb inland from the Pacific Ocean at South Oceanside toward Fire Mountain, you will cross several flat areas.
    a. About how many are there?
    b. What are their approximate elevations?
    c. What are these surfaces called, and what is their origin?

19. Is this a coastline of emergence or of submergence? Why?

Refer to the stereogram of Fraser Point, California (Figure 10.8) for these questions:

20. What is the name for the features like the steep cliffs along the coastline? How did they form?

21. What type of feature are the small rocky islands?

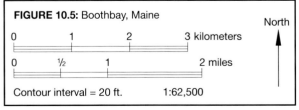

FIGURE 10.5: Boothbay, Maine

| 0 | | 1 | | 2 | | 3 kilometers |

| 0 | | ½ | | 1 | | 2 miles |

Contour interval = 20 ft.   1:62,500

North

FIGURE 10.5 Portion of the Boothbay, Maine topographic quadrangle map.

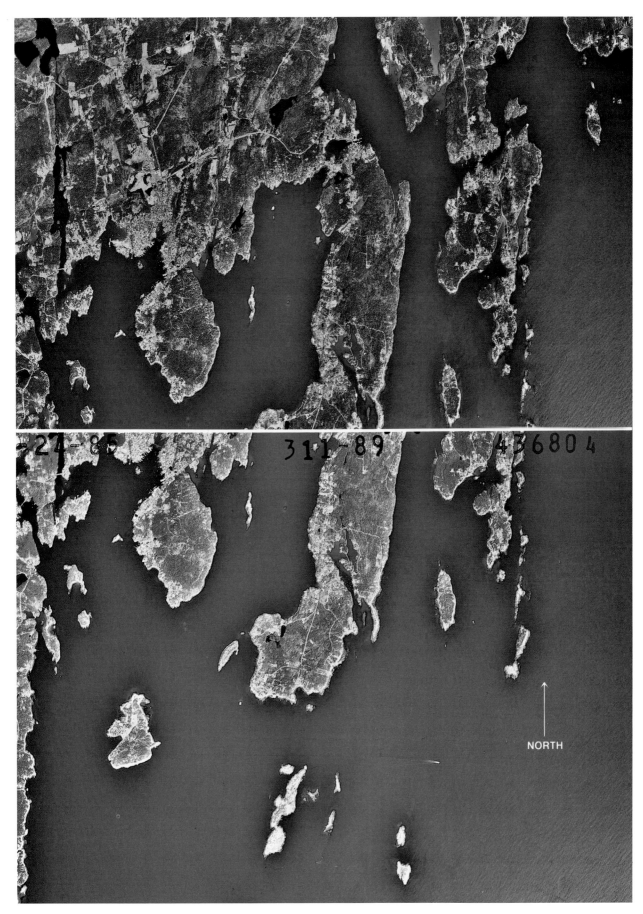

FIGURE 10.6 National high-altitude photograph (NHAP) stereogram of a portion of the Boothbay, Maine area. (USGS)

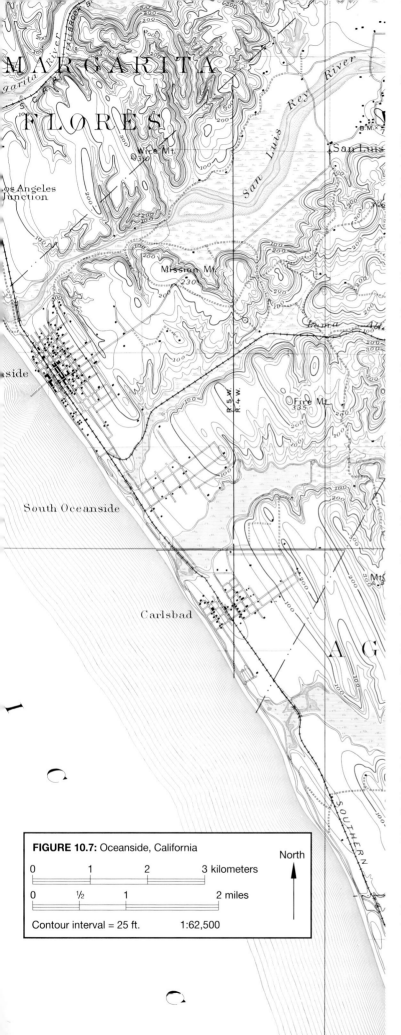

22. In the future, what is likely to happen to these islands and to the areas surrounding them?

Refer to the Point Reyes, California quadrangle (Figure 10.9) for the following questions. Point Reyes is a subtriangular landmass bounded on the west by the Pacific Ocean, on the south by Drakes Bay, and on the east by the San Andreas Fault. The fault runs along Sir Francis Drake road in the northeast corner of the map.

23. What features on the map seem to be related to the fault zone? Explain.

24. How does Point Reyes Beach differ from Point Reyes?

25. How can you tell the bedrock at Point Reyes is different from bedrock at Point Reyes Beach and Drake's Estero?

26. What is the pattern of longshore drift in Drakes Bay? How can you tell?

27. How did Drakes Estero (Spanish: estuary) form?

28. Is this a coastline of emergence or submergence? Explain.

Refer to the Seaside Park, New Jersey quadrangle (Figure 10.10) for these questions:

29. What type of feature is Goose Creek (upper left corner)?

30. What type of feature is the long narrow island that separates Barnegat Bay from the Atlantic Ocean?

31. What is the island in Question 30 composed of?

32. How high is it above sea level?

33. Is this a coastline of emergence or submergence? What is the evidence?

34. What will happen to Barnegat Bay in the future?

Refer to the Space Shuttle photograph of the Po Delta, Italy (Figure 10.11) for the following questions. The town of Adria, on the Po River in northern Italy, was a thriving seaport during Etruscan times (600 B.C.). Adria had such fame as to give its name to the Adriatic Sea, the gulf into which the Po River flows. Over the years, the Po

FIGURE 10.7 Portion of the Oceanside, California, topographic quadrangle map.

FIGURE 10.7: Oceanside, California

North

| 0 | 1 | 2 | 3 kilometers |

| 0 | ½ | 1 | 2 miles |

Contour interval = 25 ft.   1:62,500

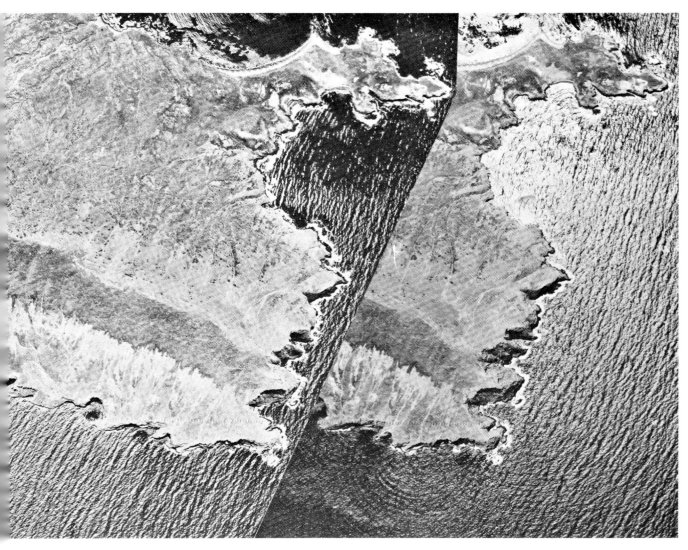

FIGURE 10.8 National high-altitude photograph (NHAP) stereogram of a portion of Fraser Point, California. (USGS)

River has deposited sand and silt in a delta. Because of the progradation of the Po Delta, Adria is no longer a seaport and now is quite far inland (Figure 10.11).

35. What has been the average annual rate of delta growth in centimeters per year (cm/yr) since Adria was a thriving seaport?

36. How many centimeters would the delta prograde during the lifetime of someone who lived to be 60 years old?

Now refer to Figure 10.12, a Space Shuttle photograph of a classical braided stream draining into an estuary on coastal Madagascar. Braided streams are choked with sediment.

37. As the braided stream is transporting huge volumes of sediment into the Indian Ocean, you might expect to see a delta prograding even beyond the estuary. Why is there no such delta?

38. What evidence can you cite to support your inference in Question 37?

FIGURE 10.9 (Following page) Portion of the Point Reyes, California topographic quadrangle map.

FIGURE 10.10 (Following page) Portion of the Seaside Park, New Jersey topographic quadrangle map.

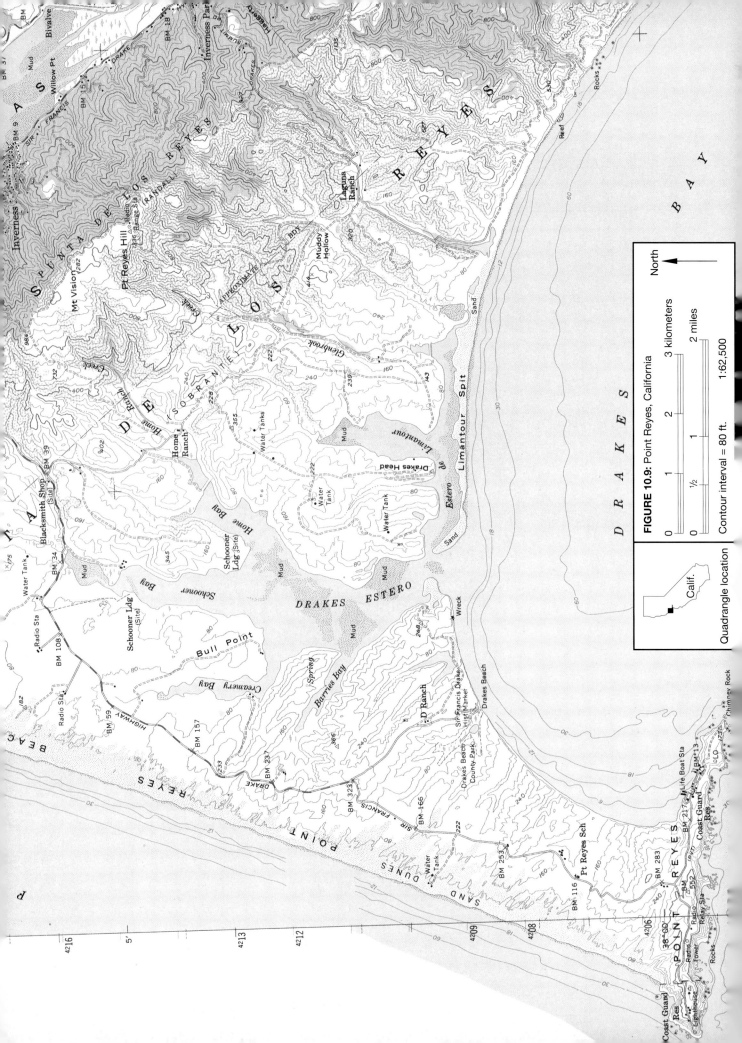

FIGURE 10.9: Point Reyes, California

Quadrangle location

Contour interval = 80 ft.

1:62,500

North

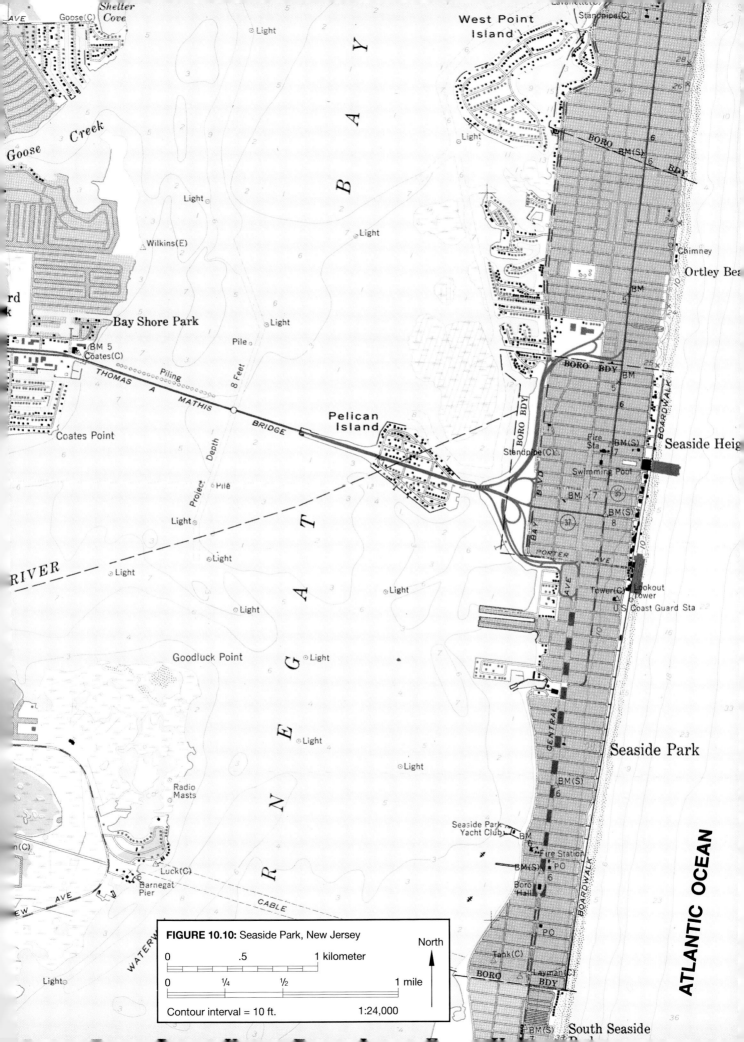

FIGURE 10.10: Seaside Park, New Jersey

| 0 | | .5 | | 1 kilometer |

| 0 | ¼ | ½ | | 1 mile |

Contour interval = 10 ft.   1:24,000

North

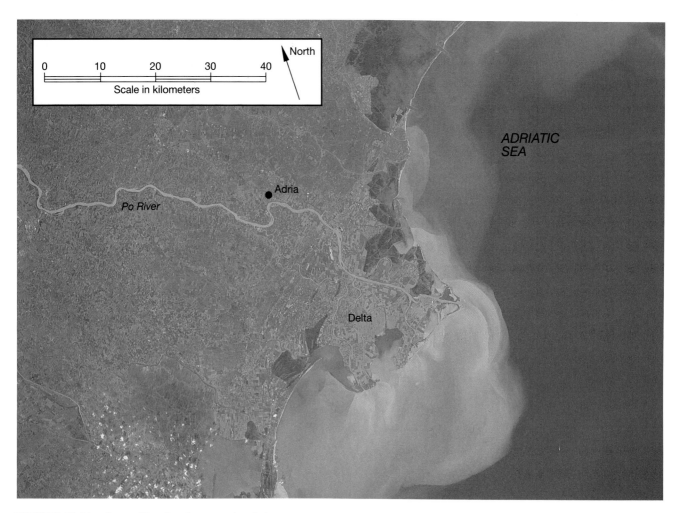

FIGURE 10.11 Space Shuttle photograph of the Po River delta region, Italy. (Photo courtesy of NASA)

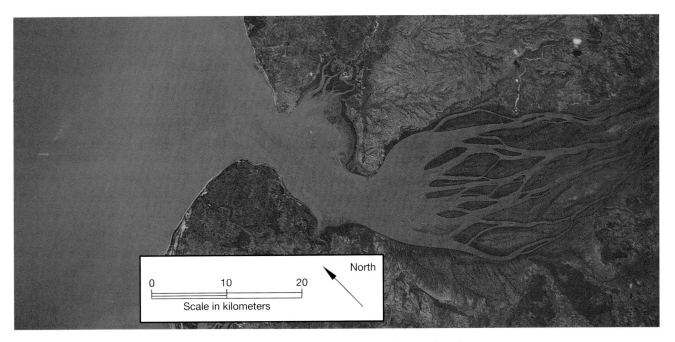

FIGURE 10.12 Space Shuttle photograph of a braided stream at Baie de Bombetoka (Bombetoka Bay) on the northern coast of Madagascar. (Photo courtesy of NASA)

ADDITIONAL QUESTIONS

Refer to the map and photographs of Saint Catherines Island, Georgia (Figure 10.13) for the following questions.

On the east-central portion of the island, note the large area of salt-marsh mud. This *living* salt marsh, full of plants, is shown on the right (west) in Figures 10.13A and B.

Also, note the linear sandy beach in Figures 10.13A and B, bounded on its seaward side (left) by another strip of salt marsh mud. However, all of the living, surficial salt marsh plants and animals have been stripped from this area. This is called **relict** (ancient) salt-marsh mud.

39. What type of sediment is probably present beneath the beach sands in Figures 10.13A and B?

40. Explain how the beach sands became located landward of the relict salt marsh mud.

41. On Figure 10.13B, draw a dashed line along the berm crest. Then label the foreshore and backshore deposits. Also label the living salt marsh and the relict salt-marsh mud.

42. Portions of the living salt marsh in Figure 10.13C recently have been buried by bodies of white sand.
    a. Where did this sand come from?
    b. What is the name given to such sand bodies?

43. The photo was taken from a landform called Aaron's Bluff. It is the headland of this part of the island. What will eventually happen to Aaron's Bluff? Why?

44. Based upon your answer in Question 43, would Aaron's Hill be a good location for a resort hotel?

45. Based upon your inferences, observations, and explanations in Questions 39 to 42, what will eventually happen to the living salt marsh in Figures 10.13B and C?

46. What can you infer about global sea level, based on your answers to Questions 6, 17, 19, 28, and 33?

47. How could the Greenhouse Effect be related to your answer in Question 46?

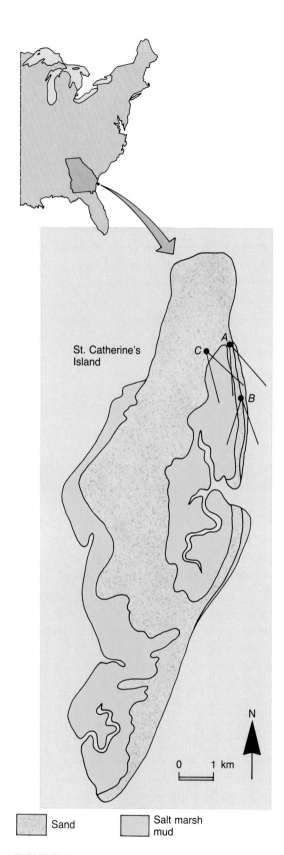

A. View south-southeast from point **A** on map, at low tide. Dark-brown "ribbon" adjacent to ocean is salt marsh mud. Light-colored area is sand.

B. View south from point **B** on map at low tide.

C. View southeast from point **C** (Aaron's Bluff) on map.

FIGURE 10.13 Saint Catherines Island, Georgia: coastal features and distribution of sand and salt-marsh mud. (Photos by R. Busch, H. Rollins, R. West)

EXERCISE ELEVEN

Desert Processes and Landforms

Charles G. Oviatt
Kansas State University

James R. Wilson
Weber State College

PURPOSE

This exercise has two parts. Part 1 familiarizes you with landforms typical of arid (desert) regions. You also will examine landforms produced by an ancient lake in what is now a desert. Part 2 familiarizes you with wind erosion and deposition (dunes).

MATERIALS

Pocket stereoscope, calculator, ruler, pencils, eraser.

PART 1—DESERT LANDFORMS

Two characteristics of desert precipitation combine to create desert landforms. First, rainfall in deserts is minimal. Second, when rainfall does occur, it generally is in the form of violent thunderstorms. The high volume of water falling from such storms causes flash floods over dry ground. These floods develop suddenly, have high discharge, and last briefly. They carve steep-walled canyons, often floored with gravel that is deposited as the flow decreases and ends. Such steep-walled canyons with gravel floors commonly are called **arroyos, wadis,** or **dry washes.**

Flash flooding in arid regions also erodes vertical cliffs along the edges of hills. When bedrock

lies roughly horizontal, such erosion creates broad, flat-topped **mesas** bounded by cliffs. In time, the mesas can erode to small, stout, barrel-like rock columns, called **buttes.**

In regions where Earth's crust has been lengthened by tensional forces (pulled apart), mountain ranges and basins develop by normal faulting (Figure 11.1). The mountain ranges are eroded by running water, which also transports the rock debris to the adjacent basins. In a humid climate, these adjacent basins might collect this water in permanent lakes. In a desert, however, precipitation usually is insufficient to fill and maintain permanent lakes. Thus, other characteristic landforms dominate the landscape.

Another factor is that climate is not constant through geologic time. Regions that now are deserts may have been more humid in the past. Landforms produced in the past, when the climate was different, still may be preserved on the present landscape. These landforms are valuable clues to understanding environmental changes.

DEFINITIONS

These desert landforms are shown in Figure 11.1, and are described here:

    alluvial fan a fan-shaped, deltalike deposit of alluvium made by a stream where it enters a level plain.

FIGURE 11.1 Some landforms typically developed in a mountainous desert region.

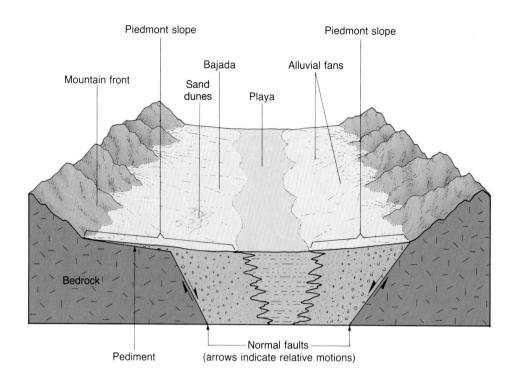

Piedmont slope

Piedmont slope

Mountain front

Bajada

Alluvial fans

Sand dunes

Playa

Bedrock

Pediment

Normal faults
(arrows indicate relative motions)

bajada a continuous apron of coalescing alluvial fans below a mountain front (Spanish, "slope").

mountain front the sharp-angled intersection where the steep lower slope of a mountain range meets the piedmont slope (a pediment or alluvial fan).

pediment a gently inclined erosion surface in the upper part of the piedmont slope. It is carved into bedrock and generally has a thin veneer of alluvium.

piedmont slope the sloping part of a basin located below the mountain front. It includes the pediment, and may include alluvial fans and bajadas.

playa the shallow, almost flat, central part of a desert basin, in which water gathers after a rain and evaporates to leave behind silt, clay, and evaporites (salts).

sand dune a small hill or linear, sinuous ridge of windblown sand.

QUESTIONS

Refer to the Frisco Peak, Utah quadrangle (Figure 11.2) and the stereogram of the Wah Wah Valley (Figure 11.3) to answer these questions:

1. What specific type of feature is the Wah Wah Valley Hardpan?

2. On Figure 11.2, identify and label the bajada, the alluvial fans, and the mountain front east of the Wah Wah Valley Hardpan.

3. A dashed blue line surrounds the Wah Wah Valley Hardpan. What does it represent?

4. In the southeastern corner of the map, note the jeep trail. In this vicinity, what do you think the alluvial fans are composed of?

5. If the Wah Wah Valley Hardpan were to fill with water, how deep could the lake become before it overflows to the northeast?

6. On the stereogram, what evidence can you identify for a former deep lake in Wah Wah Valley?

7. What is the age of the former deep lake relative to the age of the alluvial fans and bajada? (Hint: study the stereogram.)

8. How would the texture of the sediments at the surface of the alluvial fans change as you walk down the fans from the mountain front to the playa? Why?

FIGURE 11.2 (Opposite page) Portion of the Frisco Peak, Utah topographic quadrangle map.

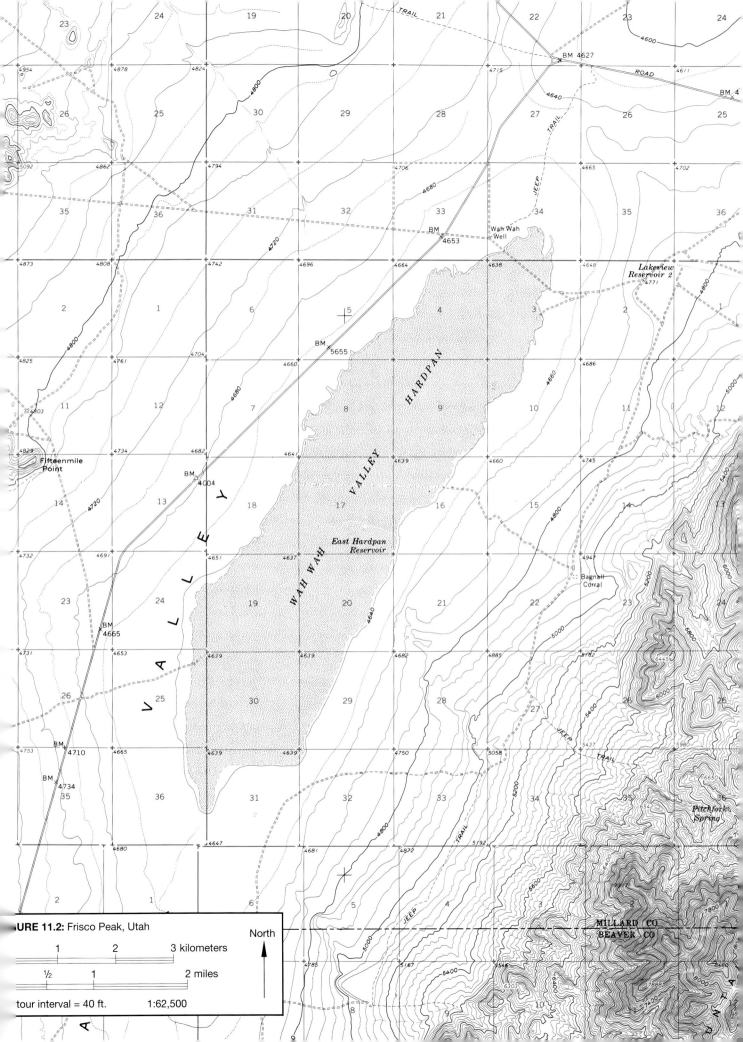

URE 11.2: Frisco Peak, Utah

North

1	2	3 kilometers

½	1	2 miles

tour interval = 40 ft.   1:62,500

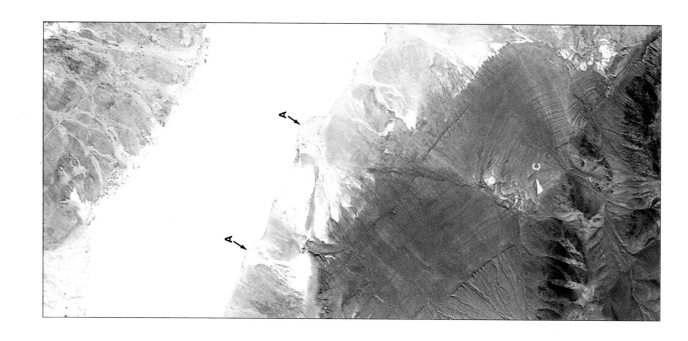

NORTH

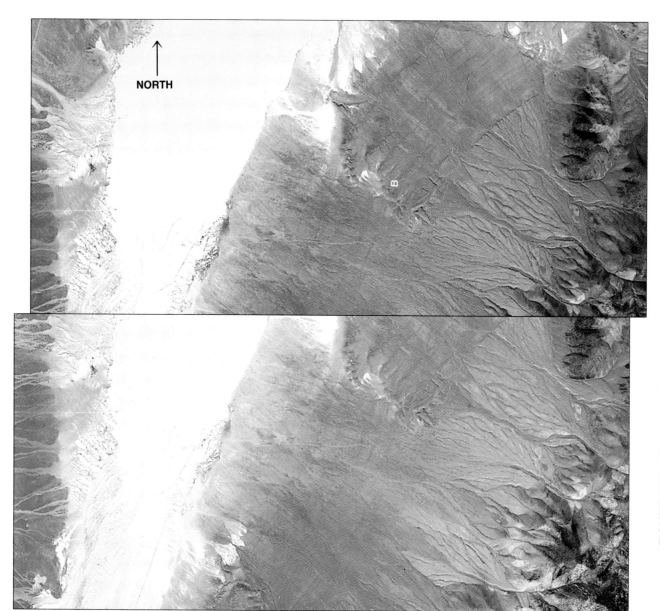

FIGURE 11.3 National high-altitude photograph (NHAP) stereogram of the Wah Wah Valley, Utah area. (USGS)

Study Figure 11.4, part of the arid Antelope Peak, Arizona quadrangle. Then answer these questions:

9. What is the hilly feature labeled **A**? How did it form?

10. How do you think the Table Top Mountains got their name?

11. What is the name of the linear landform labeled **B**? How did it form?

12. How are landforms **C** and **D** similar?

13. List the stages of development of landform **D**.

ADDITIONAL QUESTIONS

14. Refer to Figures 11.2 and 11.3. The surface of the Wah Wah Valley Hardpan consists of hard-packed mud (clay and silt) with very little salt. The surface remains dry except for brief periods immediately after rainstorms. How deep would you expect the basin's groundwater table to be, relative to the playa surface? Why?

15. In Figure 11.3, at places labeled **A**, what has caused the semicircular indentations in the playa margin?

16. The Wah Wah Valley was occupied by an arm of Lake Bonneville, a large freshwater lake that covered almost 20,000 square miles of western Utah about 15,000 years ago. On Figure 11.3, note the steplike terraces on the slope just to the north (right) of **B**. How did these terraces form?

17. Also on Figure 11.3, study the coastal landforms upslope and downslope from letter **B**. What are these depositional landforms called? How did they form in a line from upslope to downslope?

18. What was the dominant direction of longshore sediment transport as the landforms at **B** were being produced?

19. The patch of white at point **C** is tufa, a kind of chemical limestone (refer to Figure 5.23). Why is it found here?

20. Study Figure 11.3. List some ways that the landscape has changed in the 15,000 years since Lake Bonneville began drying up. Mark and describe specific features of the landscape that show the degree of landscape modification.

PART 2—WORK OF THE WIND

Water and ice are capable of moving large particles of sediment. The wind can move only smaller particles. For this reason, features resulting from wind action may be subtle or even invisible on a topographic map. (However, they may be more evident on aerial photographs, which have much higher resolution than topographic maps.) Wind-related features may be superimposed on fluvial or glacial features, particularly where recently exposed and unvegetated sediment occurs.

A lack of a dense vegetation cover is a virtual prerequisite for significant wind erosion. This lack of vegetation may occur:

1. on recently deposited sediment, such as floodplains,
2. in areas where vegetation has been destroyed by fire, overgrazing, or human activity, or
3. in dry climates where the lack of water precludes substantial vegetation.

When examining a topographic map, keep in mind that the green overprint represents only trees and shrubs. There could be an important soil-protecting grass cover present that is not indicated on the map. Your evaluation of the present climate of a topographic map area should consider surface-water features, groundwater features, and the geographic location of the area.

The most common wind-eroded landform visible on a topographic map is a small, shallow depression called a **blowout** or **deflation basin.** Such features develop where the vegetation cover has been disrupted and the sediment is being removed by the wind. Blowouts may resemble sinkholes that occur in karst areas, or kettles that occur in glaciated areas, but you can distinguish these different types of depressions from the context of other features observable on the map.

Sand transported by wind also erodes many rock surfaces by sandblasting them. **Ventifacts** are rocks having flat or scoop-shaped surfaces that were abraded in this manner.

When the wind transports and deposits sand, it creates sand dunes. The mechanism is shown in Figure 11.5. Four major types of dunes are shown in Figure 11.6 and described here:

Barchan dunes are crescent shaped. They occur where sand supply is limited and wind direction is fairly constant. Barchans generally form around shrubs or large rocks, which serve as minor barriers to sand transportation. The **horns,** or tips, of barchans point downwind.

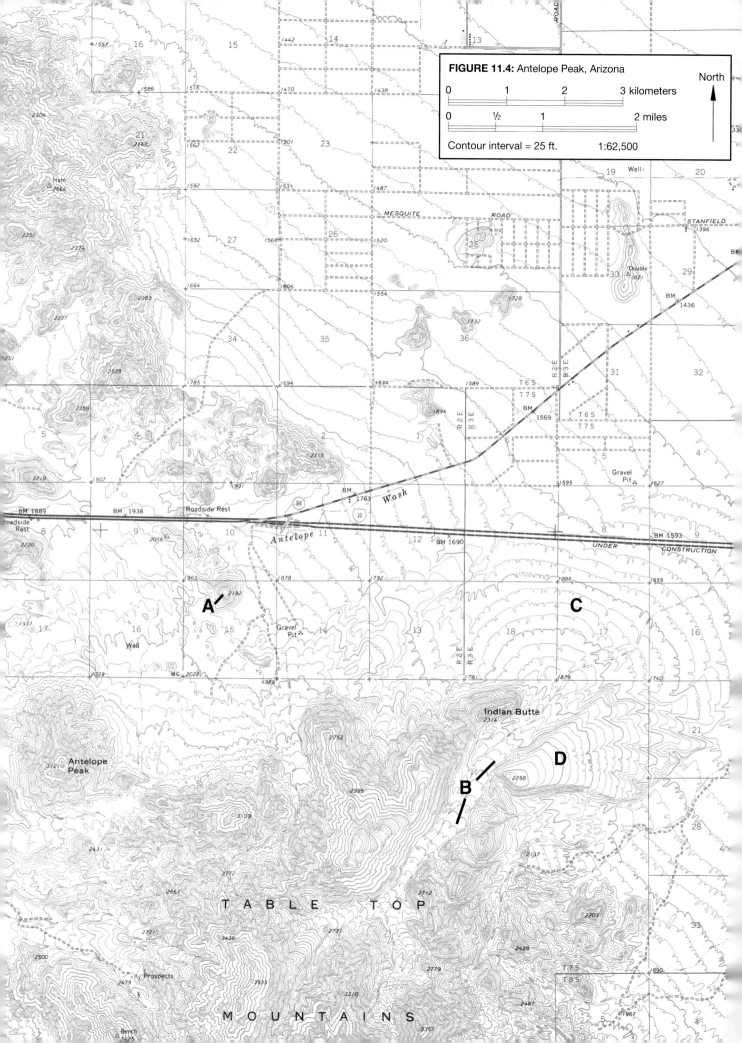

FIGURE 11.4: Antelope Peak, Arizona

North

0   1   2   3 kilometers

0   ½   1   2 miles

Contour interval = 25 ft.   1:62,500

Transverse dunes occur where sand supply is greater. They form as ridges perpendicular to the prevailing wind direction. The crests of transverse dunes generally are sinuous to very sinuous.

Parabolic dunes somewhat resemble barchans. However, their horns point the opposite direction, upwind. Parabolic dunes always form adjacent to **blowouts,** oval depressions from whence come the sandy sediments that form the parabolic dunes.

Longitudinal dunes occur in some modern deserts where sand is abundant and cross winds merge to form these high, elongated dunes. They can be quite large, up to 200 km long and up to 100 m high. The crests of longitudinal dunes generally are straight to slightly sinuous.

Dunes tend to migrate slowly in the direction of the prevailing wind (Figures 11.5 and 11.6). However, revegetation of exposed areas, due to changes in climate or land use, may stabilize them.

On topographic maps, large areas of dunes may be marked with a brown pattern (see topographic map symbols, Figure 7.7). Small groups of stabilized dunes may be indicated by contour lines, without a pattern. In the latter case, you can recognize dunes by their distinctive shape and overall pattern, or by linearity of the contour lines.

QUESTIONS

Refer to the Lakeside, Nebraska quadrangle (Figure 11.7) for these questions:

21. Describe the surface drainage of this area.

22. In sec. 16, T25N, R43W, what is the relief (in feet)?

23. Examine the hills shown on the map. Notice that most are asymmetrical, with one slope steeper than the other. Which direction does the steeper slope usually face?

24. What geologic process created these hills?

25. What specific name can be given to these hills?

26. What geologic process created the depressions shown on the map?

27. What specific name can be given to these depressions?

28. What type of earth material probably occurs in the hills?

29. Would this material be very permeable, slightly permeable, or impermeable to water?

30. How can you determine that the landscape of the area on this map is not the result of karst processes (described in Exercise Eight)?

Refer to the Clear Lake, Utah quadrangle (Figures 11.8 and 11.9) for these questions:

31. On the map, in the northwestern portion, what type of earth material is represented by the dotted pattern?

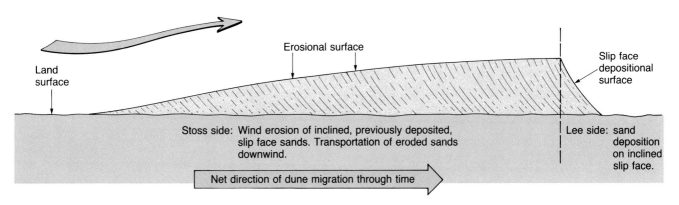

FIGURE 11.5 Hypothetical cross section through a sand dune. Wind erodes and transports sand up the *stoss* side (upwind side) of the dune. Sand rolls down the *slip face*, forming the *lee* side (downwind side) of the dune. The continuing process of wind erosion and transportation of sand on the stoss side of the dune, and simultaneous deposition of sand on the lee side of the dune, results in a net downwind migration of the dune.

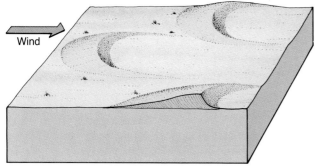

Barchan dunes

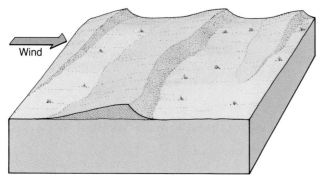

Transverse dunes

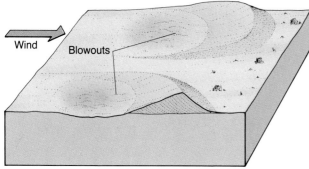

Blowouts

Parabolic dunes

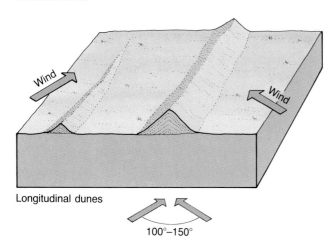

Longitudinal dunes

100°–150°

32. In NE¼ sec. 18, what is represented by the blue shaded area?

33. A few hundred feet west of the blue shaded area is a row of short brown dashes. What does this represent? Why was it constructed there?

34. Note the linear arrangement of hills in secs. 8, 17, and elsewhere on the map. How high do these hills stand above the surrounding terrain?

35. What are these long hills? How might they have formed?

36. Now, note the hills and depressions in the eastern half of sec. 8, and the western half of sec. 9. What are these depressions and hills called? How did they probably form? Record your reasoning.

37. What is the probable dominant wind direction in this area? Why?

ADDITIONAL QUESTIONS

38. Refer again to Figures 11.8 and 11.9. The area covered by these figures is part of a very large depression, or closed basin. Knowing this, and knowing the type of sediment that composes the features you have observed on the map, what was this large basin in the past?

Use Figure 11.7 for these additional questions about the Lakeside quadrangle:

39. The large number of lakes represents a water table that is above the land surface in the basins. Make a contour map of the water-table surface by using the elevations shown on the lakes and drawing directly on the map. Use a 5-foot contour interval.

40. What is the direction of groundwater flow?

FIGURE 11.6 Four common types of sand dunes. Note their basic morphology and internal stratification relative to wind direction.

FIGURE 11.7 (Opposite page) Portion of the Lakeside, Nebraska topographic quadrangle map.

FIGURE 11.7: Lakeside, Nebraska

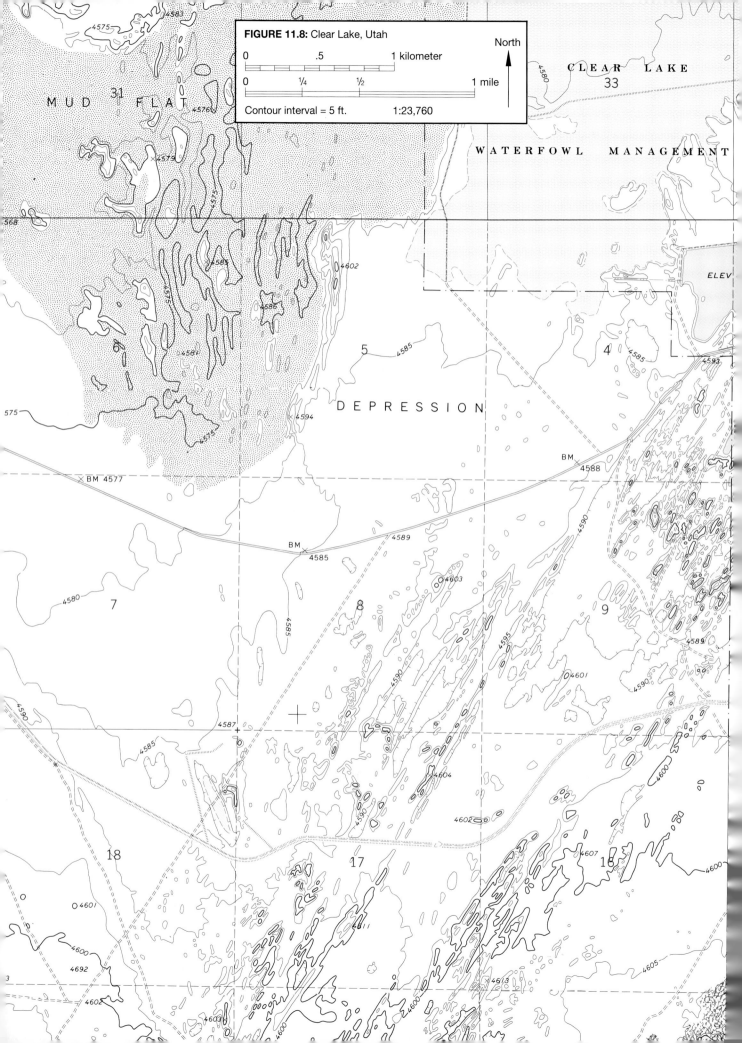

FIGURE 11.8: Clear Lake, Utah

0 .5 1 kilometer

0 ¼ ½ 1 mile

Contour interval = 5 ft.   1:23,760

North

FIGURE 11.8 (Opposite page) Portion of the Clear Lake, Utah topographic quadrangle map.

41. Calculate the gradient (slope) of the water table in feet/mile from Jennings Lake (northeast edge of map) to the lake in sec. 29, T26N, R43W.

42. Refer to the ventifact in Figure 11.10. This is one of many such rocks in a local area, all of which were worn this way. In this area, from which direction does the prevailing wind likely blow? Explain your answer.

43. Examine the **star dunes** in Figure 11.11. What kind of wind pattern do you think would cause this kind of dune form? Explain your reasoning.

44. Examine the dunes in Figure 11.12. What kind of wind pattern do you think would cause this kind of dune form? Explain your reasoning.

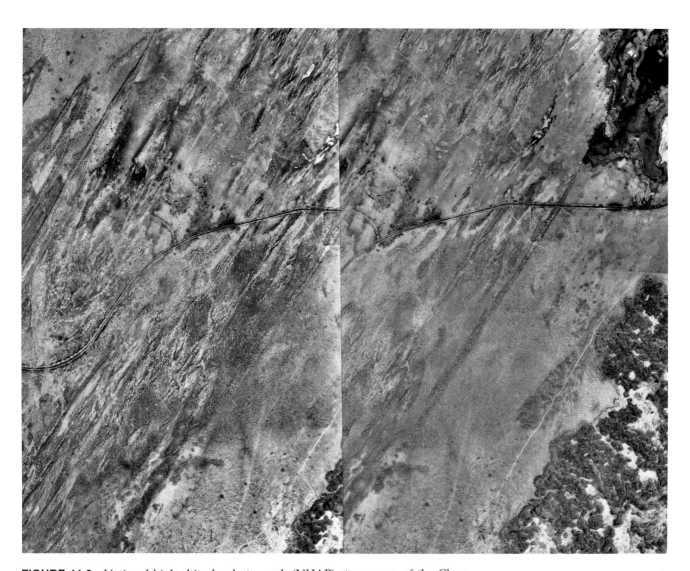

FIGURE 11.9 National high-altitude photograph (NHAP) stereogram of the Clear Lake, Utah area. Stereogram covers sections 16 and 15 (and southern portions of secs. 9 and 10) on Figure 11.8. Stereogram scale is the same as map scale on Figure 11.8. (USGS)

FIGURE 11.10 Photograph (actual size) of a sandblasted rock, or *ventifact*. Note the three flat surfaces, which were abraded by windblown sand. (Photo by R. Busch)

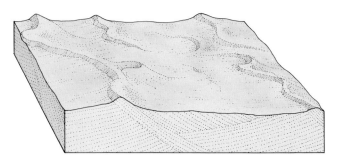

FIGURE 11.12 Unidentified sand dunes.

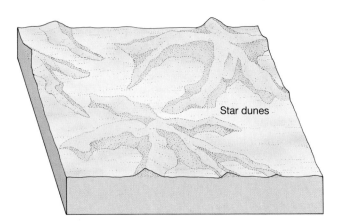

FIGURE 11.11 Star dunes.

EXERCISE TWELVE

Glacial Processes and Landforms

Nancy A. Van Wagoner
Sharon Laska
Acadia University, Nova Scotia

Kenton E. Strickland
Wright State University—
Lake Campus

PURPOSE

This exercise helps you understand the origin of glacial features. Part 1 presents features of mountain glaciation, and Part 2 looks at features of continental glaciation.

MATERIALS

Ruler, pencil, eraser, pocket stereoscope.

INTRODUCTION

Glaciers are large ice masses that form on land areas which are cold enough and have enough moisture to sustain them. They build up where the winter **accumulation** of snow and ice exceeds the summer **ablation** or **wastage**. Ablation (wastage) is the loss of snow and ice by melting and by *sublimation* (evaporation directly from the solid state, without melting). Accumulation commonly occurs in snowfields, regions of permanent snow cover.

Glaciers can be divided into two zones, accumulation and ablation (Figure 12.1). As snow and ice collect in the **zone of accumulation,** they become compacted and highly recrystallized under their own weight. The mass then begins to slide and flow downslope, like a very viscous (thick)

fluid, in response to gravity. This process continues until glaciers move into the **zone of ablation,** where melting/sublimation of ice exceeds the production of ice in the accumulation zone. The **snowline** is the boundary between the zones of accumulation and ablation. The bottom end of the glacier is the **terminus.**

It helps to understand a glacier by viewing it as a river of ice. The "headwater" is the zone of accumulation, and the "mouth" is the terminus. Like a river, glaciers erode rocks, transport their load (tons of rock debris), and deposit their load "downstream" (down-glacier).

The downslope movement and extreme weight of glaciers cause them to scrape and plow (push) rock materials that they encounter. They *pluck* rock material by freezing around it and ripping it from bedrock, incorporating it into the glacial ice. This rock debris then can be transported many kilometers by a glacier. The debris also gives glacial ice its great abrasive power. As the heavy rock-filled ice moves over the land, it scrapes surfaces like a giant sheet of sandpaper.

Rock debris falling from valley walls commonly accumulates on the surface of a moving glacier and is transported downslope. Thus, glaciers transport huge quantities of sediment, not only *in*, but also *on* the ice.

When a glacier melts, it deposits its load of rocky gravel, sand, silt, and clay. These deposits

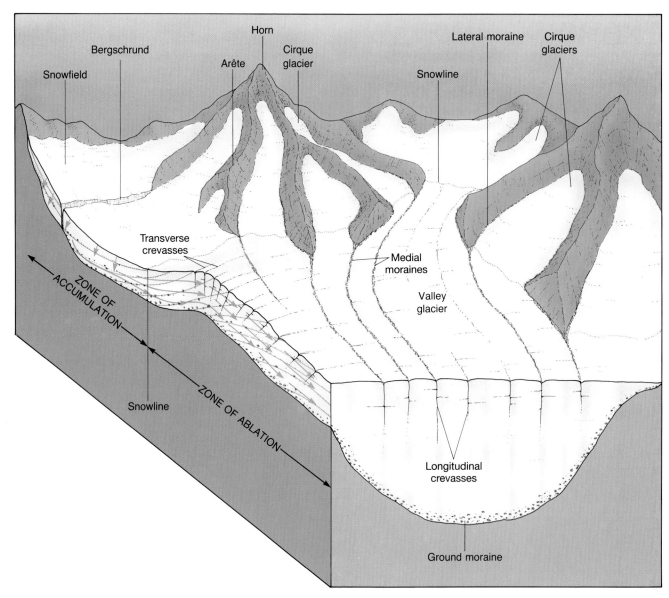

FIGURE 12.1 Active mountain glaciation, in a hypothetical region. Note cutaway view of glacial ice, showing flow lines and direction (blue lines and arrows).

collectively are called **drift.** Drift that accumulates directly from the melting ice is unstratified (unsorted by size) and is called **till.** However, drift that is transported by water becomes sorted by size, and is called **stratified drift.** Wind also can transport the sand, silt, and clay particles from drift deposits. Wind-transported glacial material can form dunes or **loess** deposits (wind-deposited, unstratified accumulations of clayey silt).

There are four major types of glaciers. The first three are variants of **mountain glaciation** (Figure 12.1):

Cirque glacier a small, semicircular glacier that forms on the sides of mountains.

Valley glacier a long glacier that flows in existing stream valleys in mountains.

Piedmont glacier a coalescence of two or more valley glaciers at the foot (break in slope) of a mountain range.

The fourth type of glacier develops on major portions of continents, and thus is called **continental glaciation:**

Ice sheet vast pancake-shaped ice mounds that develop around Earth's North Polar and South

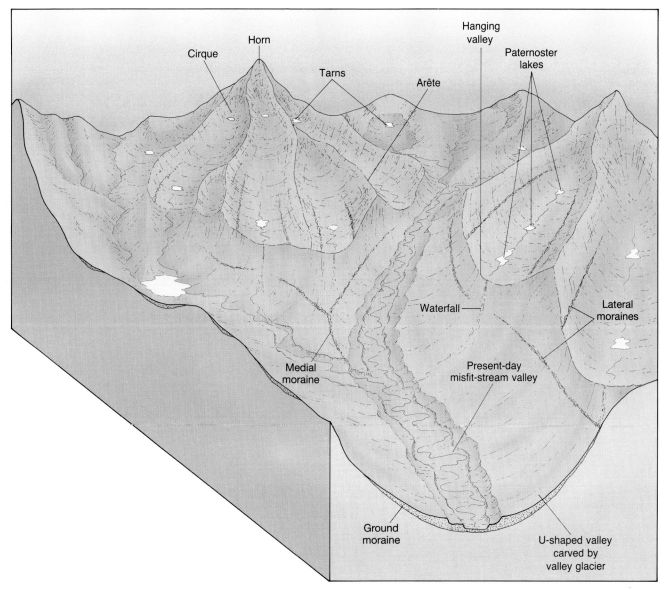

FIGURE 12.2 The same region in Figure 12.1, showing erosion features remaining after total ablation of glacial ice.

Polar regions. They spread over large areas of continents and flow independently of minor topographic features beneath them. The Antarctic Ice Sheet, covering the entire continent of Antarctica, is an example.

PART 1—MOUNTAIN GLACIATION

Mountain glaciation is characterized by cirque glaciers, valley glaciers, and piedmont glaciers. Poorly developed mountain glaciation involves only cirques; the best-developed mountain glaciation involves all three types. In some cases, valley and piedmont glaciers are so well developed that only the highest peaks and ridges extend above the ice. Mountain glaciation also is called **alpine glaciation,** because it is the type seen in Europe's Alps.

Figure 12.1 shows a region with mountain glaciation. Note the extensive **snowfield** in the zone of accumulation. The **snowline** is the elevation above which the snowfield is developed.

Also note several types of **crevasses** (deep cracks) in Figure 12.1. At the upper end of the glacier is the large **bergschrund** (German, "mountain crack") that separates the flowing ice from the relatively immobile portion of the snowfield. Observe the difference between transverse crevasses (perpendicular to the flow direction) and longitudinal crevasses (aligned with the direction of flow).

Figure 12.2 shows the results of mountain glaciation after the glaciers have completely ablated.

For your convenience, we have summarized distinctive glacial landforms in three figures:

• *erosional* features in Figure 12.3
• *depositional* features in Figure 12.4
• *water bodies* in Figure 12.5.

Note that some features are identical in mountain glaciation and continental glaciation, but others are unique to one or the other. Before you proceed to the questions, study the descriptions in these three figures, and compare them with the visuals in Figures 12.1 and 12.2.

QUESTIONS—PART 1

1. In Figure 12.6, examine the typical stream cobble and typical glacial cobble. Explain how two different physical-abrasion processes—river abrasion versus glacial abrasion—can produce such different cobbles.

2. Examine Figures 12.7 and 12.8. Locate the features labeled **A** through **H** (some are on one

FIGURE 12.3 *Erosional features of glaciated regions.*

EROSIONAL FEATURES OF GLACIATED REGIONS	
Cirque	Bowl-shaped depression on a high mountain slope, formed by a cirque glacier
Arête	Sharp, jagged, knife-edge ridge between two cirques or glaciated valleys
Col	Mountain pass formed by the headward erosion of cirques
Horn	Steep-sided, pyramid-shaped peak produced by headward erosion of several cirques
Headwall	Steep slope or rock cliff at the upslope end of a glaciated valley or cirque
Glacial trough	U-shaped, steep-walled, glaciated valley formed by the scouring action of a valley glacier
Hanging valley	Glacial trough of a tributary glacier, elevated above the main trough
Roche moutonnée	Asymmetrical knoll or small hill of bedrock, formed by glacial abrasion on the smooth stoss side (side from which the glacier came) and by plucking (prying and pulling by glacial ice) on the less-smooth lee side (down-glacier side)
Glacial striations and grooves	Parallel linear scratches and grooves in bedrock surfaces, resulting from glacial scouring
Glacial polish	Smooth bedrock surfaces caused by glacial abrasion (sanding action of glaciers analogous to sanding of wood with sandpaper)

FIGURE 12.4 *Depositional features* of glaciated regions.

DEPOSITIONAL FEATURES OF GLACIATED REGIONS	
Ground moraine	Sheetlike layer (blanket) of till left on the landscape by a receding (wasting) glacier
Terminal moraine	Ridge of till that forms at the farthest advance of a glacier
Recessional moraine	Ridge of till that forms at terminus of a glacier, behind (up-glacier) and generally parallel to the terminal moraine; formed during a temporary halt (stand) in recession of a wasting glacier
Lateral moraine	Ridge of till formed from melting ice and mass wasting at the side of a valley glacier
Medial moraine	Ridge of till either in transit or deposited along the boundary between two tributary glaciers that have merged to form a larger valley glacier
Drumlin	Streamlined hill, asymmetrical in lengthwise profile, commonly composed of till; ideally with a steep slope facing the direction from which the ice came, and a gentle slope that points down-glacier
Erratic	Boulder or smaller fragment of rock resting far from its source on bedrock of a different type
Boulder train	Linear (sometimes sinuous) deposit of erratics that extends from the source of the erratics to various points along the path of ice advance (transport)
Outwash	Sediment transported by meltwater from a glacier and deposited in front of (down-slope from) the terminus of the melting glacier
Outwash plain	Plain formed by blanketlike deposition of outwash; usually an outwash braid plane, formed by the coalescence of many braided streams having their origins along a common glacial terminus
Valley train	Long, narrow sheet of outwash (outwash braid plain of one braided stream, or floodplain of a meandering stream) that extends far beyond the terminus of a glacier
Kame	Steep-sided mound of stratified drift that formed in contact with glacial ice
Esker	Long, narrow, sinuous ridge of stratified drift deposited by meltwater streams flowing under glacial ice or in tunnels within the glacial ice
Beach line	Landward edge of a shoreline of a lake formed from damming of glacial meltwater, or temporary ponding of glacial meltwater in a topographic depression
Glacial-lake deposits	Layers of sediment in the lake bed, deltas, or beaches of a glacial lake
Loess	Unstratified sheets of clayey silt and silty clay transported beyond the margins of a glacier by wind and/or braided streams; it is compact and able to resist significant erosion when exposed in steep slopes or cliffs

FIGURE 12.5 *Water bodies* of glaciated regions.

WATER BODIES OF GLACIATED REGIONS	
Tarn	Small lake in a cirque
Scoured lake	Lake in a depression formed from glacial scouring (scraping, digging)
Paternoster lakes	Chain of small lakes in a glacial trough
Finger lake	Lake formed by natural damming of a glacial trough
Kettle lake or kettle hole	Small, rounded lake or water-saturated depression in glacial drift, formed by melting of an isolated, detached block of ice left behind by a glacier in retreat (melting back)
Swale	Shallow lake or water-saturated area formed in a slight depression of a hummocky ground moraine
Marginal lake	Lake formed at the margin (edge) of a glacier as a result of accumulating meltwater; the upslope edge of the lake is the melting glacier itself
Meltwater stream	Stream of water derived from melting glacial ice, which flows under the ice, on the ice, along the margins of the ice, or beyond the margins of the ice
Misfit stream	Stream that is not large enough to have cut the valley it occupies
Marsh or swamp	Saturated, poorly drained areas that are permanently or intermittently covered with water and have grassy vegetation (swamp) or shrubs and trees (marsh)

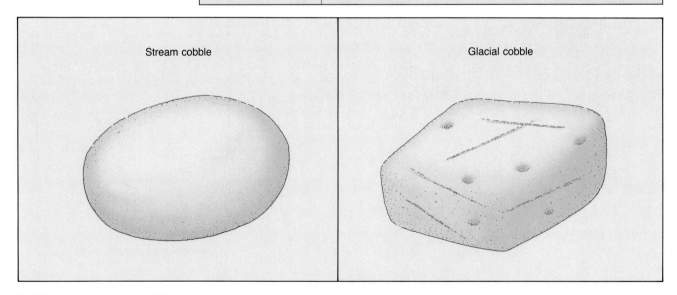

Stream cobble

Glacial cobble

FIGURE 12.6 Note the differences between a stream cobble and a glacial cobble. Stream cobbles are rounded-to-well-rounded and have smooth surfaces. Glacial cobbles are angular or faceted, and have many scratch marks. (A cobble is a clast between a pebble and a boulder in size, 64–256 mm diameter.)

FIGURE 12.7 Oblique aerial photograph of the Coast Mountains, British Columbia, Canada.

photo, some are on the other, and some appear on both). Name each feature and describe how it formed.

3. Imagine that you are doing some geologic mapping in the area of Figure 12.7. You find a boulder at point **X** that contains visible gold. Would you go to area **L, M,** or **N** to find the source outcrop? Why?

4. In Figure 12.8, you find a similar gold-bearing boulder at point **Y.** How many different valleys must you search to find the source?

Refer to the Siffleur River, Alberta quadrangle (Figure 12.9) for these questions:

5. What is the name given to features like Marmot Mountain and Conical Peak? How do such features form?

6. The boundary between Improvement Districts 9 and 10 follows a ridge from the Siffleur River Valley to Mount Kentigern. What type of ridge is this? How did it form?

7. Near the northern edge of the map, what type of valley is located above the falls west of the Siffleur River? How did it form?

8. What type of lake is at the headwaters of the stream that forms these falls?

FIGURE 12.8 Oblique aerial photograph, western Northwest Territories, Canada.

FIGURE 12.9 (Opposite page) Portion of the Siffleur River, Alberta, Canada topographic quadrangle map.

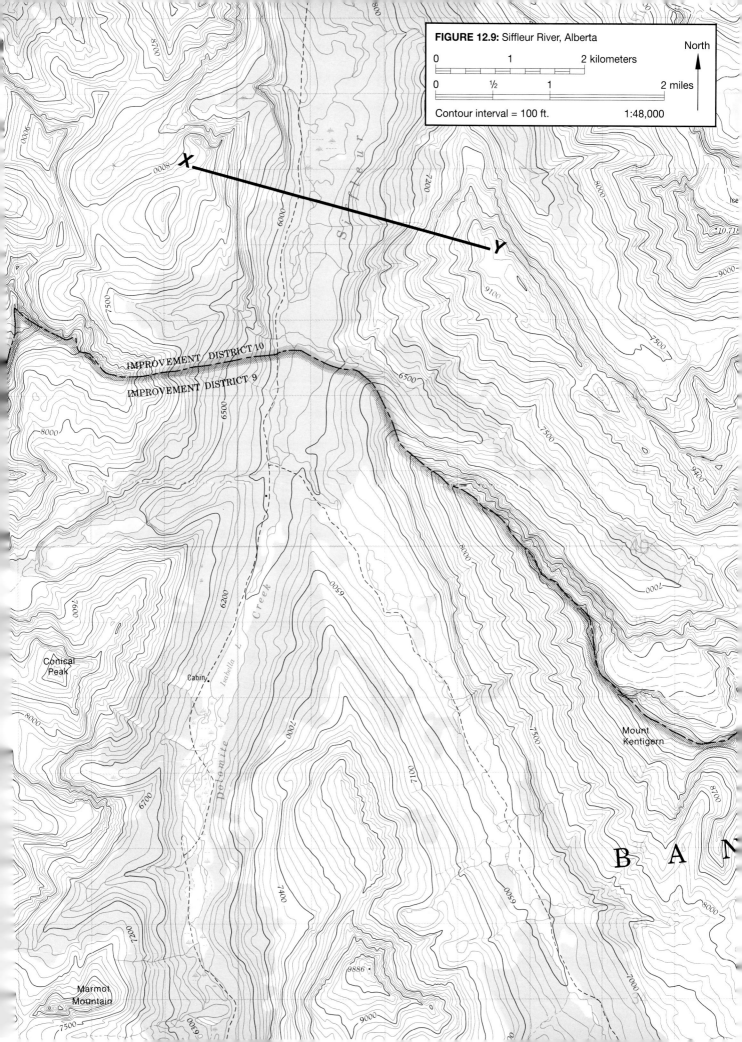

FIGURE 12.9: Siffleur River, Alberta

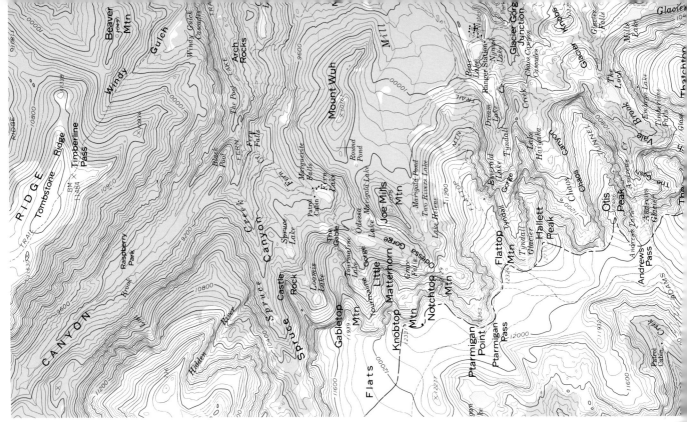

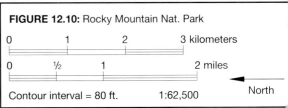

FIGURE 12.10: Rocky Mountain Nat. Park

0   1   2   3 kilometers

0   ½   1   2 miles

Contour interval = 80 ft.   1:62,500   North

FIGURE 12.10 Portion of the Rocky Mountain National Park topographic quadrangle map.

9. Imagine the topographic profile along **X–Y**. Is this a normal profile for a river valley? Why?

10. Why does the profile of Question 9 have the shape that it does?

11. What other features produced by mountain glaciation can you see on this map?

Refer to Figure 12.10, a portion of Rocky Mountain National Park, to answer these questions:

12. In the southwestern quadrant of the map, find Flattop Mountain and Hallett Peak. Note the small glacier between them.
    a. What is its name?
    b. What type of glacier is it?
    c. Give several lines of evidence that this glacier may have been larger in the past.
    d. Meltwater from the present glacier flows in which direction? In what stream?

13. About a mile northwest of the center of the map, find Loomis Lake. What kind of feature is it? How did it form?

14. What other features of mountain glaciation are present in this area?

Refer to Figure 12.11, a portion of the Anchorage (B–2), Alaska quadrangle, for the following questions. In the southwestern corner, note the Harvard Arm of Prince William Sound. The famous *Exxon Valdez* oil spill occurred just south of this area (it did not affect Harvard Arm).

15. Observe the Harvard Glacier and its many **tributary glaciers** (small valley glaciers that feed into, and merge with, the main valley glacier).

FIGURE 12.11 (Opposite page) Portion of the Anchorage B–2, Alaska topographic quadrangle map.

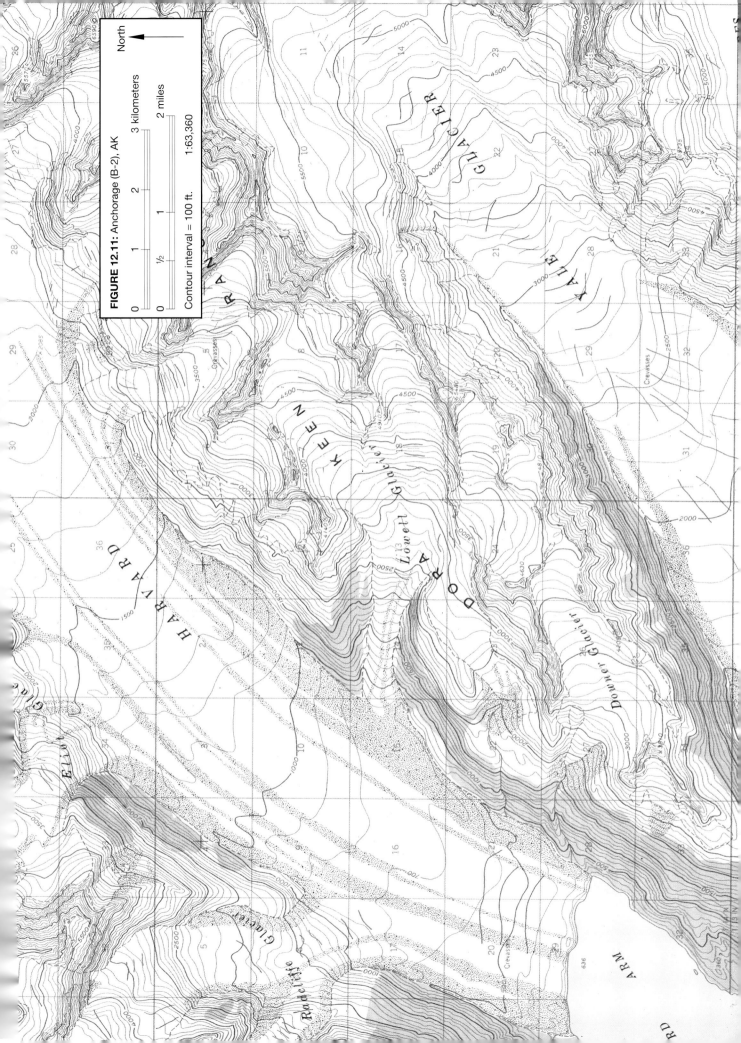

FIGURE 12.11: Anchorage (B-2), AK

North

| 0 | 1 | 2 | 3 kilometers |
| 0 | ½ | 1 | 2 miles |

Contour interval = 100 ft.   1:63,360

Also notice that Harvard Glacier is about the size of the valley glacier that once flowed in the Siffleur River Valley of Alberta (refer back to Figure 12.9). Based on your knowledge of the shape of the glaciated Siffleur River Valley, and taking into account the slopes of the Harvard Glacier Valley, estimate the thickness of ice that is below sea level where Harvard Glacier enters Harvard Arm. Explain your reasoning.

16. What are the linear features on Harvard Glacier that are indicated by the brown stipled pattern? How do they form?

17. Notice the crevasses within a mile of the glacier's terminus. What specific kind of crevasses are they? Why do you think they formed only on this part of the glacier?

18. Find the Yale Glacier in the southeastern corner of the map. Notice the *transverse* crevasses around the label "Yale." Also note that other visible parts of this glacier have well-developed *longitudinal* crevasses. Explain why you think each type of crevasse occurs where it does.

19. Between the Harvard and Yale glaciers, notice how the Dora Keen Range is streamlined and thins to the southwest. How could you use this information to infer how ice has flowed in regions where glaciers are no longer present?

PART 2—CONTINENTAL GLACIATION

During the Pleistocene Epoch or "Ice Age" that ended about 10,000 years ago, thick ice sheets covered virtually all of Canada, large parts of Alaska, and the northern contiguous United States. These continental glaciers produced a variety of characteristic landforms (Figures 12.12 and 12.13).

Recognizing and interpreting these landforms is important in conducting work such as regional soil analyses, studies of surface drainage and water supply, and exploration for sources of sand and gravel. Boulder tracing and geochemical studies of glacial till can lead to discovery of metallic ore deposits. The thousands of lakes in the Precambrian Shield area of Canada also are a legacy of this continental glaciation, as are the fertile soils of the north-central United States. Study Figures 12.12 and 12.13 together with the descriptions in Figures 12.3, 12.4, and 12.5.

The Antarctic ice sheet is the largest modern continental glacier. Its area is larger than the United States and Mexico combined. Its maximum thickness is 2.65 miles (4.26 km), and it probably contains about two-thirds of the fresh water on Earth! During recent droughts in parts of the United States, some people have proposed mining of the Antarctic ice sheet for freshwater ice. These large blocks of ice would be towed by ships to U.S. port cities, where they would melt and provide fresh water.

QUESTIONS—PART 2

Refer to Figure 12.14, part of the Peterborough, Ontario quadrangle, for the following questions. This area lies north of Lake Ontario.

20. Study the size and shape of the oblong hills. What type of feature are they? How did they form?

21. In what direction did the ice move over this area? Explain.

22. What sort of sediment would you expect to find in a drumlin? Would it be well stratified and well sorted? Explain.

23. Find the red highway, Route 7, that crosses the upper part of the map. About 1¼ inches below the number 7, what is the long, narrow feature that trends northeast-southwest? How did it form? Explain.

24. What size of sediment would you expect to find in the feature you just described in Question 23? Would it be well stratified and well sorted? Why?

25. This map contains large areas of swamp, also known as "mosquito hatchery" or "moose pasture." How did these areas form?

Refer to Figure 12.15, part of the Miniota, Manitoba/Saskatchewan quadrangle, for the following questions. This area is located in western Manitoba, about 70 miles (112 km) north of the Canada-U.S. border.

26. There are many small lakes on this map. What type of lakes are they? How did they form?

27. These lakes all are intermittent sloughs (swamps), and very few are fed or drained by streams. When these lakes fill, where does the water come from? Where does the water go when the lakes dry up?

28. How can you distinguish this landscape from a karst landscape (Exercise Eight)? Explain which features are the same and which are different.

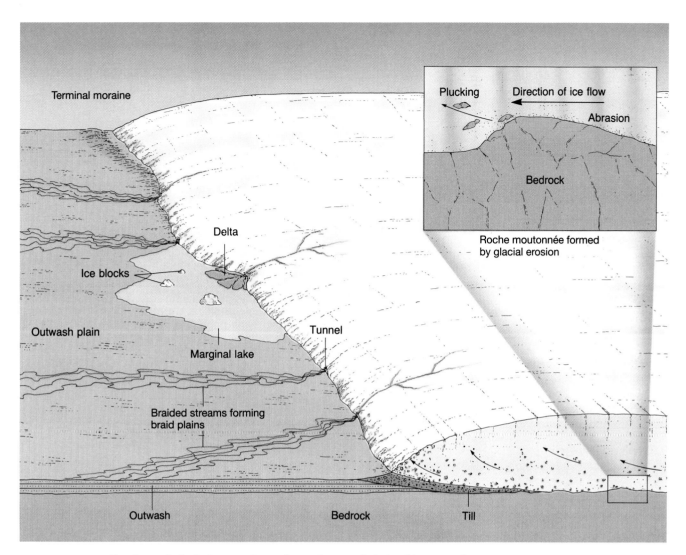

FIGURE 12.12 Continental glaciation produces these characteristic landforms at the beginning of ice wastage (decrease in glacier size due to severe ablation).

QUESTIONS—APPLYING WHAT YOU'VE LEARNED

Now we will apply what you have learned about mountain glaciation and continental glaciation. Refer to Figure 12.16, a portion of the Mt. Rainier, Washington quadrangle, and Figure 12.17, the accompanying stereogram.

29. What kinds of glaciers presently are located on Mt. Rainier?

30. Is this an example of mountain glaciation or continental glaciation?

31. List the *erosional* features (from Figure 12.3) that have been caused by glaciers in this region.

32. List the *depositional* features (from Figure 12.4) caused by glaciers in the Mt. Rainier region.

33. Considering your answers, what evidence is there that the glaciers of the Mt. Rainier region once were more extensive than today?

34. Note the obvious radial drainage pattern (Figure 9.3) that is developed in this region. Many ice sheets also move radially. Do you think that the glaciation associated with Mt. Rainier could ever have been regarded as an example of an ice sheet, based on the evidence remaining in the area? Explain your answer.

Refer to Figure 12.18, a portion of the Whitewater, Wisconsin quadrangle, and Figure 12.19, the accompanying stereogram, for these questions:

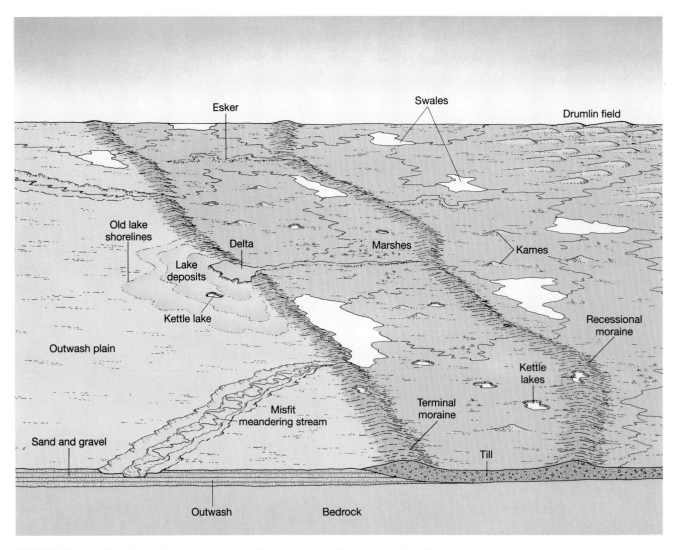

Esker   Swales   Drumlin field

Old lake
shorelines   Delta   Marshes   Kames

Lake
deposits

Kettle lake

Outwash plain   Recessional
moraine

Kettle
lakes

Misfit
meandering stream   Terminal
moraine

Sand and gravel   Till

Outwash   Bedrock

FIGURE 12.13 Continental glaciation leaves behind these characteristic landforms after complete ice wastage (compare to partial wastage in Figure 12.12).

35. List the features of glaciated regions from Figures 12.3 and 12.4 that are present in this region.

36. Based on your answer to Question 35, what kind of glaciation (mountain versus continental) has shaped this landscape?

37. Describe what direction the ice flowed over this region. Cite evidence for your inference.

38. What kinds of lakes are present in this region, and how did they form? (Refer to Figure 12.5.)

39. In the southeastern corner of the map, the forested area probably is what kind of feature?

40. Note the swampy and marshy area running from the west-central edge of the map to the northeastern corner. Describe the probable origin of this feature (more than one answer is possible).

ADDITIONAL QUESTIONS

41. List the features from Figures 12.3 and 12.4 that are commonly found in regions affected by *mountain* glaciation.

FIGURE 12.14 (Opposite page) Portion of the Peterborough, Ontario, Canada topographic quadrangle map.

FIGURE 12.14: Peterborough, Ontario

0   1   2 kilometers

0   ½   1   2 miles

North

Contour interval = 25 ft.   1:48,000

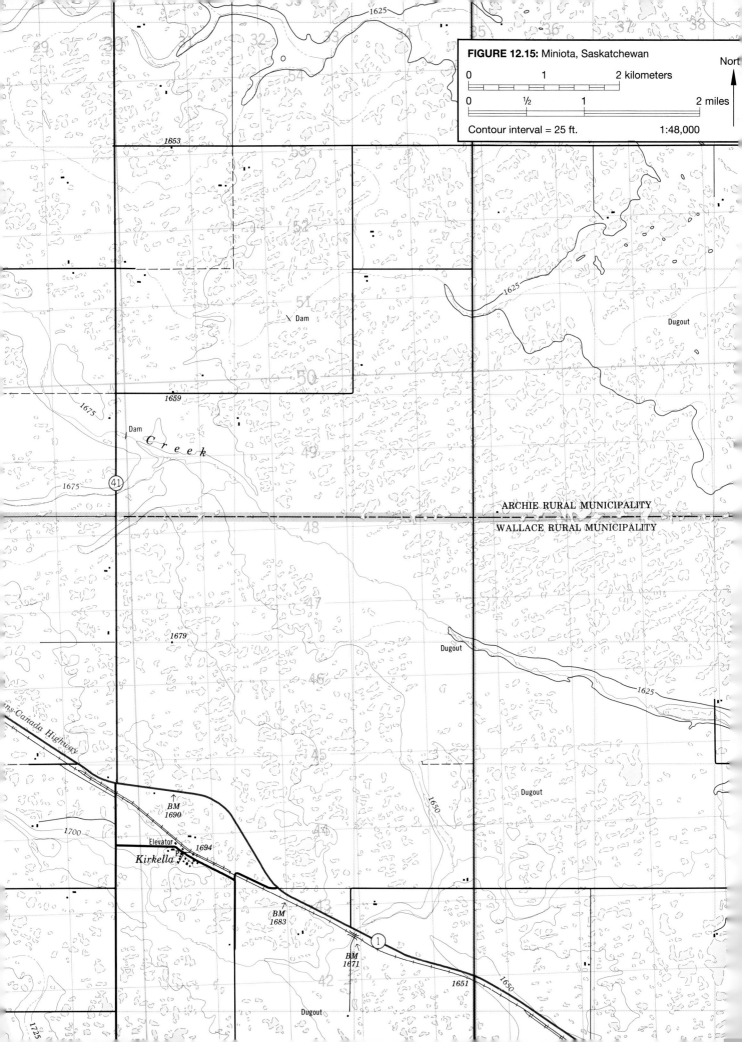

FIGURE 12.15: Miniota, Saskatchewan

North

| 0 | | | 1 | | 2 kilometers |

| 0 | ½ | 1 | 2 miles |

Contour interval = 25 ft.   1:48,000

ARCHIE RURAL MUNICIPALITY

WALLACE RURAL MUNICIPALITY

Creek

Dam

Dam

Dugout

Dugout

Dugout

Dugout

Trans-Canada Highway

Kirkella

Elevator

BM 1690

BM 1694

BM 1683

BM 1671

1653

1625

1625

1625

1659

1675

1675

1679

1650

1690

1694

1700

1725

1683

1671

1651

1650

29 30 32 33 34 35 36 37 38

54

53

52

51

50

49

48

47

46

45

44

43

42

41

FIGURE 12.15 (Opposite page) Portion of the Miniota, Manitoba/Saskatchewan, Canada topographic quadrangle map.

42. List the features from Figures 12.3 and 12.4 that are commonly found in regions affected by *continental* glaciation.

43. Based on your answers to Questions 41 and 42, plus your knowledge of regions studied during this exercise, answer these questions:
   a. Which type of glaciation (mountain or continental) produces a record on the landscape of mostly *erosional* features?
   b. Which kind of glaciation (mountain or continental) produces a record on the landscape of mostly *depositional* features?

44. What kinds of water bodies typify regions that have been subjected to *mountain* glaciation? (Refer to Figure 12.5.)

45. What kinds of water bodies typify regions that have been subjected to *continental* glaciation? (Refer to Figure 12.5.)

The Antarctic ice sheet contains about two-thirds of the fresh water on Earth. As noted, during recent droughts in the United States, some people have proposed mining huge blocks of Antarctic ice and towing them to U.S. ports, where they would melt to provide abundant fresh water.

46. What problems might be encountered during mining and towing of such huge blocks of ice? What would make the task difficult?

47. Would water from such a source require treatment or filtering? Explain.

FIGURE 12.16 (Following page) Portion of the Mt. Rainier, Washington topographic map.

FIGURE 12.17 (Following page) National high-altitude photograph (NHAP, color-infrared) stereogram of the Mt. Rainier, Washington region. (USGS)

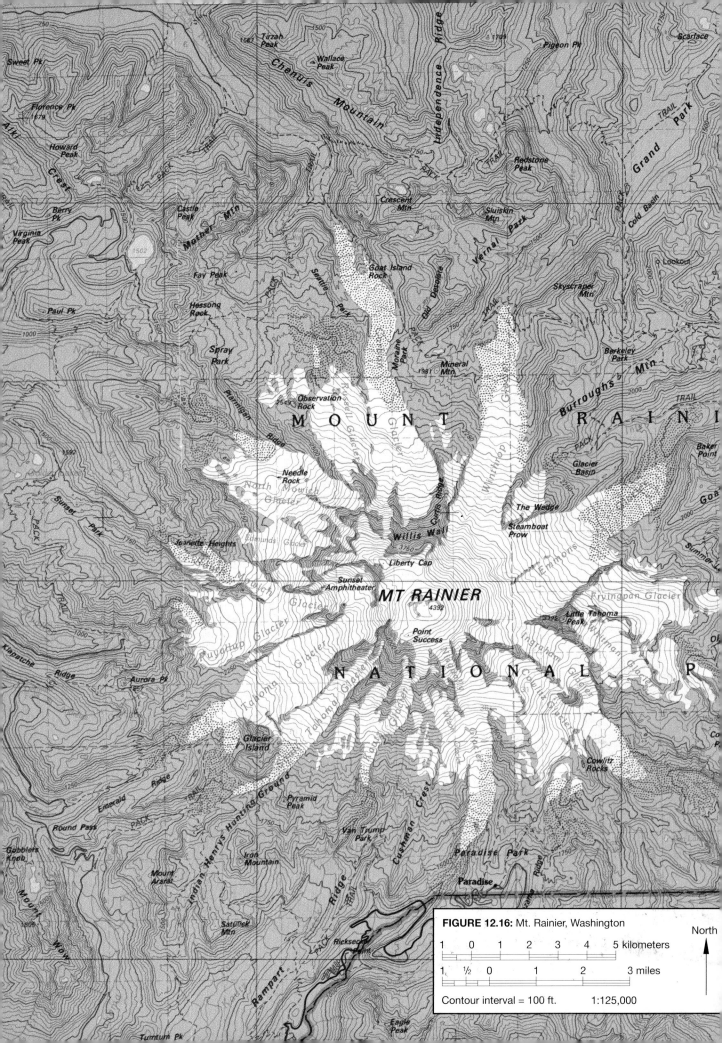

FIGURE 12.16: Mt. Rainier, Washington

| 1 | 0 | 1 | 2 | 3 | 4 | 5 kilometers |

| 1 | ½ | 0 | 1 | 2 | 3 miles |

Contour interval = 100 ft.   1:125,000

North

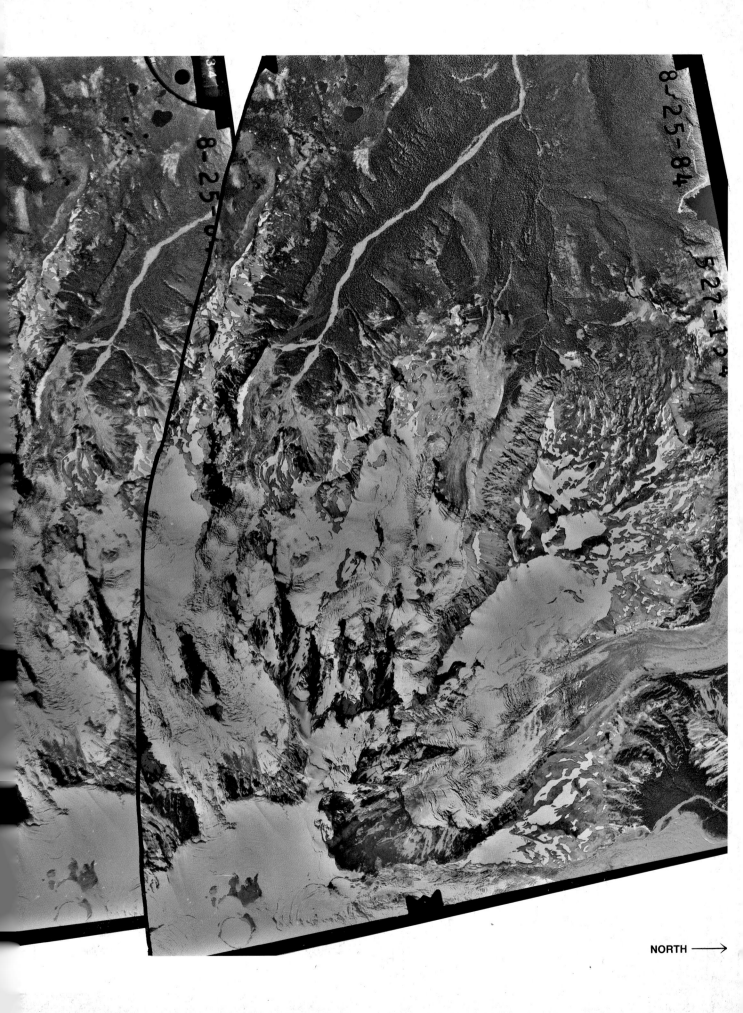

8-25-84

8-25-84

8-25-84 527-19⁴

NORTH →

FIGURE 12.18: Whitewater, Wisconsin

North

0   1   2   3 kilometers

0   ½   1   2 miles

Contour interval = 20 ft.   1:62,500

FIGURE 12.18 (Opposite page) Portion of the Whitewater, Wisconsin topographic quadrangle map.

FIGURE 12.19 National high-altitude photograph (NHAP, color-infrared) stereogram of the Whitewater, Wisconsin region. (USGS)

EXERCISE THIRTEEN

Dating of Rocks and Geologic Events

Jonathan Bushee
Raman J. Singh
Northern Kentucky University

PURPOSE

Geologists commonly examine surficial exposures of rocks and sediments in two-dimensional, vertical cross sections such as road cuts, stream valleys, and cliffs. This exercise will enhance your ability to decipher the chronological geologic history displayed in such exposures.

MATERIALS

Pencil, eraser, ruler, calculator.

THE PRINCIPLES

A geologist's initial challenge in the field is to subdivide the existing rock sequence into mappable units that can be traced throughout the field area, or **correlated** from one site to the next. This subdivision is made on the basis of color, texture, or composition. Such mappable units are called **formations.** Their subdivisions are called **members.** The boundaries between formations or members are **contacts.**

In 1669 a Danish naturalist, Nicholas Steno, outlined two basic principles for determining relative age in sedimentary rocks: the Principle of Original Horizontality and the Principle of Super-

position. These two principles, and others discovered by geologists, are as follows:

Principle of Original Horizontality Sedimentary rock layers (strata) originally were deposited as horizontal layers of sediment. If strata are no longer horizontal, it is because they have been displaced by movements in Earth's crust.

Principle of Original Lateral Continuity Sedimentary rock layers, and lava flows, extend laterally in all directions until they thin to their termination *(pinch out)* or reach the edges of their basins of deposition.

Principle of Superposition In any *undisturbed* sequence of strata, the oldest stratum is at the bottom of the sequence, and the youngest stratum is at the top.

Principle of Inclusions Any piece of rock (clast) that has become included in another rock, or in sediment, must be *older* than the rock or sediment into which it has been incorporated. Such a clast (commonly a rock fragment, crystal, or fossil) is an **inclusion.** The surrounding body of rock/sediment is the **matrix** or **groundmass.** Thus, an inclusion is older than its matrix.

Principle of Unconformities An unconformity is a rock surface that represents a gap in the geologic record. It is like a page missing from a book. An unconformity can be a buried surface on which no sediment was deposited for a while, or a

196

buried surface that was eroded. Unconformities range from local to continent-wide.

   Principle of Cross Cutting   Any geologic feature that *cuts across* a rock or sediment must be *younger* than the rock or sediment it cuts across. Such cross-cutting features include a fracture (a crack in rock), a fault (a fracture along which movement has occurred), or an intrusive mass of rock.

APPLYING THE PRINCIPLES

Figures 13.1 through 13.13 show you how these principles are used.

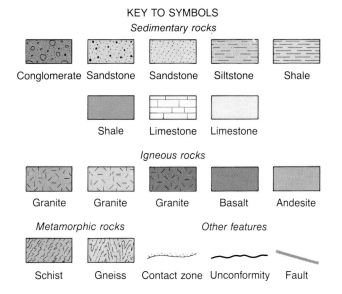

KEY TO SYMBOLS
Sedimentary rocks

| Conglomerate | Sandstone | Sandstone | Siltstone | Shale |

| Shale | Limestone | Limestone |

Igneous rocks

| Granite | Granite | Granite | Basalt | Andesite |

| *Metamorphic rocks* | | | *Other features* | |
| Schist | Gneiss | Contact zone | Unconformity | Fault |

Relative Ages of Sedimentary Rocks

Sedimentary rocks result from the deposition of sediments, layer by layer, on Earth's surface.

1. Horizontal rocks (Figure 13.1). A simple illustration of the principle of superposition.
2. Folded rocks (Figure 13.2). The rocks have been deformed by folding. If a series of strata is folded, the folding happened more recently than the age of the youngest rock affected.
3. A sedimentary layer that lies with an angular discordance on other rocks is the youngest (Figure 13.3).
4. If a series of strata is folded into an **anticline,** then the *oldest* formation is in the core of the fold (Figure 13.4).
5. If a series of strata is folded into a **syncline,** then the *youngest* formation is in the core of

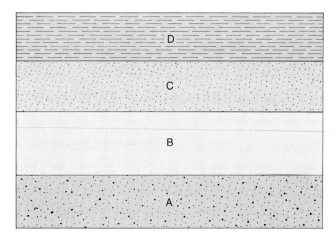

FIGURE 13.1   Geologic cross section. Rock layer **A** is the oldest. Layer **D** is the youngest.

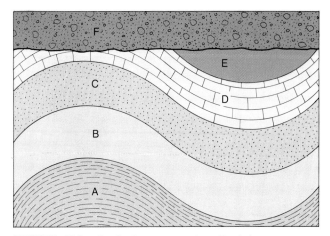

FIGURE 13.2   Geologic cross section. Rock layer **A** is the oldest. Layer **F** is the youngest. Folding and erosion occurred after **E** was deposited, but before layer **F** was deposited.

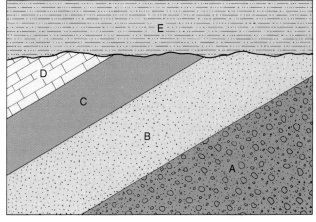

FIGURE 13.3   Geologic cross section. Formation **A** is the oldest. Formation **E** is the youngest. Tilting and erosion occurred after **D** was deposited, but before **E** was deposited.

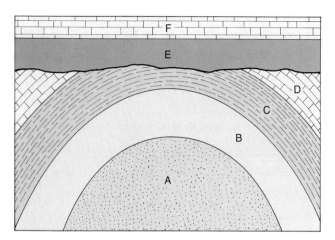

FIGURE 13.4 Geologic cross section. Formation **A** is the oldest. Formation **F** is the youngest. Folding and erosion occurred after **D** was deposited, but before **E** was deposited.

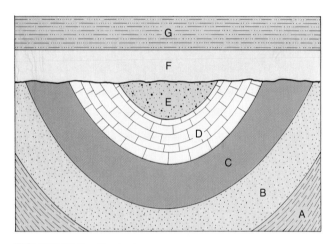

FIGURE 13.5 Geologic cross section. Formation **A** is the oldest. Formation **G** is the youngest. Folding and erosion occurred after **E** was deposited, but before **F** was deposited.

the fold (Figure 13.5), disregarding any strata that were deposited after folding.

6. Sedimentary rocks that contain pebbles or other inclusions are younger than the rocks from which the inclusions were derived (Figure 13.6).

Relative Ages of Igneous Rocks

Igneous rocks are the products of cooling and hardening of magma or lava. *Where* they have formed determines their relative age:

- *Within Earth's crust,* an **intrusive** rock body must be *younger* than the rock it has intruded. (The intruded, preexisting rock is called **country rock.**)

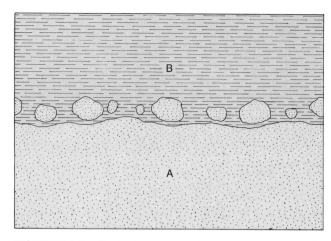

FIGURE 13.6 Geologic cross section. Formation **A** is the older. Formation **B** is the younger. Erosion occurred after **A** was deposited, but before **B** was deposited.

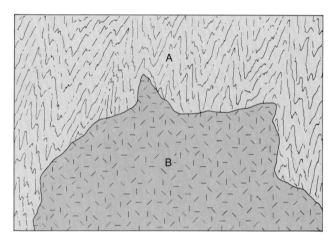

FIGURE 13.7 Geologic cross section. Granite **B** is younger than country rock **A.**

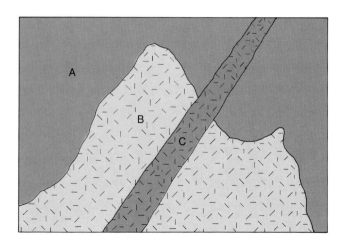

FIGURE 13.8 Geologic cross section. Granite **B** is younger than country rock **A**. Dike **C** is younger than granite **B**.

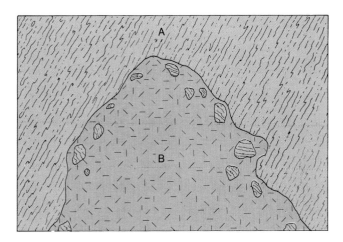

FIGURE 13.9 Geologic cross section. Granite **B** is younger than country rock **A**.

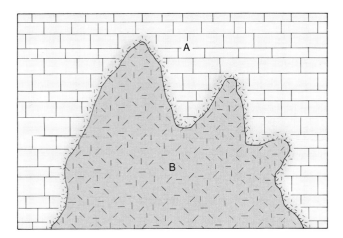

FIGURE 13.10 Geologic cross section. Granite **B** is younger than contact-metamorphosed country rock **A**.

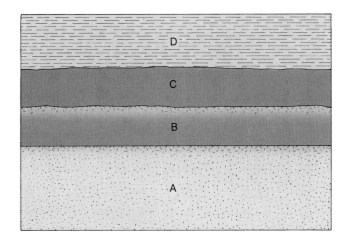

FIGURE 13.11 Geologic cross section. Lava flow **B** is younger than country rock **A**. Lava flow **C** is younger than lava flow **B**. Formation **D** is younger than lava flow **C**.

- *At Earth's surface,* an **extrusive** rock body such as a lava flow or ash bed must be *younger* than the underlying rocks. (But if this extrusive rock is buried, it must be *older* than the overlying rocks.)

7. If a body of granite crosscuts another rock, the granite is the younger (Figure 13.7).
8. If a body of granite is crosscut by a dike, the dike is the younger (Figure 13.8).
9. If a body of granite contains inclusions (unmelted fragments) of another rock, the granite is the younger (Figure 13.9).
10. Younger intrusive rocks produce contact metamorphic zones along their contacts with the older rocks (Figure 13.10).
11. Lava flows contact-metamorphose older rocks at their basal contacts (Figure 13.11).

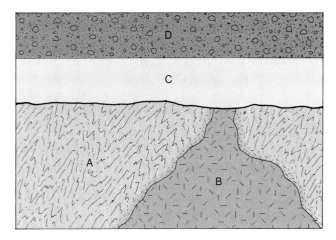

FIGURE 13.12 Geologic cross section. Schist **A** is older than granite **B**. Granite **B** is older than formation **C**.

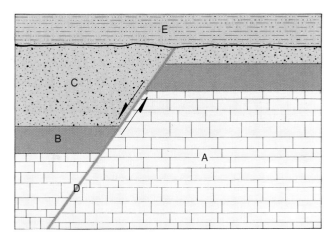

FIGURE 13.13 Geologic cross section. Formation **A** is the oldest. Formation **E** is the youngest. Fault **D** is younger than **C**, but older than **E**.

Relative Ages of Regionally Metamorphosed Rocks

Metamorphosed rocks form at depth in Earth's crust by recrystallization of previously formed rocks.

12. Metamorphic rocks are older than the igneous rocks which have intruded them. They also are older than any layered rocks that have been deposited on top of them (Figure 13.12).

Relative Ages of Faults

Faults are fractures (planar or gently curved) along which rocks have been displaced.

13. If rocks are faulted, the faulting occurred after formation of the youngest rock affected by the fault (Figure 13.13).

QUESTIONS

1. Are only sedimentary rocks used for relative age determinations? Explain.

2. Consider how mud accumulates in layers at the bottom of a mud puddle, storm after storm. The mud puddle is actually a basin of deposition.
   a. Describe the process, step by step, of how the strata form in the puddle.
   b. How far do the strata extend?
   c. Are there hidden unconformities in the mud at the bottom of a mud puddle? Where are they?
   d. What name do we give to these hidden unconformities? (Refer back to Exercise Five, if you are uncertain.)
   e. How do these unconformities form in the mud puddle?
   f. How much actual time do the unconformities generally represent, relative to the time represented by the accumulation of sediment that form the strata?

3. Refer to the vertical geologic cross sections in Figures 13.14, 13.15, 13.16, and 13.17. Determine the relative ages of rock bodies and features marked with letters. Indicate their relative age relationships by writing their letters on the blanks, oldest (bottom) to youngest (top). On Figures 13.16 and 13.17, indicate (by writing on the figure) all zones where you would expect contact metamorphism. Keep in mind the mode of origin of the various rock types, and the principles for determining relative age. Always start with the question: *What was there first?* (More than one solution is possible for Figures 13.16 and 13.17.)

4. Carefully examine Figure 13.18, a surface mine (strip mine) in northeastern Pennsylvania's anthracite coal mining district. Describe all of the events that have happened to the fossil plants,

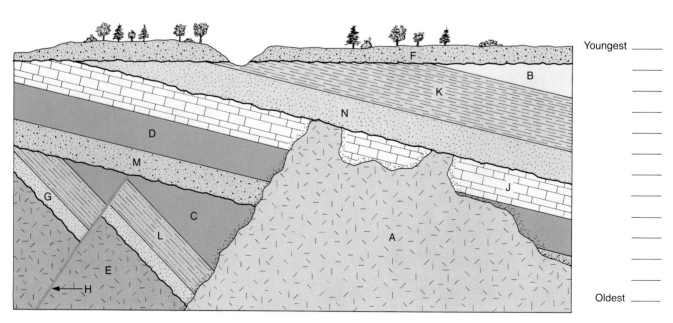

FIGURE 13.14 Relative age relationships in a geologic cross section.

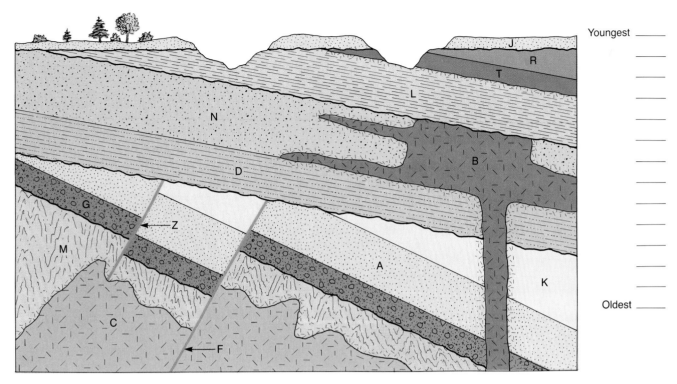

FIGURE 13.15 Relative age relationships in a geologic cross section.

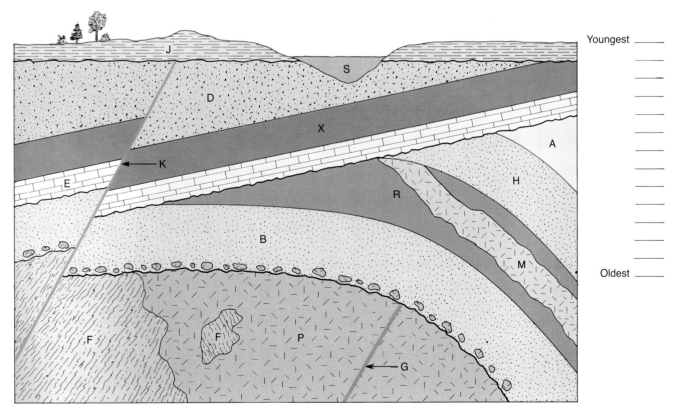

FIGURE 13.16 Relative age relationships in a geologic cross section.

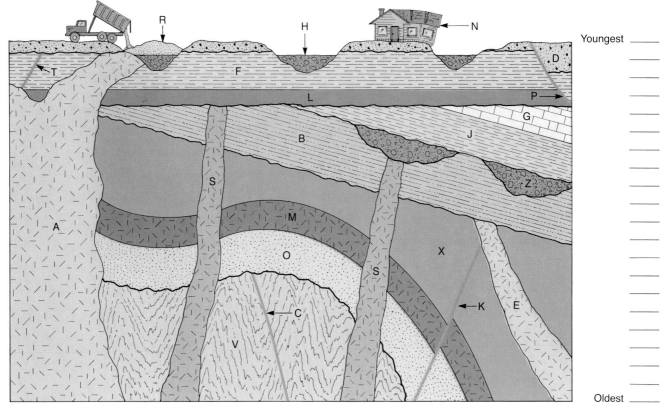

FIGURE 13.17 Relative age relationships in a geologic cross section.

from when they were live trees to when they were exposed by bulldozers. (Note that your response may differ from those of others, because more than one inference is possible about the geologic history of this site. *Be prepared to discuss your reasoning with the other members of your class.*)

5. Carefully examine Figure 13.19, an exposure of sedimentary rocks and a sill in northeastern New Mexico. Assume that the sill was relatively horizontal when it intruded as magma. Now, answer these questions:
   a. Was the fault present when the sill intruded this region? How can you tell?
   b. How much displacement occurred along the fault after the sill intruded? Explain your answer.
   c. Although there is evidence of fault displacement after emplacement of the sill, it is impossible to determine from the photograph whether the sill was molten (liquid) or solid rock when the post-intrusion displacement

occurred. Where would you look to find out if fault displacement occurred before the sill cooled? What information would you look for? Explain your answer.

ADDITIONAL QUESTIONS

6. Layers of rock are analogous to the pages of a book. Why?

7. How is "reading" geological history from layers of rock different from reading a book, in terms of how the pages are arranged from top to bottom (front to back) of the book? (Hint: imagine a book on a table and how you would go about "reading" geologic history.)

8. Describe the usual textural characteristics of sediments that occur directly on top of unconformities.

9. Are all unconformities surfaces above which rock or sediment has been removed? Explain.

West

East

Coal

Fossiliferous sandstone

Fossiliferous
sandstone

Fossil
plants

FIGURE 13.18 Surface mine
(strip mine) in northeastern
Pennsylvania, from which
anthracite coal is being
extracted. Closeup shows
sandstone block with abundant
plant fragments. (Photo by
R. Busch)

Sill having an absolute age of about 25 million years

Sedimentary rocks

2 m

1

0

FIGURE 13.19 Surface mine (strip mine) in northern New Mexico, from which bituminous coal is being extracted. Note sill, sedimentary rocks, and fault. (Photo by R. Busch)

EXERCISE FOURTEEN
Structural Geology

Michael J. Hozik
William R. Parrott, Jr.
Raymond W. Talkington
Stockton State College

PURPOSE

This exercise develops your ability to define, describe, and interpret geological structures in three dimensions. To do this, we will use three-dimensional block diagrams, geologic maps, and geologic cross sections.

MATERIALS

Ruler, set of colored pencils, paper, pencil, eraser.

INTRODUCTION

Structural geology is the study of how rocks or sediments are arranged when first formed, and how they are deformed afterward. Rock/sediment deformation is caused by *stress* (directed pressure). Deformation (such as a change in shape) caused by this stress is called *strain*. Therefore, much of structural geology involves deciphering stress and strain relations.

Generally, geologists can see how rocks or sediments are positioned only at Earth's *surface*. Geologists record this two-dimensional information on geologic maps like those you will use in this exercise. From the information on such maps, they then *infer* the three-dimensional arrangement of the rocks/sediments. From this 3-D picture, the structural geology of an area can be interpreted.

DEFINITIONS

Three representations of Earth are commonly used by structural geologists. These are the geologic map, cross section, and block diagram:

geologic map shows the distribution of rocks at Earth's surface. The rocks commonly are divided into mappable units that can be recognized and traced across the map area. This division is made on the basis of color, texture, or composition. Such mappable units are called **formations.** They may be subdivided into **members.** The boundaries between geologic units are **contacts.** A geologic map also may show the topography of the land surface with contour lines.

geologic cross section a drawing of a vertical slice through Earth, with the material in front of it removed—a cutaway view. It shows the arrangement of rock units and their contacts. A good cross section also shows the topography of the land surface, like a topographic profile.

block diagram a combination of the geologic map and cross section. It looks like a solid block, with a geologic map on top and a geologic cross section on each of its visible sides. You will work with six block diagrams in this exercise.

Because we are dealing with the three-dimensional arrangement of rocks, both at and beneath Earth's surface, we need a system to describe rock orientation, or attitude. Strike and dip serve this purpose (see Figures 14.1 and 14.2):

strike the *compass direction* of a line formed by the intersection of a horizontal plane (like the surface of a lake) and an inclined stratum, fault, fracture, or other surface (Figure 14.1). Because it is a compass direction, strike usually is expressed relative to north or south. Hence, strike is expressed as "north X degrees east," or "south X degrees west." (Refer back to Exercise Seven if necessary.)

dip the *angle* between a horizontal plane and the inclined stratum, fault, or fracture. As you can see in Figure 14.1, a thin stream of water poured onto an inclined surface always runs down the surface parallel to dip. The inclination of the water line down from the horizontal plane is the **dip angle.** Dip always is measured perpendicular to strike.

This "water-on-the-rock method" for finding the direction and angle of dip is very useful. Because strike is perpendicular to dip, strike easily

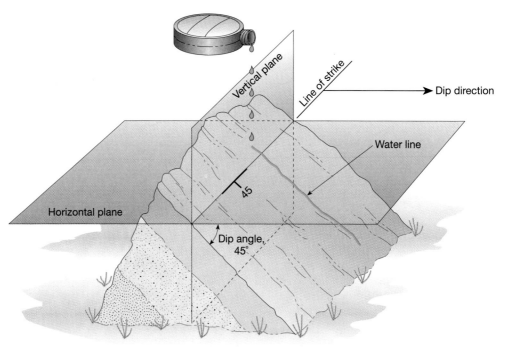

FIGURE 14.1 Strike and dip of a rock outcrop. *Strike* is the direction of a line formed by the intersection of rock strata and a horizontal plane. *Dip* is the maximum angle of inclination of the strata, always measured perpendicular to the line of strike (looking straight down on it, in map view). Water poured onto a dipping stratum drains along the angle of dip. The **T** and **45** together form the standard strike-and-dip symbol: the top of the **T** is the line of strike; the short upright of the **T** shows the dip direction; and the **45** is the dip angle in degrees.

FIGURE 14.2 How to read strike-and-dip symbols. In the left example, strike runs 45° east of north (N45°E), and the rocks dip 30° toward the southeast (30°SE). Strike and dip always are given in this order: N45°E, 30°SE. Compare to the example on the right.

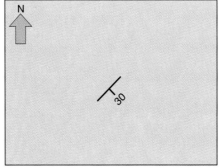

N45°E, 30°SE

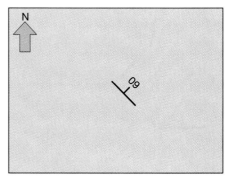

N45°W, 60°NE

can be determined relative to the water line. The direction that the water runs down an inclined geologic surface is the **dip direction**, and must be expressed together with the **dip angle** (e.g., 24° west).

Strike and dip are shown on maps by use of T-shaped symbols (Figure 14.2). The long line shows strike direction, and the short line shows dip direction. Again, dip always is drawn perpendicular to the line of strike. The short line "points" downdip. The accompanying numerals indicate the dip angle in degrees.

TYPES OF STRUCTURES

Structural geologists must locate, observe, and interpret many different structures. Fundamentally, these include unconformities, faults, and folds.

Unconformities are of three common types (Figure 14.3):

1. **Disconformity** an unconformity between *parallel* strata. The disconformity itself may be a very irregular surface, as shown.

2. **Angular unconformity** an unconformity between *nonparallel* strata.
3. **Nonconformity** an unconformity between sedimentary rock/sediment and *nonsedimentary* rock.

Faults are of two general classes, those having mostly vertical movement, and those having mostly lateral movement (Figure 14.4):

1. Vertical-motion faults are of two types, **normal faults** and **reverse faults.** Each is named by noting the *sense of motion* of the top block relative to the bottom block, regardless of which one actually has moved. Simply assume that the bottom block (foot wall) has not moved, and then determine which direction the top block (hanging wall) appears to have moved. If the top block appears to have moved downward, as gravity would normally pull it, then the fault is a **normal fault.** If the top block appears to have moved upward, the reverse of the way gravity would pull it, then the fault is a **reverse fault.**
2. Horizontal-motion faults are **lateral faults** (or **strike-slip faults**). Shown in the figure is a

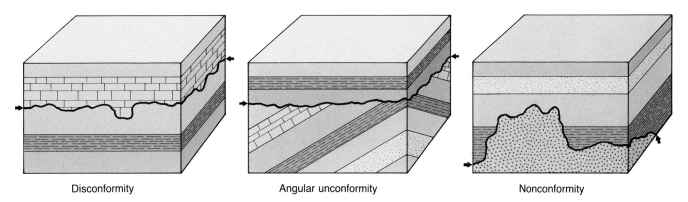

Disconformity   Angular unconformity   Nonconformity

FIGURE 14.3 Unconformities—the three common types. Arrows mark the unconformity surfaces.

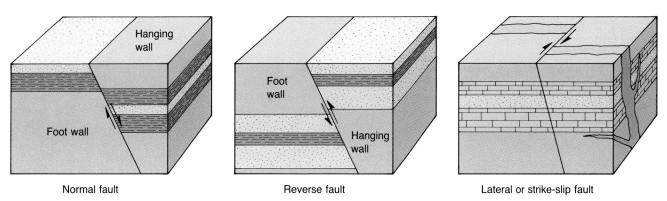

Normal fault   Reverse fault   Lateral or strike-slip fault

FIGURE 14.4 Faults—the three common types. Arrows show the direction of movement of each block. (Also refer back to Figure 1.12.)

207

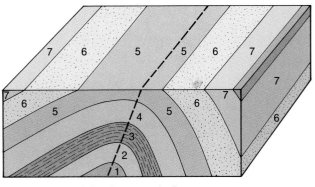

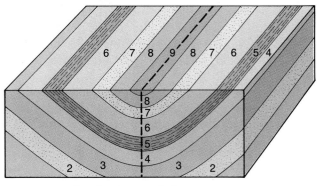

Anticline (asymmetrical)   Syncline (symmetrical)

FIGURE 14.5 Folds—the two common types. Numbers indicate relative ages of the rock units. Lowest number (**1** or **2**) in each diagram = oldest unit, deposited first. Highest number in each diagram (**7** or **9**) = youngest unit, deposited last. Heavy dashed lines mark axial planes of the folds (see Figure 14.6).

right-lateral fault. If you stand on one side of the fault and look across it, the rocks on the opposite side of the fault appear to have moved to the right. *Left-lateral faults* have the opposite sense of motion. They also are called strike-slip faults because they slip along the direction of strike of the fault plane.

Folds basically are upward or downward (Figure 14.5):

1. **Antiforms** are "upfolds" or "convex folds." If the *oldest* rocks are in the middle, they are called **anticlines.**
2. **Synforms** are "downfolds" or "concave folds." If the *youngest* rocks are in the middle, they are called **synclines.**

In a fold, each stratum is bent around an imaginary axis, like the crease in folded paper. This is the **fold axis** (or **hinge line**). For all strata in a fold, the fold axes lie within the **axial plane** of the fold (Figure 14.6A).

The fold axis may not be horizontal, but rather plunge into Earth, called a **plunging fold** (Figures 14.6B and 14.7). **Plunge** is the angle between the fold axis and horizontal. The **trend** of the plunge is the compass direction, measured in the direction that the axis is inclined downward.

Folds commonly have two sides, or **limbs,** one on each side of the axial plane (Figure 14.6). However, **monoclines** have two axial planes that separate two nearly horizontal limbs from a more steeply inclined limb (Figure 14.8).

Domes and basins are large, circular structures formed when strata are warped upward (domes) or downward (basins). Strata are oldest at the center of a dome, and youngest at the center of a basin.

Geologic maps use many symbols to describe structures; some are shown in Figure 14.9. Figure 14.10 provides simple rules for interpreting geologic maps.

STRUCTURE MODELS AND QUESTIONS

It is easiest to learn about geologic structures through the use of three-dimensional models. We provide six models, printed on heavy paper, at the back of this manual. Carefully remove them from the book, so you can fold them into blocks. To fold them, follow the procedure in Figure 14.11.

Structure Model 1

This model shows a light brown (speckled) formation striking due north and dipping 25° to the west. A second formation (gray) strikes due north and is vertical (dip angle = 90°).

1. Note that both formations have the same thickness, but the one dipping 25° to the west makes a much wider band on the geologic map (top). Why?

We have printed the complete map for you, and the vertical cross sections on the south, east, and west sides. Now complete the vertical cross section on the north side. Also, draw on the map a strike and dip symbol on the bed that dips 25° to the west. Then draw a strike and dip symbol for the vertical bed (see Figure 14.9 for the strike and dip symbol for a vertical bed).

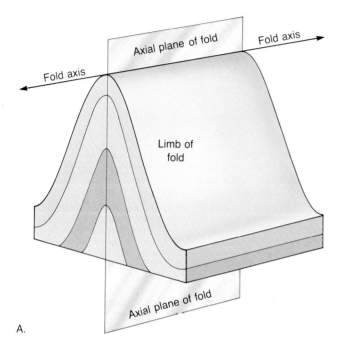

A.

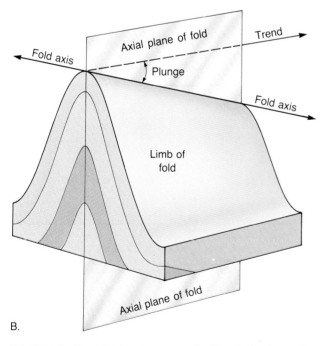

B.

FIGURE 14.6 Fold terminology. A. Simple horizontal fold. B. More complex plunging fold. Note that the fold axis plunges into Earth, but the *trend* is the compass direction on the surface.

Structure Model 2

This model is slightly more complicated than the previous one. Complete the north and east sides of the block. Notice that the rock units define a fold. This fold is an antiform, because the strata are convex upward. We say it is nonplunging, because its axis is horizontal. (Consult Figure 14.6 for the differences between plunging and nonplunging folds if you are uncertain about this.) On the geologic map, draw strike and dip symbols showing the orientations of unit **E** at points **I**, **II**, **III**, and **IV**.

2. How do the strikes at all four locations compare with each other?

3. How does the dip direction at points **I** and **II** compare with the dip direction at points **III** and **IV**? In your answer, include the dip direction at all four points.

4. Draw the proper symbol along the axis of the structure (refer to Figure 14.9).

Structure Model 3

Complete all four cross sections, using as guides the geologic map on top of the block and the incomplete cross section at the south end. On the map, draw strike and dip symbols showing the orientation of unit **C** at points **I**, **II**, **III**, and **IV**.

5. How do the strikes of all four locations compare with each other?

6. How does the dip direction at points **I** and **II** compare with the dip direction at points **III** and **IV**? Include the dip direction at all four points in your answer.

7. Is this fold plunging or nonplunging? Is it an antiform or a synform?

8. How much variation is there in the strike at all points in a nonplunging fold?

9. Draw the proper symbol along the axis of the structure (refer to Figure 14.9).

Structure Model 4

This model shows a plunging antiform and an unconformity. The antiform plunges to the north, following the general rule that *anticlines plunge in the direction in which the fold closes* (refer to rules, Figure 14.10). Complete the north and east sides of the block. Draw strike and dip symbols on the map at points **I**, **II**, **III**, **IV**, and **V**.

10. How do the directions of strike and dip differ from those in Model 2?

FIGURE 14.7 Plunging folds. A. Before erosion. Imaginary plane above strata is the *horizontal datum plane,* from which all data are measured. B. After erosion. Eroded plunging folds are exposed at the land surface.

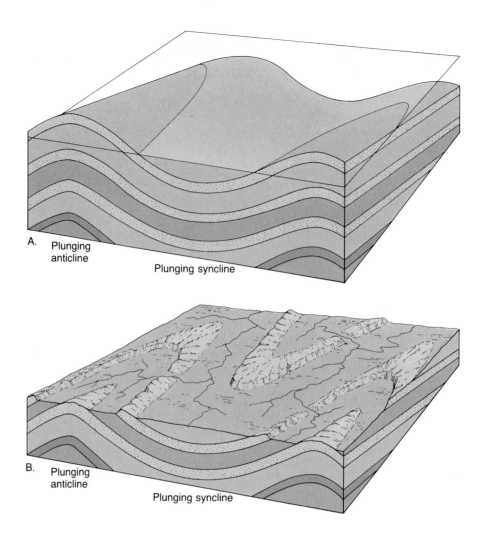

A. Plunging anticline
Plunging syncline

B. Plunging anticline
Plunging syncline

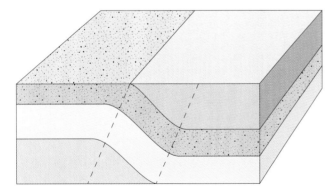

FIGURE 14.8 Monocline. Not all folds have two limbs. The monocline is a fold inclined in only one direction. A monocline has two axial planes (dashed) that separate two nearly horizontal limbs from a more steeply inclined limb.

11. What type of unconformity is at the base of unit **I**?

12. Draw the proper symbol along the axis of the structure. Indicate the direction of plunge. (Refer to Figure 14.9.)

13. Draw the proper symbol on the geologic map to indicate the orientation of beds in formation **I** (refer to Figure 14.9).

Structure Model 5

This model shows a plunging synform. Complete the north and east sides of the diagram. Draw strike and dip symbols on the map at points **I, II, III, IV,** and **V** to show the orientation of layer **G**. *Synforms plunge in the direction in which the fold opens* (refer to rules, Figure 14.10).

14. In which direction does this synform plunge?

15. Draw the proper symbol along the axis of the structure. Indicate the direction of plunge (refer to Figure 14.9).

Structure Model 6

This model shows a fault that strikes due west and dips 45° to the north. At point **I**, draw a strike and dip symbol showing the *orientation of the fault.* On the west edge of the block, draw arrows parallel to the fault, indicating relative motion. Label the hanging wall and the foot wall.

16. Is this fault a normal or a reverse fault? Why?

Complete the east side of the block. Draw arrows parallel to the fault to show the relative motion. Now look at the geologic map and at points **II** and **III**. Write **U** on the side that went up and **D** on the side that went down. At points **IV** and **V**, draw strike and dip symbols for unit **B**.

17. On the geologic map, what happens to the contact between units **A** and **B** where it crosses the fault?

The general rule is that, as erosion of the land proceeds, *contacts migrate downdip.*

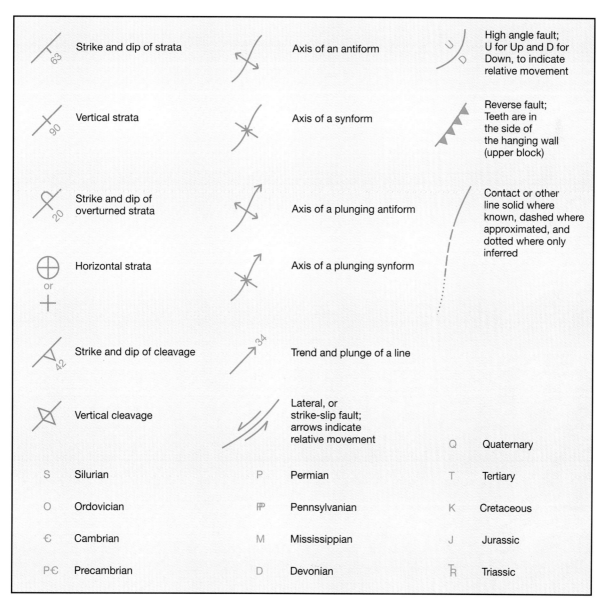

Strike and dip of strata	Axis of an antiform	High angle fault; U for Up and D for Down, to indicate relative movement
Vertical strata	Axis of a synform	Reverse fault; Teeth are in the side of the hanging wall (upper block)
Strike and dip of overturned strata	Axis of a plunging antiform	Contact or other line solid where known, dashed where approximated, and dotted where only inferred
Horizontal strata or	Axis of a plunging synform	
Strike and dip of cleavage	Trend and plunge of a line	
Vertical cleavage	Lateral, or strike-slip fault; arrows indicate relative movement	Q Quaternary
S Silurian	P Permian	T Tertiary
O Ordovician	ℙ Pennsylvanian	K Cretaceous
Ҽ Cambrian	M Mississippian	J Jurassic
PҼ Precambrian	D Devonian	Ҍ Triassic

FIGURE 14.9 Structural symbols and abbreviations used on geologic maps. (For rock symbols, see Exercise Thirteen, Figure 13.1.)

FIGURE 14.10 Simple rules used by geologists to interpret geologic maps.

A SET OF SIMPLE RULES FOR INTERPRETING GEOLOGIC MAPS

1. Contacts between horizontal beds are parallel to topographic contours along those contacts.
2. Anticlines have their oldest beds in the center.
3. Synclines have their youngest beds in the center.
4. Anticlines plunge toward the nose (closed end) of the structure.
5. Synclines plunge toward the open end of the structure.
6. Contacts of horizontal beds, or of beds that have a dip lower than stream gradient, "V" upsteam.
7. Contacts of beds that have a dip greater than stream gradient "V" downstream.
8. Vertical beds do not "V" or migrate with erosion.
9. The upthrown blocks of faults tend to be eroded more than downthrown blocks.
10. Contacts migrate downdip upon erosion.
11. True dip angles can only be seen in cross section if the cross section is perpendicular to the fault or to the strike of the beds.

FORMING THE STRUCTURE MODELS

1. Lay the paper with the model on it face down in front of you. Orient the long dimension of the paper up-and-down, as if you were going to read a normal typewritten page.

2. Carefully curl back one side until you can see the solid black line that runs all the way from the top to the bottom of the page. Crease the paper exactly along that line.

3. Now repeat this process for the other side of the paper.

4. Unfold the two sides, and curl back the top until you see the solid black line that runs across the page. Crease the paper exactly along that line.

5. Now repeat this process for the bottom of the paper.

6. To make a block, you still need to do something about the extra material where the corners are. In each corner there is a dashed line. Start at one corner and push that line toward the inside of the block. Fold the sides down so that they match, and crease the flap you folded in. Your crease should be approximately along the dashed line. Do the same thing with the other three corners.

7. If the block is folded correctly, the top will be flat and the strata will match on the map (top) and on the cross sections (sides).

8. The block will not really stay together without tape, but do not tape it. You will find that it is easier to draw on the block if you can unfold it and lay it out flat.

9. Write your name on the blank inside of the block so that your instructor can identify your work when you hand it in.

FIGURE 14.11 Forming the structure models.

18. Is this true in this example?

19. Could the same offset have been produced by strike-slip motion?

GEOLOGIC MAPS AND QUESTIONS

Refer to Figure 14.12, a portion of the Bright Angel, Arizona quadrangle, including parts of the Grand Canyon. This is a topographic map like those you have used in previous exercises, but with geologic information superimposed. It shows where various rocks **crop out,** or where they are exposed at the surface. (Sometimes they are obscured by soil or vegetation, but it is where they *would be* exposed if not obscured.) In the southwestern United States, the semiarid climate prevents the formation of much soil, so rock formations and the contacts between them are largely visible in the field. In the explanation on the page facing the map, the formations are listed in the order of their age (youngest at top).

Examine the map and the explanation, and answer these questions:

20. What is the name of the oldest unit? In terms of geography and elevation, where is this unit exposed? (Note: Printing colors vary slightly between the map and the explanation. To find formations, use both the color and the formation designation, such as Pk, pCb.)

21. How old is the Kaibab Formation? (Give geologic period.)

22. In terms of geography and elevation, where is this unit exposed?

23. What is the youngest unit?

24. Note the pattern of the contour lines. Why do the contacts of most of the geologic formations mimic the contour lines? (Refer to rules, Figure 14.10.)

25. How do the contour lines indicate that the Redwall Limestone is a cliff-forming unit in the map area?

26. Would the Redwall Limestone be a cliff-former in a region of heavy rainfall? Why or why not?

27. Is the Hermit Shale a cliff-former?

28. Is the Supai Formation a cliff-former?

29. Approximately how thick is the Paleozoic sequence (Appendix 1) in this area? (You will find the contour lines helpful here.) What must you assume about how the rocks are oriented to make this estimation?

On this map, contacts between rock units are shown by thin black lines. Faults are shown as heavy black lines, dotted where covered by younger rock units. In the northwestern quadrant of the map, find the Cheops Pyramid, and the fault passing through it. Note how this fault offset the Dox and Shinumo Formations *before* the Tapeats Sandstone was deposited. Before continuing, make sure you clearly see how the map depicts these relationships among the Tapeats, Dox, and Shinumo.

30. In the southeastern quadrant, find the Cremation Fault. Identify the youngest formation affected by the Cremation Fault. Which formation was deposited first, after the faulting occurred?

31. In the southwestern quadrant, find the Pipe Fault and the Bright Angel Fault. Study the interesting relationship of these two faults. Now, Identify the youngest formation affected by the portion of the Pipe Fault that lies northwest of the Bright Angel Fault. Which formation was deposited first, after the fault had occurred?

32. Examine the portion of the Pipe Fault southeast of the Bright Angel Fault. When was this portion active?

33. According to the fine print in the explanation, what may have happened in the area during the Silurian Period?

Refer to Figure 14.13. This geologic map shows part of Somerset County, Pennsylvania, a bituminous coal mining area. Examine the map and you will see that the only difference from the Bright Angel geologic map is the addition of red contour lines. These are not topographic contours; we will discuss them shortly, but disregard them for now. This is an interesting area to study, both economically and structurally. In the stratigraphic column on the page facing the map, note the economic resources, especially the Upper Kittanning coal.

34. The contour interval on the Bright Angel quadrangle is 50 feet. But on this map, C.I. = 20 feet. Why are these different contour intervals used?

35. In the west-central part of the map, at the eastern crest of Glade Mountain (you will have to look closely for these localities), what is the

EXPLANATION

FIGURE 14.12 Geologic map (opposite) showing formations and some structural features for a portion of the Grand Canyon, on the Bright Angel quadrangle in northern Arizona. North is toward the binding. Explanation on this page identifies the formations.

Quaternary

Landslide — CENOZOIC

Laramide Revolution

Triassic

Tkm — Moenkopi Formation — MESOZOIC

Permian

Pk — Kaibab Formation

Pt — Toroweap Formation

Pc — Coconino Sandstone

Ph — Hermit Shale

Permian and Pennsylvanian

PPs — Supai Formation

Mississippian

Mr — Redwall Limestone

Cambrian

Cm — Muav Formation

Includes unclassified Middle Cambrian strata at top. Devonian Temple Butte Limestone occurs here and there filling channels eroded in upper part of the formation.

Cba — Bright Angel Formation

Ct — Tapeats Sandstone

PALEOZOIC

Map Scale — North

0	½	1	2 miles
0	3000	6000	9000	12,000 feet
0	0.5	1	2	3 kilometers

Grand Canyon Revolution and Grand Canyon Peneplain.

Upper Precambrian

pCr — Rama Formation
Diabase plugs, dikes, and sills intrusive into older formations.

pCd — Dox Formation

pCs — Shinumo Sandstone

pCh — Hakatai Shale

pCb — Bass Limestone

Arizonan Revolution and Arizonan Plain.

Lower Precambrian

pCz — Zoroaster Granite
Stocks and pegmatite dikes intrusive into older formations.

pCbs — Brahma Schist
Principally metamorphosed basic rocks presumably of volcanic origin.

pCv — Vishnu Schist
Meta-sediments with minor meta-volcanics.

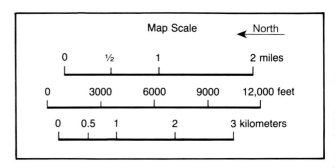
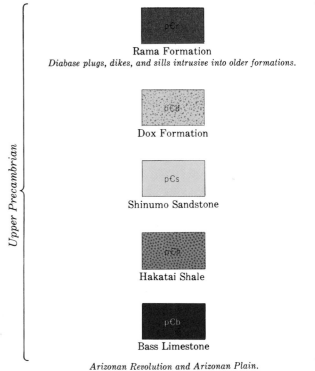
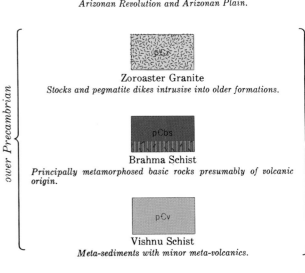

214

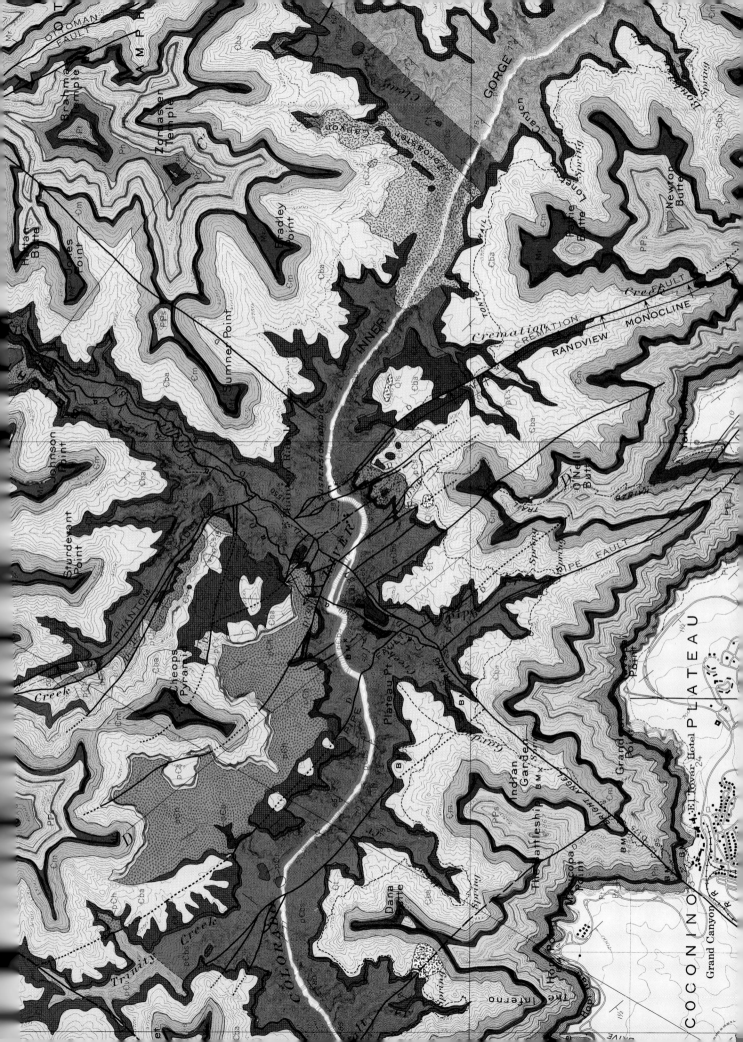

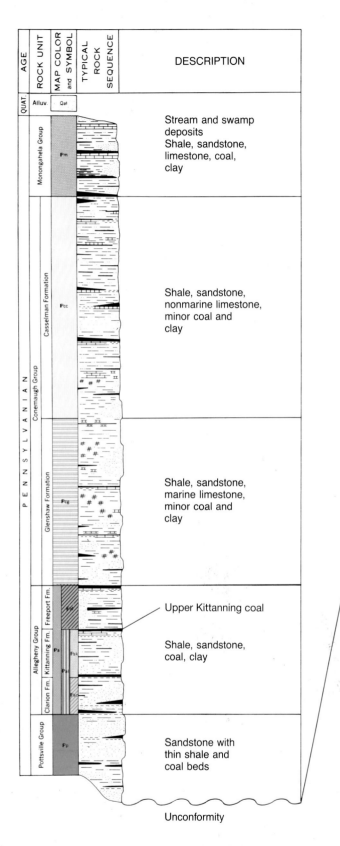

AGE	ROCK UNIT	MAP COLOR and SYMBOL	TYPICAL ROCK SEQUENCE	DESCRIPTION
QUAT.	Alluv.	Qal		
P E N N S Y L V A N I A N	Monongahela Group	Pm		Stream and swamp deposits Shale, sandstone, limestone, coal, clay
	Conemaugh Group — Casselman Formation	Pcc		Shale, sandstone, nonmarine limestone, minor coal and clay
	Conemaugh Group — Glenshaw Formation	Pcg		Shale, sandstone, marine limestone, minor coal and clay
	Allegheny Group — Freeport Fm. / Kittanning Fm. / Clarion Fm.	Pf / Pak / Pa / Pal / Pac		Upper Kittanning coal — Shale, sandstone, coal, clay
	Pottsville Group	Pp		Sandstone with thin shale and coal beds

Unconformity

FIGURE 14.13 Geologic map (opposite) for a portion of Somerset County in southwestern Pennsylvania. Structure contours (red) are on the Upper Kittanning coal seam. North is toward the binding. On this page is a stratigraphic column for the area. (From Flint, Norman K., 1981, *Geology and Mineral Resources of Southern Somerset County*, Pennsylvania Geological Survey Bulletin C56A)

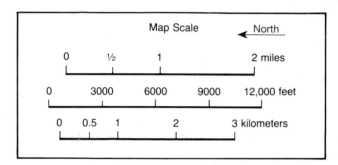

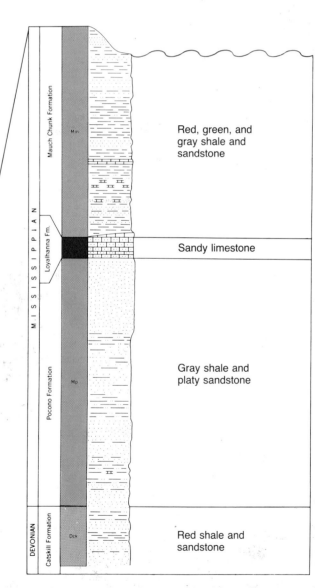

M I S S I S S I P P I A N	Mauch Chunk Formation	Mm
	Loyalhanna Fm.	
	Pocono Formation	Mp
DEVONIAN	Catskill Formation	Dck

Red, green, and gray shale and sandstone

Sandy limestone

Gray shale and platy sandstone

Red shale and sandstone

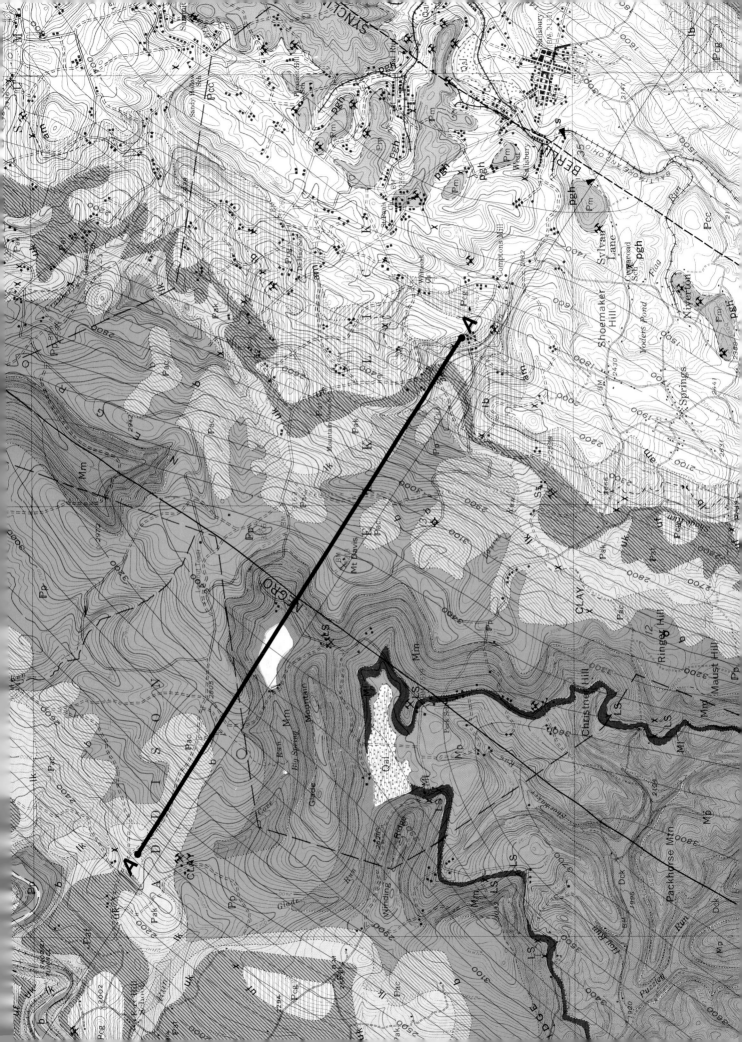

elevation of the contact between the two units exposed there?

36. The contact is between what two units?

37. Refer to the stratigraphic column. Coals are represented as black intervals on the typical rock sequence. The Upper Kittanning coal unit is near the top of the Kittanning Formation. Does the Upper Kittanning coal occur above or below the contact mentioned in Question 36?

38. In the southeastern part of the map, along the Berlin syncline, find the abandoned coal mine, 1½ miles north of the center of Salisbury. (It is just below the "n" in Coal Run). What is the elevation of this point? (Note it for a later question.)

39. Would the Upper Kittanning coal unit lie at or below ground level here?

40. What is the difference in elevation between this site (abandoned coal mine) and the one in Question 35?

The red lines on this map are **structure contours.** They are like topographic contours, but instead of giving the elevation above sea level of the land surface, they show the *elevation above sea level of a specified geologic surface.* In this case, the geologic surface is the top of the Upper Kittanning coal.

Figure 14.14 shows two views of a coal bed like the Upper Kittanning. The profile (side view) shows how the land surface and coal bed surface can intersect. The map view shows the same intersection by using topographic contours (for the surface) and structure contours (for the coal bed). The dashed line indicates where the two intersect, which is where the coal crops out at the surface.

FIGURE 14.14 Profile (top) and map view (bottom) of a coal bed.

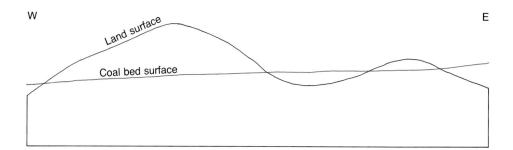

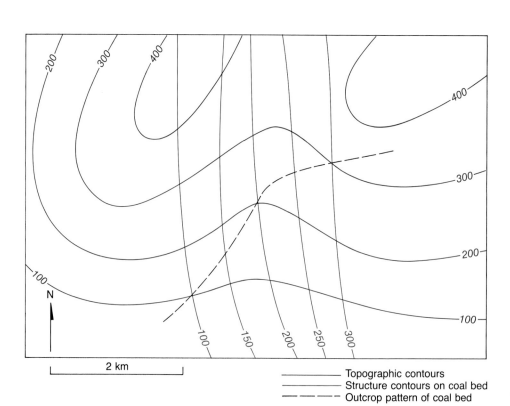

2 km

——— Topographic contours
——— Structure contours on coal bed
– – – Outcrop pattern of coal bed

(Geologists who work for surface-mining companies use these maps to find outcrops where coal can be easily mined at the surface.)

Here are rules to remember about structure contours:

- If a structure contour is *lower* than the topographic contour, the geologic surface is buried underground.
- If a structure contour is *identical* to the topographic contour, the geologic surface is at ground level, and crops out (although it may be concealed by vegetation, soil, or alluvium).
- If a structure contour is *higher* than the topographic contour, the geologic surface is above the ground. In other words, it is up in the air, and there is nothing there. What happened? The geologic surface has been eroded away.

41. Returning to Figure 14.13, use both the structure contours and the topographic contours to determine the depth to the coal at the abandoned mine in Question 38. In other words, how many feet is the mine below the surface?

42. Based on what you learned from Figure 14.14, where would you look on this map to find outcrops of the coal unit?

43. How might a mining geologist use structure contours to estimate the costs of mining at a given place?

ADDITIONAL QUESTIONS

Refer to Figure 14.13, and note line *A–A'*. On the topographic profile of this line provided in Figure 14.15, do the following:

44. Plot the line of the Upper Kittanning coal (use red pencil) on the geologic cross section (Figure 14.15).

45. Mark points on the geologic cross section (Figure 14.15) that represent contacts between rock units.

46. Extend these contacts (from Question 45) throughout the subsurface portion of the geologic cross section.

47. Use colored pencils to tint the rock units of the geologic cross section (Figure 14.15). Use colors similar to those on the map.

48. Draw a line on the geologic cross section (Figure 14.15) representing the edge of the axial plane of the anticline, and label it.

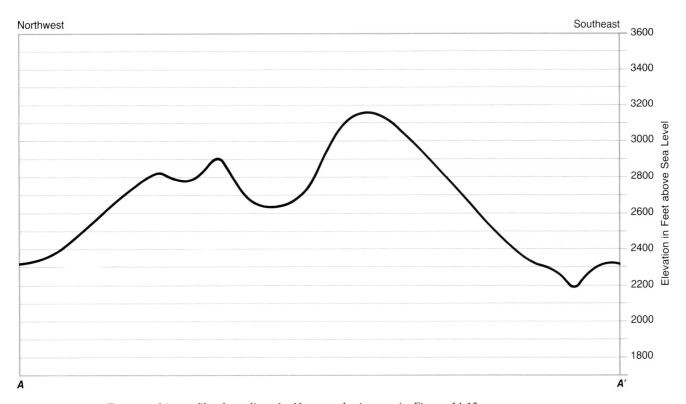

FIGURE 14.15 Topographic profile along line *A–A'* on geologic map in Figure 14.13.

EXERCISE FIFTEEN

Subsurface Geology and Fossil Fuel Exploration

Monte D. Wilson
Boise State University

PURPOSE

This exercise shows how to use geologic principles to interpret data from exploration wells. The goal is to discover the subsurface geology, so that economic resources can be located. A problem in subsurface mapping and oil exploration also is provided.

MATERIALS

Protractor, pencil, eraser, colored pencils.

INTRODUCTION

Opportunities to directly observe rocks below the surface of the land are limited to a few mines, tunnels, and caves. Much more is learned about subsurface geology by interpreting data obtained from wells drilled for hydrocarbons (oil and gas) and water. Geologists compile information from each well into a **well log,** or **well record,** which shows the sequence of rocks penetrated by the drill. The log shows each rock unit penetrated, describes its lithology and thickness, and notes any gas, oil, or water encountered. Geologists also use the data from well logs to create maps that show rock thick-

nesses and attitudes in the subsurface, especially in oil exploration.

HYDROCARBON TRAPS

Hydrocarbon traps "trap" oil and gas. These traps cause hydrocarbons to accumulate and remain stored underground. The traps result either from geologic structures or from porosity/permeability relationships in the rock, or a combination of the two. Recall from Exercise Eight ("Groundwater Processes and Use") that **porosity** is the percentage of void space in a rock body (e.g., fractures, holes), and that **permeability** is a measure of how well fluids can pass through a rock body. For a rock to be permeable, its pore spaces must be interconnected. These same principles apply to oil and gas, as well as to water.

Understanding the behavior of fluids in rocks is essential in the search for resources. The key is the difference between permeable and impermeable rocks:

- *Permeable rocks* permit water, oil, and gas to travel through them, or to be stored in them. Permeable rocks of hydrocarbon reservoirs are called **reservoir rocks** (Figure 15.1).
- *Impermeable rocks* impede (trap) the movement of water, oil, and gas. Impermeable rocks that im-

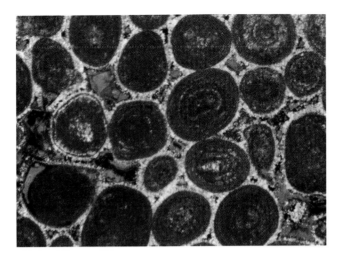

FIGURE 15.1 Photomicrograph of oolitic limestone. The limestone was soaked in pink epoxy resin to reveal extensive pore spaces (porosity) in the rock. Area shown is 6 mm wide.

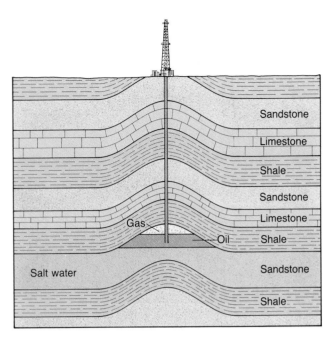

FIGURE 15.2 Oil well drilled into an idealized vertical geologic cross section. Note vertical positions of gas, oil, and salt water in the hydrocarbon trap.

pede or trap hydrocarbons are called **confining beds** or **cap rocks** (e.g., the mudstone in Figure 5.31).

Oil and gas are less dense than water. Thus, in a container of oil, gas, and water, the hydrocarbons rise above the denser water. This explains why, in any hydrocarbon trap, you commonly will encounter gas in the highest part, oil beneath the gas, and water in the lowest part.

Figure 15.2 shows an idealized structural trap. An anticlinal structure has created an area where fluids can concentrate. Water, oil, and gas are trapped in a permeable sandstone (reservoir rock) beneath an impermeable shale (confining bed or cap rock). The sandstone is porous, as well as permeable, and most of its porosity is filled with water, oil, and gas.

Note that gas is present in the highest portion of the reservoir, oil is between the gas and the water, and salt water is in the lowest portion of the reservoir. The total accumulation of oil and gas trapped in the reservoir is called the **pool**. As you can see, the best place to drill a well for hydrocarbons is where the reservoir (and the pool) attains its greatest elevation (in this case, the peak of an anticline). This is why the study of structural geology is so important in resource exploration.

There are two major types of hydrocarbon traps (Figure 15.3). **Structural traps** are produced by folding and/or faulting. **Stratigraphic traps** are produced by lithologic variations. Occasionally, combination **structural-stratigraphic traps** are en-

countered. In Figure 15.3, the unconformity-related trap was formed by a combination of folding, erosion, and sedimentation, which produced horizontal confining beds overlying the inclined reservoir rocks.

PROBLEM 1 AND QUESTIONS

Figure 15.4 is a cross section of five wells drilled along a west-east line. Figure 15.5 provides well logs for these wells. These logs record the rock units and faults intersected by each well, and the dips of these units and faults. You also need to know the lithologic descriptions of the rock units:

Unit 1. Cross-bedded eolian sandstone
Unit 2. Brown-to-gray siltstone with shale zones and some coal seams
Unit 3. Parallel-bedded, poorly sorted sandstone
Unit 4. Conglomerate
Unit 5. Poorly sorted sandstone with some clay, silt, pebbles
Unit 6. Black, clayey shale
Unit 7. Parallel-bedded, well-sorted, coarse-grained sandstone
Unit 8. Black shale
Unit 9. Gray limestone

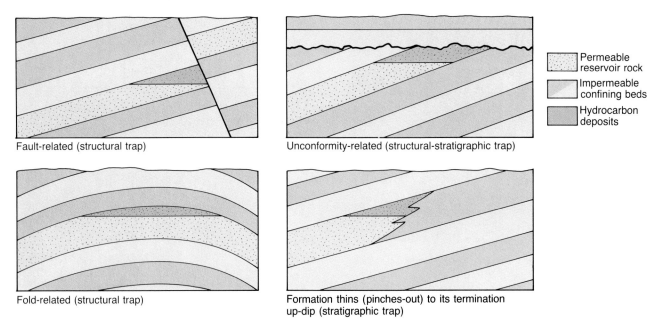

FIGURE 15.3 Common types of hydrocarbon traps as they appear in geologic cross sections.

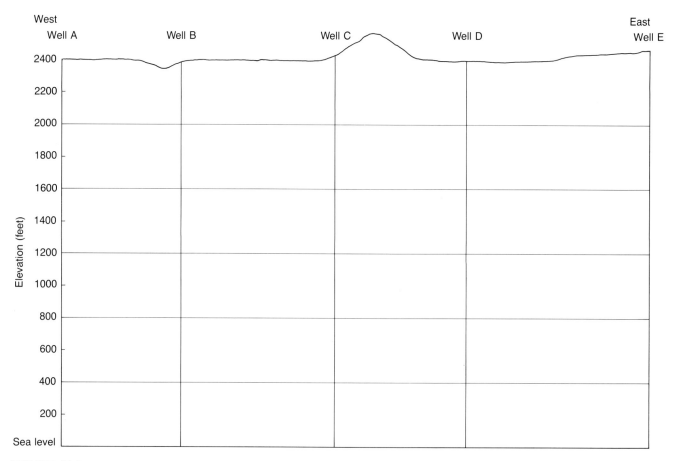

FIGURE 15.4 Cross section showing well locations.

Well A

2400–2100	Unit 1, horizontal
2100–2050	Unit 2, horizontal
2050–1700	Unit 3, dips westward 15°
1700–1150	Unit 4, dips westward 15°
1150– 800	Unit 5, dips westward 15°
800– 550	Unit 6, dips westward 15°
550– 200	Unit 7, dips westward 15°
Bottom of well	

Well B

2300–2100	Unit 1, horizontal
2100–1980	Unit 2, horizontal
1980–1650	Unit 3, dips westward 15°
1650	Fault; dips eastward 60°
1650–1350	Unit 4, dips westward 15°
1350–1000	Unit 5, dips westward 15°
1000– 750	Unit 6, dips westward 15°
750– 200	Unit 7, dips westward 15°
200–sea level	Unit 8, dips westward 15°
Bottom of well	

Well C

2350–2100	Unit 1, horizontal
2100–1900	Unit 2, horizontal; coal seam at 1950
1900–1700	Unit 3, dips westward 15°
1700–1150	Unit 4, dips westward 15°

1150– 800	Unit 5, dips westward 15°
800– 550	Unit 6, dips westward 15°
550– 200	Unit 7, dips westward 15°
200	Fault; dips eastward 60°
200– 100	Unit 9, dips westward 15°
Bottom of well	

Well D

2300–2100	Unit 1, horizontal
2100–1800	Unit 2, horizontal; coal seam at 1950
1800–1350	Unit 4, horizontal
1350–1000	Unit 5, horizontal
1000– 750	Unit 6, horizontal
750– 200	Unit 7, horizontal
200– 100	Unit 8, horizontal
Bottom of well	

Well E

2400–2100	Unit 1, horizontal
2100–1650	Unit 2, horizontal; coal seams at 1950 and 1850
1650–1450	Unit 3, dips eastward 21°
1450– 900	Unit 4, dips eastward 21°
900– 550	Unit 5, dips eastward 21°
550– 300	Unit 6, dips eastward 21°
300– 200	Unit 7, dips eastward 21°
Bottom of well	

FIGURE 15.5   Logs for wells shown in Figure 15.4.

Refer to the cross section and logs. On each well (vertical line), mark with ticks the elevations of the contacts between units (lightly in pencil). For example, in well **A,** unit 1 extends from the surface (2400 feet) to 2100 feet, so make tick marks at these points; unit 2 extends from 2100 to 2050 feet, so make ticks at these points; and so on. Label each unit number lightly beside each column, between the ticks.

Pay careful attention to the *dip angles* indicated. When you make tick marks, it is very helpful to angle them approximately to indicate dip (use a protractor). This is especially true if you encounter any *faults* in the cross section.

When you have all units plotted in the five wells, connect corresponding points between wells. (You are "correlating" well logs when you do this. You are preparing a subsurface cross section of the type actually constructed by petroleum-exploration geologists.)

From the lithologic descriptions given, you can fill in some of the rock units with patterns— for example, sandstone (dots), conglomerate (tiny

circles), and coal (solid black). You may wish to use the symbols given in the key to Figure 13.1.

1. What is the nature and geologic origin of the bottom contact of Unit 2?

2. Why is coal not found in wells **A** and **B,** whereas two coal seams are found in well **E?**

3. Wells **A** and **E** are **dry holes,** so-called because they produced no hydrocarbons. But the others produce petroleum. An oil pool is penetrated in well **B** from 750 feet to 650 feet, in well **C** from 550 down to 500 feet, and in well **D** from 750 down to 500 feet. Sketch the oil pools on the cross section and explain why the oil was trapped there.

4. Why is there no oil in either well **A** or well **E?**

5. Using the principles of original horizontality, superposition, and cross cutting (refer back to Exercise Thirteen if necessary), describe the sequence of events that developed this geologic situation.

PROBLEM 2 AND QUESTIONS

Geologists and geological engineers often must determine the attitude of a surface (e.g., the top or base of a rock unit), or the thickness variation of a rock body. This information is very useful when exploring for hydrocarbons or water, or for any type of construction that involves excavation. Therefore, geologists and geological engineers commonly use two types of maps:

- **Structure contour maps,** which use contour lines to show the configuration of the top of a rock unit (or sometimes the base of a rock unit, whichever is more useful). In other words, they illustrate the configuration of a surface, relative to sea level or to some other horizontal datum. (Examples are shown in Exercise Fourteen, Figures 14.13 and 14.14.)
- **Isopach maps,** which show the variation in thickness of a rock unit.

    In this problem, you will construct a structure-contour map. You will use it, in combination with an isopach map, to predict the location of a new hydrocarbon well. Start on Figure 15.6 by adding the elevation contours to make it a complete structure-contour map. (Use a contour interval of 100 feet.) Draw the contours with a red pencil. Historically, some wells have produced oil and gas (black dots), whereas others produced only salt water (dry-hole symbols—circles with ticks). Using a green pencil, color areas underlain by salt water.

6. What type of trap is present in this map area?

7. Imagine that this is an old hydrocarbon field in which all wells have been abandoned (sealed with concrete). Consider Figures 15.6 and 15.7, then mark the exact location on Figure 15.6 that is the best place to drill a new hydrocarbon well.

8. Specify the precise location of your proposed well by determining its section number (Public Land Survey System, Figure 7.4), and the quarter of a quarter within it.

9. Why is this the best place to drill?

10. How deep must you drill to get to the bottom of the reservoir sandstone?

FIGURE 15.6 Map of a township in the Public Land Survey System, showing elevations of points in wells where they contacted the top of a reservoir sandstone. Elevations are in feet above mean sea level. Solid black dots represent "producers," wells that produced oil and/or gas. Open circles with ticks represent "dry holes," wells that produced nothing at all, or only salt water.

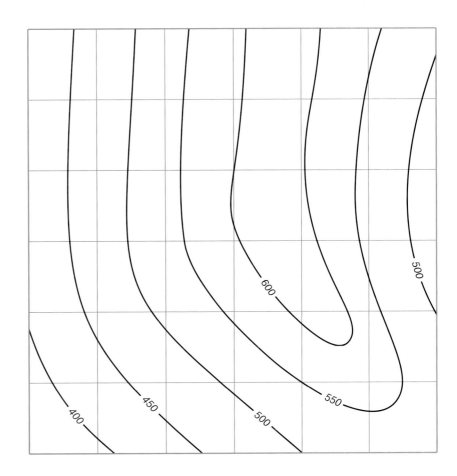

FIGURE 15.7 Isopach map showing thickness of the sandstone formation in Figure 15.6.

EXERCISE SIXTEEN

Earthquakes

**Department of Geology and
Planetary Science
University of Pittsburgh**

PURPOSE

This exercise familiarizes you with the procedures for locating the epicenter of an earthquake.

MATERIALS

Drafting compass, pencil, eraser, ruler, calculator.

INTRODUCTION

Earthquakes are vibrations caused by large releases of energy. Such energy releases accompany fault movements, asteroid impacts, volcanic eruptions, explosions, and movements of magma. Thus, these vibrations can originate both in Earth's crust and beneath it. Earth vibrations are elastic waves that travel through Earth materials, radiating away from their point of origin, the **focus.** The point on the Earth's surface directly above the focus is the **epicenter.**

SEISMIC WAVES AND SEISMOGRAMS

The waves radiating through Earth away from the focus are recorded on a **seismograph.** The recording it produces is a **seismogram** (Figure 16.2). Seis-mographs can detect several types of **body waves,** which are waves that travel through Earth's "body" rather than along the surface, and radiate in all directions from the focus. Two of these body waves are used to locate earthquake epicenters:

- **"P"-waves,** or **longitudinal waves:** "P" for primary, because they travel fastest and arrive at seismographs first. (They are compressional or "push-pull" waves.)
- **"S"-waves,** or **transverse waves:** "S" for secondary, because they travel more slowly and arrive at seismographs after P-waves. (They are perpendicular or "side-to-side" waves.)

Seismographs also detect surface waves, called **"L"-waves** or **Love waves** (named for A. E. H. Love, who discovered them). L-waves travel along Earth's surface—a longer route—and thus are recorded after the S-waves and P-waves arrive at the seismograph. Because P-waves and S-waves arrive at seismic stations before the slower L-waves, they collectively are called *preliminary waves.*

TRAVEL-TIME CURVES

Figure 16.1 shows **travel-time curves,** graphs that indicate how long it takes each type of seismic wave to travel a distance, measured on Earth's surface. Note the curvature of the S and P lines, and the nearly straight line for the surface (L) waves.

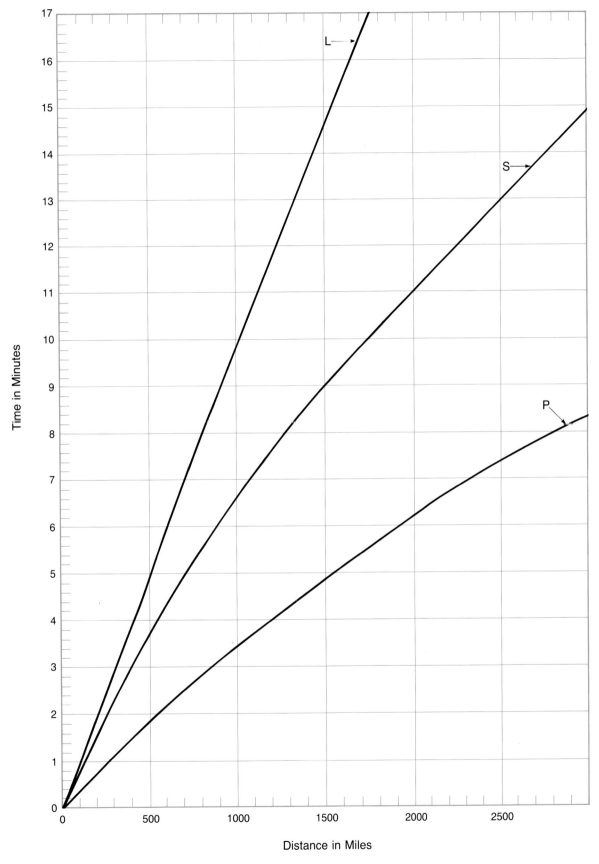

FIGURE 16.1 Travel-time curves for P-waves, S-waves, and L-waves.

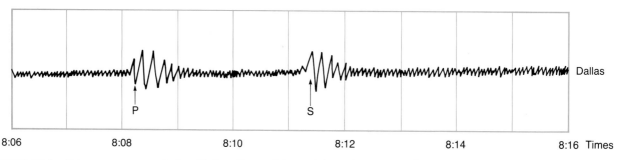

FIGURE 16.2 Seismogram recorded at Dallas, Texas. Most of the seismogram shows only minor background deviations (short zigzags) from a horizontal line, such as the interval recorded between 8:06 and 8:08. Large vertical deviations indicate motions caused by the P-waves and S-waves of an earthquake (note arrows with labels). By making detailed measurements with a ruler, you can determine that the first P-wave motion began at 8:08.2, and the first S-wave motion began at 8.11.3.

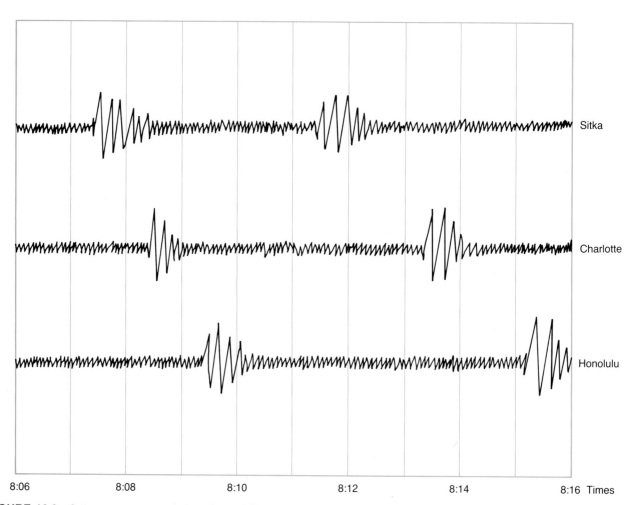

FIGURE 16.3 Seismograms recorded at three different locations for the same earthquake. Times shown have been standardized to Charlotte, NC to simplify comparison.

228 EXERCISE SIXTEEN

The difference between the S-wave arrival time and the P-wave arrival time corresponds to the distance of the seismograph from the focus of the earthquake. This time difference can be converted readily into distance, using the travel-time curves.

For example, study Figure 16.2, a seismogram recorded in Dallas, Texas. Note the zigzags indicating the arrival of P-waves and the zigzags indicating the arrival of S-waves, labeled on the figure. The P-waves began to arrive at 8:08.2, and the S-waves began to arrive at 8:11.3 (3.1 minutes after the P-waves). In other words, the difference in arrival times between the S-waves and P-waves is 3.1 minutes.

To determine the distance from the seismograph to the earthquake's focus, use the travel-time curves in this manner:

1. On Figure 16.1, lay a strip of blank paper along the time axis. Mark two dots on the edge of the paper corresponding to a 3.1-minute time interval (0 and 3.1).
2. Keeping the edge of the paper parallel to the vertical lines, slide the paper up along the **S** and **P** curves until the two dots lie exactly on the **S** and **P** curves.
3. A vertical line through the **S** and **P** curves at these points should intersect the horizontal axis at 1000 miles. This is the distance between the seismograph at Dallas and the earthquake's focus. Because earthquakes occur within, or slightly below, Earth's thin crust, this distance also approximates the distance to the earthquake epicenter. So, you know that the earthquake happened 1000 miles from Dallas, but you don't know specifically where. To determine that, you need seismograms from three recording stations, as you will see shortly.

To determine the time at which the earthquake occurred, project a horizontal line to the time axis of the graph, from the point where the vertical line (from preceding paragraph) passes through the P-wave travel-time curve. This indicates that the earthquake occurred 3.5 minutes before the first P-wave arrived at Dallas. The first P-wave arrived in Dallas at 8:08.2, so the earthquake occurred at 8:04.7.

QUESTIONS

Refer to Figure 16.3 for seismograms of an earthquake recorded at three stations in Alaska, North Carolina, and Hawaii.

1. Estimate, to the nearest tenth of a minute, the times of first arrival of the P-waves and S-waves at each station in Figure 16.3. Then, subtract S minus P:

	First P arrival	First S arrival	S minus P
Sitka, AK	_____	_____	_____
Charlotte, NC	_____	_____	_____
Honolulu, HI	_____	_____	_____

2. Using the S-minus-P times, estimate the distances from the epicenter that correspond to these values. (Refer to Figure 16.1, and follow steps 1, 2, and 3 as you did for the Dallas example.)

Sitka, AK	_____	miles
Charlotte, NC	_____	miles
Honolulu, HI	_____	miles

3. Next, find the earthquake's epicenter, using the distances just obtained.
   a. First locate and mark the three seismic stations on the world map in Figure 16.4. (Refer to Figures 7.1 and 7.2 for additional information, if needed.)

   Sitka, AK: 57° N latitude, 135° W longitude
   Charlotte, NC: 35° N latitude, 81° W longitude
   Honolulu, HI: 21° N latitude, 158° W longitude

   b. Use a drafting compass to draw a circle around each seismic station. Make the radius equal to the distance between the station and the epicenter, as determined in Question 2. (Use the scale on Figure 16.4 to set this radius on your drafting compass.) The circles you draw should intersect at one point. This point is the epicenter. (If the three circles do not quite intersect at a single point, find a point that is equidistant from the three edges of the circles, and use this as the epicenter.) The location of the earthquake's epicenter is: Latitude _____ longitude _____

4. What is the origin time of the earthquake (at what time did it occur)?

5. At what time did the L-waves from this earthquake begin to arrive at the Sitka station?

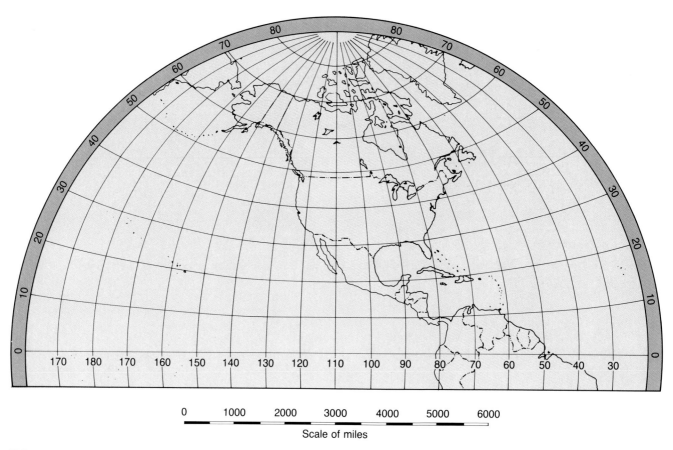

FIGURE 16.4 Map of Earth, for use in plotting data and locating the earthquake's epicenter.

EXERCISE SEVENTEEN

Earth's Magnetic Field: Reversals of Direction

James H. Shea
University of Wisconsin, Parkside

(Original version published in
Journal of Geological Education,
1986, 34:320–34.)

PURPOSE

This exercise focuses upon the direction of Earth's magnetic field and its history of reversals.

MATERIALS

Pencil, eraser, ruler, calculator.

INTRODUCTION

Earth's magnetic field is a **vector field**—it is composed of lines of force having both strength and direction. It is as though a large bar magnet resided within Earth, because Earth has both a magnetic north pole and a magnetic south pole. The lines of force arc out through space from the south magnetic pole and arc back into the north magnetic pole. These lines of force have two characteristics important in geology, inclination and declination:

- **Inclination** is the plunge of lines of magnetic force, or the angle at which they dip with respect to a horizontal plane.
- **Declination** was defined in Exercise Seven as the angle between the direction of true north (geographic north) and the direction of magnetic north. That is, in map-reading, we use declination specifically in reference to modern geography and Earth's modern magnetic field.

However, in studies of ancient magnetism (paleomagnetism), we use the term declination differently. Thus, in this exercise:

- **Declination** is the angle between the *present-day geographic north* direction and the *ancient magnetic north* direction (Figure 17.1).

The present north magnetic pole is located in the Arctic Islands of Canada. If you look upon Earth as a bar magnet, this location actually is a "south" magnetic pole, because it attracts the "north" pole of magnets and the "north-seeking pole" of compasses. Nevertheless, we will call the present magnetic pole in Canada the "north magnetic pole" in this exercise, because its location is in the geographic north.

Iron-rich minerals, such as magnetite (Fe_3O_4), can acquire and retain the directional signature of Earth's magnetic field at their time of formation. This ancient magnetism is called **paleomagnetism**. Magnetic minerals lose this magnetism if heated above their **Curie Point** of about 580°C. Only when they cool below the Curie point do heated minerals (i.e., those in igneous or metamorphic rocks) retain the signature of Earth's magnetic field for the time and place where they cooled. Sedimentary minerals, such as iron-bearing limonite ($Fe_2O_3 \cdot nH_2O$), commonly form well below the Curie point and therefore commonly exhibit magnetic signatures.

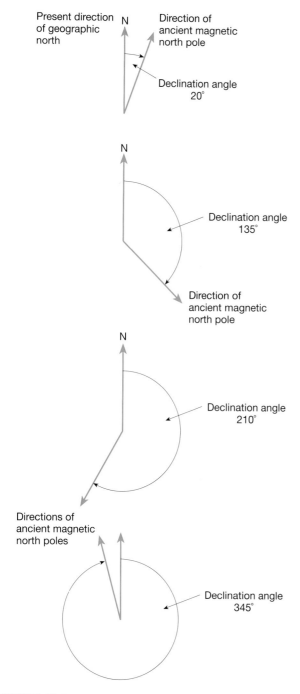

FIGURE 17.1 Relation among geographic north, compass direction, and declination angle, showing examples for each of the four quadrants. Note that declination always is measured in a clockwise direction, starting from geographic north.

QUESTIONS

Figure 17.2 lists magnetic declinations of some rock samples, mostly basaltic lavas. Figure 17.3 shows where these samples were obtained. Each of the 150 data sets represents the average magnetic declination of several samples from the particular locality.

1. Briefly examine the data in Figure 17.2. Are you able to detect any pattern(s) in the data? If so, describe the pattern(s) and their significance.

   The next step is to determine whether the magnetic declination depends on the *locality* where the rock samples were collected, or on *some other factor*. To begin, ask yourself: does the declination of Earth's magnetic field *today* vary with locality? Does the north pole of a compass point roughly toward geographic north, no matter where the compass is located on Earth's surface? Or, does the needle point generally north at some places, generally south at other places, and in various other directions at other places?

   You can check your answers in another way by looking at the data in Figure 17.2. Some localities (e.g., Argentina, California, Hawaii, Iceland, and Nunivak Island in Alaska) are represented by several data sets. Record the declinations at these localities in Figure 17.4.

2. Do all of the rock samples collected from Nunivak Island have approximately the same declination?

3. Do all of the rock samples from *any* one locality (from which a substantial number of samples were taken) have the same declination?

4. What is the total range of declinations in:
   a. Argentina?
   b. California?
   c. Hawaii?
   d. Iceland?
   e. Nunivak Island?

5. Is the amount of variation in declination at each locality substantially more, about equal to, or substantially less than the overall variation among all localities?

6. In general, do the data from rocks from any of these localities suggest that declination varies systematically with locality?

7. From your brief examination of the relationship of declination to geographic locality, what conclusion can you draw?

Use Figure 17.5 to tally the number of times that each declination value occurs within the basic data set of Figure 17.2. (Figure 17.5 does not include all possible declinations; do not concern yourself with this now.)

8. Explain why declinations of 359° on Figure 17.5 are shown adjacent to 0°, instead of at the end of the list, below 195°.

9. Did Figure 17.2 include any declinations that you could not record on Figure 17.5?

As you fill in Figure 17.5, it will become clear why only 62 of the 360 possible declination values were provided on the tally sheet. The number of times that each declination occurred is its *frequency* of occurrence. On Figure 17.6, plot the frequency of occurrence of each declination from Figure 17.5.

10. Describe the pattern revealed by your completed graph in Figure 17.6.

11. Keeping in mind the fact that your completed graph in Figure 17.6 shows only 56 of the 360 possible declinations, explain the significance of the pattern.

ADDITIONAL QUESTIONS

You have discovered that Earth's magnetic field has two basic states. In one state, the north-seeking point of a compass needle points toward or near to Earth's geographic North Pole (declination values of 347–359° and 0–14°). This kind of magnetic polarity is called *normal*, simply because this is the condition of Earth's magnetic field today. In the other state, the north-seeking point of a compass points at or near to Earth's geographic South Pole (declination values of 167–194°). This kind of magnetic polarity is called *reversed*.

This, however, creates a bit of a problem: Earth's magnetic field cannot simultaneously be both normal and reversed. If you are convinced that the rocks have preserved an accurate record of the state of the magnetic field (and all of the evidence suggests that they have), then there is only one logical conclusion: Earth's magnetic field has undergone periodic **reversals.** At times the field has been in a normal state, but at other times it has been in a reversed state.

Could continental drift be responsible for the reversed orientations in the paleomagnetic record? It might, except that large tectonic plates would have fairly *uniform* declination angles over major

continental areas. But, as you have seen, this is not the case.

The pattern of magnetic polarity that you discovered, and your conclusion about periodic reversals, is the same conclusion that was reached by early researchers of paleomagnetic phenomena. At the time, they also were perplexed, because the occurrence of magnetic polarity reversals seemed unlikely. To give you some idea of their reluctance to accept what the data revealed, the existence of polar reversals was first suggested in 1906, but almost 60 years went by before the scientific community finally accepted their occurrence, and began to work out details and make use of reversals in the mid-1960s!

Your next step is to determine whether magnetic polarity has varied in any systematic way through time. Figure 17.2 includes the ages of rocks in each of the 150 data sets. There are at least two ways to determine if an age pattern exists. You could copy each of the appropriate data sets onto cards, and then sort the cards by age (this also can be done with a computer). Or, you could plot the ages and polarities on a time line, which we will do here.

On Figure 17.7, plot only those samples from Figure 17.2 having ages of 2 my or younger ("my" stands for "megayears" or "million years"). Indicate the polarity of each datum by writing **N** (normal) or **R** (reversed) beside each age that you plot. Also write the sample number (No.) beside each age (very helpful should you need to check for mistakes). For example, your first entry should read R-1 (reversed polarity, sample 1) on the 1.52 my line.

After you have completed plotting the data on Figure 17.7, complete Figure 17.8 to show the times when Earth's magnetic field reversed itself. (A reversal means that the field reversed itself either from normal to reversed, or from reversed to normal.) Also refer to the caption for Figure 17.8 for essential instructions.

For each reversal, you will need to give both a maximum age (column 2) and a minimum age (column 3). For example, the data show that the field was reversed 0.73 my ago (based on a data set from New Mexico), but that some time before 0.69 my ago it had reversed itself to the normal polarity condition (based on a data set from California).

Note that you cannot tell from your data exactly when the reversal actually occurred within the 0.04 my (40,000 years) between the two limiting dates. This is the "total uncertainty" for that

No.	Degrees of declination	Locality	Age In my
1	179	Comoro Is.	1.52
2	2	Nunivak Is.	4.24
3	182	Iceland	3.78
4	354	Hawaii	3.18
5	349	New Zealand	2.58
6	355	Argentina	0.25
7	185	Madeira Is.	3.09
8	180	New Mexico	0.73
9	1	Society Is.	2.64
10	179	California	3.60
11	10	Iceland	3.18
12	2	Nunivak Is.	0.50
13	4	Australia	0.59
14	194	California	1.01
15	353	France	0.61
16	5	Canary Is.	3.85
17	184	Norfolk Is.	2.38
18	177	Mauritius Is.	2.01
19	180	Argentina	3.57
20	1	Society Is.	0.53
21	0	Pribilof Is.	4.18
22	181	Argentina	3.59
23	180	California	1.16
24	179	Canary Is.	4.36
25	179	Sicily	2.93
26	182	Mauritius Is.	3.08
27	178	Iceland	4.32
28	358	Reunion Is.	4.41
29	359	California	3.35
30	181	California	3.66
31	183	New Mexico	0.75
32	359	Nunivak Is.	1.70
33	177	Argentina	1.91
34	5	Nunivak Is.	0.03
35	178	New Mexico	4.34
36	182	Madeira Is.	1.07
37	181	Hawaii	2.23
38	359	Philippine Is.	2.57
39	180	Norfolk Is.	1.67
40	350	Iceland	1.67
41	0	Australia	4.46
42	180	Iceland	2.95
43	179	Norfolk Is.	2.41
44	174	Madeira Is.	1.04
45	176	Japan	1.46
46	178	Comoro Is.	3.75
47	180	Reunion Is.	1.97
48	178	Canary Is.	0.90
49	0	Society Is.	3.26
50	176	California	3.11
51	180	Australia	2.31
52	186	California	3.57
53	179	Galapagos Is.	4.09
54	4	California	0.69
55	357	Society Is.	2.57
56	182	Argentina	3.64
57	179	Pribilof Is.	1.91
58	1	Reunion Is.	2.01
59	2	Canary Is.	3.85
60	183	Nevada	3.71
61	181	Argentina	1.47
62	181	New Mexico	1.12
63	180	Iceland	3.54
64	356	Reunion Is.	0.22
65	3	Libya	0.42
66	181	Canary Is.	0.85
67	168	Society Is.	0.85
68	357	Galapagos Is.	0.31
69	183	France	1.20
70	347	Galapagos Is.	0.09
71	177	Hawaii	2.27
72	358	Pribilof Is.	0.13
73	167	Canary Is.	3.58
74	0	Argentina	2.63
75	14	Argentina	1.71
76	358	Hawaii	3.38
77	188	Idaho	1.40
78	359	Society Is.	3.92
79	2	France	0.96
80	357	Mauritius Is.	2.80
81	192	Hawaii	1.35
82	186	Australia	3.65
83	178	Iceland	2.48
84	183	Pribilof Is.	1.64
85	181	Australia	0.83
86	0	Norfolk Is.	2.50
87	1	Canary Is.	0.54
88	1	Nunivak Is.	3.24
89	173	Norfolk Is.	2.42
90	175	California	2.23
91	350	Tanzania	1.79
92	1	California	0.08
93	0	Argentina	0.17
94	357	New Mexico	0.55
95	181	Tanzania	2.08
96	182	Reunion Is.	1.05
97	356	California	4.48
98	0	Canary Is.	0.18
99	170	Nunivak Is.	3.40
100	175	New Mexico	4.49
101	178	Madeira Is.	0.75
102	358	Reunion Is.	2.14
103	180	Nunivak Is.	0.86
104	3	California	0.48
105	359	Cocos Is.	2.14
106	180	New Mexico	1.40
107	178	Cocos Is.	1.98
108	177	Victoria, Aust.	4.02
109	356	Argentina	3.03
110	355	Hawaii	0.14
111	184	New Mexico	1.06
112	0	Philippine Is.	2.87
113	359	Hawaii	2.90
114	5	Australia	3.21

No.	Degrees of declination	Locality	Age In my	No.	Degrees of declination	Locality	Age In my
115	358	Society Is.	0.43	133	0	California	3.40
116	352	Nunivak Is.	0.93	134	172	Iceland	1.36
117	11	California	2.52	135	358	Iceland	3.95
118	183	Australia	2.26	136	177	Nevada	3.43
119	3	Nunivak Is.	3.36	137	182	Norfolk Is.	2.46
120	186	Nunivak Is.	1.58	138	8	Hawaii	4.45
121	184	California	1.93	139	185	California	4.31
122	179	Japan	1.65	140	180	Society Is.	1.55
123	190	Iceland	1.64	141	4	Nunivak Is.	4.14
124	182	Argentina	3.78	142	0	Mauritius Is.	0.48
125	0	Hawaii	3.36	143	180	Mauritius Is.	3.06
126	181	Norfolk Is.	3.11	144	187	Canary Is.	2.26
127	193	California	4.08	145	180	Japan	3.99
128	175	Nevada	3.59	146	359	New Mexico	0.45
129	180	Japan	1.25	147	173	Canary Is.	1.60
130	3	California	4.42	148	354	Reunion Is.	0.11
131	179	Argentina	1.20	149	6	Pribilof Is.	1.83
132	2	Madeira Is.	1.68	150	179	Mauritius Is.	3.42

FIGURE 17.2 Magnetic declinations of rock formations worldwide. Most were measured from basaltic lava flows. In table heading, my = age in million years. (Polarity and age data from Manikinen, E. A., and Dalrymple, G. B., 1978, *Journal of Physical Research* 84:615–26)

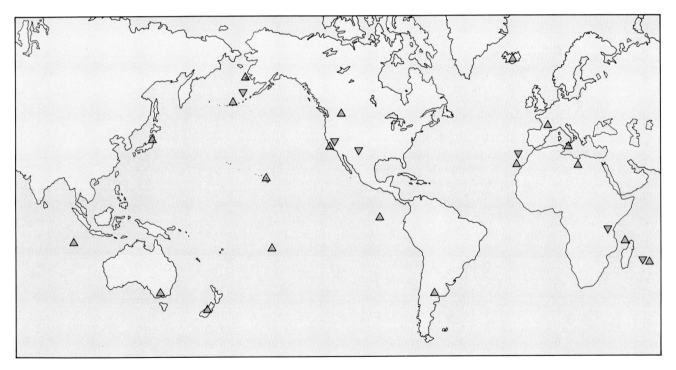

FIGURE 17.3 Map showing approximate localities from which samples were collected for the data in Figure 17.2. Note global distribution.

No.	Locality	Declination	No.	Locality	Declination
———	California	—————————————	———	Iceland	—————————————
———	California	—————————————	———	Iceland	—————————————
———	California	—————————————	———	Iceland	—————————————
———	California	—————————————	———	Iceland	—————————————
———	California	—————————————	———	Iceland	—————————————
———	California	—————————————	———	Iceland	—————————————
———	California	—————————————	———	Iceland	—————————————
———	California	—————————————	———	Iceland	—————————————
———	California	—————————————	———	Iceland	—————————————
———	California	—————————————	———	Iceland	—————————————
———	California	—————————————	———	Hawaii	—————————————
———	California	—————————————	———	Hawaii	—————————————
———	California	—————————————	———	Hawaii	—————————————
———	California	—————————————	———	Hawaii	—————————————
———	California	—————————————	———	Hawaii	—————————————
———	California	—————————————	———	Hawaii	—————————————
———	California	—————————————	———	Hawaii	—————————————
———	California	—————————————	———	Hawaii	—————————————
———	Argentina	—————————————	———	Hawaii	—————————————
———	Argentina	—————————————	———	Nunivak	—————————————
———	Argentina	—————————————	———	Nunivak	—————————————
———	Argentina	—————————————	———	Nunivak	—————————————
———	Argentina	—————————————	———	Nunivak	—————————————
———	Argentina	—————————————	———	Nunivak	—————————————
———	Argentina	—————————————	———	Nunivak	—————————————
———	Argentina	—————————————	———	Nunivak	—————————————
———	Argentina	—————————————	———	Nunivak	—————————————
———	Argentina	—————————————	———	Nunivak	—————————————
———	Argentina	—————————————	———	Nunivak	—————————————
———	Argentina	—————————————	———	Nunivak	—————————————

FIGURE 17.4 Data sheet for determining whether declination varies systematically with locality. Complete the sheet by entering the appropriate numbers from Figure 17.2.

particular reversal, and it has been recorded in the fourth column of Figure 17.8. Reversals are never instantaneous; they generally take about 5000 years (0.005 my) to complete. The uncertainty, however, generally is greater than this.

In the next column (fifth) of Figure 17.8, write your best estimate of the age of each reversal. The best estimate in each case is halfway between the maximum and minimum ages, plus or minus half of the total uncertainty.

Next, complete the last column in Figure 17.8 by calculating the length of the various magnetic polarity intervals between reversals. For example, the duration of the most recent period of reversed polarity is the difference between the ages of the reversals that bound that interval (0.915 my −

0.710 my = 205,000 years). *Write the durations in years, rather than in millions of years.*

The first three rows of Figure 17.8 have been completed to assist you in filling out the remainder of the chart. After you have completed your polar-reversal time scale for the last two million years, compare it to the one in your textbook.

12. Are the two time scales the same?

13. If not, account for any differences.

14. Is there any regularity to the timing of the magnetic reversals? Are all of the durations about equal?

15. How long was the shortest interval of constant magnetic polarity between any two reversals?

345 ———————	165 ———————
346 ———————	166 ———————
347 ———————	167 ———————
348 ———————	168 ———————
349 ———————	169 ———————
350 ———————	170 ———————
351 ———————	171 ———————
352 ———————	172 ———————
353 ———————	173 ———————
354 ———————	174 ———————
355 ———————	175 ———————
356 ———————	176 ———————
357 ———————	177 ———————
358 ———————	178 ———————
359 ———————	179 ———————
0 ———————	180 ———————
1 ———————	181 ———————
2 ———————	182 ———————
3 ———————	183 ———————
4 ———————	184 ———————
5 ———————	185 ———————
6 ———————	186 ———————
7 ———————	187 ———————
8 ———————	188 ———————
9 ———————	189 ———————
10 ———————	190 ———————
11 ———————	191 ———————
12 ———————	192 ———————
13 ———————	193 ———————
14 ———————	194 ———————
15 ———————	195 ———————

FIGURE 17.5 Tally sheet for declinations. Numbers shown are in degrees.

16. How long was the longest interval between reversals?

17. Is it possible that the data with which you have worked have caused you to miss any reversals? Explain.

18. Explain the fact that at 1.67 my there are conflicting data as to magnetic polarity. Data set number 40 (from Iceland) suggests that Earth's magnetic field was normal at that time, whereas data set number 39 (from Norfolk Island) indicates that the field was reversed.

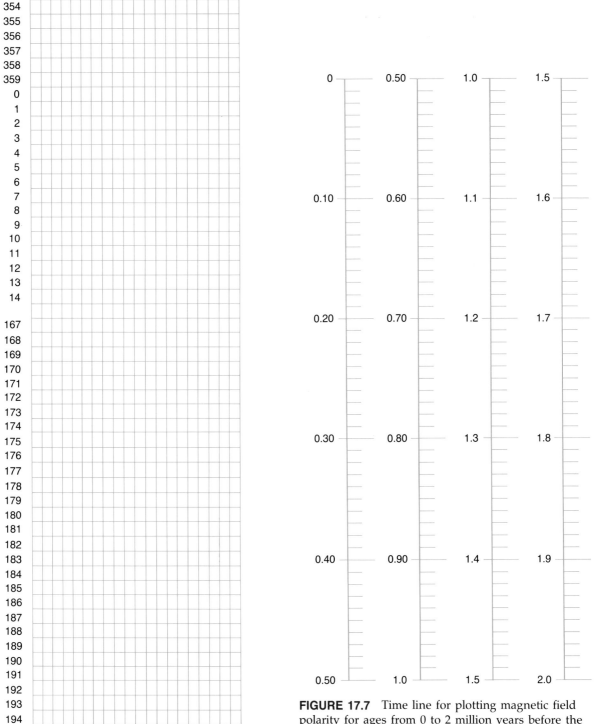

FIGURE 17.6 Grid for plotting declination frequencies.

FIGURE 17.7 Time line for plotting magnetic field polarity for ages from 0 to 2 million years before the present. (Units are Ma, or millions of years before the present.)

Reversal number	Max. age	Min. age	Total uncertainty	Best estimate	Duration in years (polarity)
	0	0	0	0	
1	0.73	0.69	0.04	0.710 ± 0.02	710,000 (N)
2	0.93	0.90	0.03	0.915 ± 0.015	205,000 (R)
3	____	____	____	____	____
4	____	____	____	____	____
5	____	____	____	____	____
6	____	____	____	____	____
7	____	____	____	____	____
8	____	____	____	____	____
9	____	____	____	____	____
10	____	____	____	____	____
11	____	____	____	____	____
12	____	____	____	____	____
13	____	____	____	____	____
14	____	____	____	____	____
15	____	____	____	____	____
16	____	____	____	____	____
17	____	____	____	____	____
18	____	____	____	____	____
19	____	____	____	____	____
20	____	____	____	____	____
21	____	____	____	____	____

FIGURE 17.8 Maximum and minimum age estimates for magnetic polarity reversals, total uncertainty for ages, best estimate of ages, and durations of magnetic polarity intervals during the past 2.0 million years. Begin with the youngest reversal at the top of the figure and work in millions of years. The *total uncertainty* is the difference between the maximum and minimum ages. The *best estimate* of the age is halfway between the maximum and minimum, plus-or-minus half of the uncertainty. The *duration in years* is the length of the polarity interval following the reversal. Thus, for *Reversal Number 1*, the duration of the current magnetic polarity interval is 0.710 ± 0.02 million years. (The numbers for the most recent two intervals are provided to guide you in completing the chart.)

EXERCISE EIGHTEEN

Magnetic Intensity Anomalies and Seafloor Spreading

James H. Shea
University of Wisconsin, Parkside

(Original version published in Journal of Geological Education, 1988, 36:290–305.)

PURPOSE

This exercise shows you the crucial role played by magnetic-intensity measurements in confirming the Vine-Matthews-Morley hypothesis, which led to the plate tectonics theory.

MATERIALS

Pencil, eraser, several sheets of graph paper (10 divisions to the inch by 10 divisions to the inch), ruler, calculator.

INTRODUCTION

After World War II, the pace of research accelerated greatly on Earth magnetism. For example, in England, much effort was devoted to measuring the magnetism of individual rock samples of various ages from various localities. The goal was to determine the location of the magnetic poles over the course of geologic time. This work involved determining the orientation of the **paleomagnetic fields** preserved in rocks from the time they were formed.

By about 1955, this work began to support the conclusions of Alfred Wegener, Frank Taylor, and Alexander Du Toit regarding continental drift. By the early 1960s, this work also strongly suggested that Earth's magnetic field had reversed its polarity sporadically through time.

Another line of research on magnetism involved towing a magnetometer behind oceanographic research vessels to measure variations of magnetic field *intensity* (strength) from place to place. The strength of Earth's magnetic field is relatively low, and ranges between about 30 microteslas at the equator and about 50 microteslas at the poles. (For comparison, small magnets used to hold reminder notes to refrigerator doors have a surface intensity of about 50,000 microteslas, about 1000 times that of Earth's field.

The **tesla** is a unit of magnetic field strength, named after Croatian inventor Nikola Tesla, who emigrated to the United States in 1884 and made many contributions in electricity, magnetism, and radio transmission. A **microtesla** is a millionth of a tesla, and a **nanotesla** is a billionth of a tesla.

Magnetic Anomalies

Magnetic anomalies are deviations from the average magnetic intensity in a given area. For example, in the area where magnetic-intensity profiles were taken for this exercise, the magnetic intensity ranges from 44,000 to 50,000 nanoteslas. The anomalies range over approximately ±800 nanoteslas, less than 2% of the total intensity.

Magnetic-intensity data obtained from the ocean floors were for some years more puzzling than useful. The first **magnetic profiles** (lines or ships' tracks along which magnetic intensity is measured) were made in the late 1940s. Regardless of where they were made, all showed the same general pattern: alternating peaks of relatively high intensity **(positive anomalies)** and valleys of relatively low intensity **(negative anomalies)**—see Figure 18.1.

Unfortunately, the positive and negative magnetic anomalies seemed to bear no relation to any known topographic or structural aspect of the oceanic crust. Nor did the positive and negative anomalies of one profile seem to be related to those of any other profile. In fact, the value of magnetic-intensity studies at that time was in such low repute that a golden opportunity very nearly was missed!

In 1955, the U.S. Coast and Geodetic Survey vessel, *Pioneer*, was scheduled to begin an oceanographic survey off the west coast of the United States. The survey involved cruising a series of precisely located east-west lines, spaced 8 km apart (5 miles), and extending from as near the shoreline as possible out to 550 km from the shore (342 miles). However, when Henry Menard of Scripps Institute of Oceanography suggested that a magnetic survey could be made simultaneously with the other work, officials balked. Fortunately, Menard's view prevailed, and scientists from Scripps got on board and had the magnetometer towed behind the ship.

The critical difference between the profiles made on the *Pioneer* survey and those done earlier was that the new survey provided a long series of closely spaced profiles. By contrast, earlier profiles had been made as opportunities presented themselves in widely separated geographic areas.

Almost immediately, the new survey began to yield results. The researchers realized they could match positive and negative anomaly peaks on adjacent profiles and trace patterns of magnetic anomalies for hundreds of kilometers. Nothing like this pattern of striped magnetic anomalies, called **paleomagnetic striping,** had been seen before. Its origin would remain a complete mystery for years.

In 1963, however, a solution to the mystery was proposed. A doctoral candidate at Cambridge University in England (Fred Vine) and his dissertation advisor (Drummond Matthews), and—independently—a Canadian geologist (Lawrence Morley) suggested that the magnetic anomalies resulted from interaction of two phenomena: seafloor spreading and reversals of Earth's magnetic field. The existence of both phenomena was a matter of some disagreement among scientists.

Polar-Reversal Time Scale

As Vine, Matthews, and Morley pondered magnetic anomalies, geologists A. Cox, R. B. Doell, and G. B. Dalrymple at the U.S. Geological Survey in Menlo Park, California, were preparing to publish the first polar-reversal time scale. Their time scale showed that Earth's magnetic field has undergone sporadic **reversals**—that is, the north and south magnetic poles periodically have exchanged positions, as explained in Exercise Seventeen. Reversals generally occur over about 5000 years, and intervals of constant polarity between reversals are extremely variable, ranging from about 20,000 to 730,000 years.

During times of *normal* polarity, the north-seeking needle of a compass points in the general direction of the geographic North Pole. During times of *reversed* polarity, the north-seeking needle of a compass would point in the general direction of the geographic South Pole. *A reversal occurs whenever Earth's field changes from normal to reversed, or from reversed to normal.*

The other aspect of the Vine-Matthews-Morley (VMM) hypothesis involved a then-revolutionary idea about the behavior of oceanic crust. In 1960, H. H. Hess of Princeton University suggested that the seafloor spreads apart at oceanic ridges and moves away from oceanic ridges like a giant conveyor belt, as new oceanic crust is created at ridges. As the oceanic crust moves, it carries the continents with it. Hess's idea was thus a variant of the theory of continental drift, and it received little support from the scientific community until about 1966.

The VMM hypothesis proposed that the magnetic anomalies formed in this way: At the oceanic ridges, as new minerals (notably magnetite) in basalts cool below their Curie temperatures, their magnetic fields align themselves with Earth's magnetic field at that time. (The **Curie temperature** of a mineral is the temperature *below which* it becomes magnetic—about 580°C—and aligns itself with Earth's magnetic field.)

If the field is in the reversed state at that time, then the magnetism will be aligned with the north-seeking poles generally oriented toward geographic south. All magnetic minerals formed during that period of reversed polarity will have that orientation. These rocks thus form a band along the oceanic ridge crest with a width that is directly related to the length of time the field remains in a reversed state, and to the rate at which seafloor spreading occurs.

Later, when Earth's field undergoes a reversal to normal polarity, and new magnetic minerals in new basalt cool below their Curie temperatures, their magnetism will align itself so that the north-seeking poles are pointed generally toward the north. Then, as time passes, along the ridge crest where new oceanic crust is forming, the band of such rocks will gradually widen as seafloor spreading continues. This will continue until another reversal occurs.

At any given time, except immediately after a reversal, the magnetic fields of rocks near the crest of oceanic ridges will be aligned so that they add to, and slightly strengthen, the magnetic fields above them. This additive effect happens because they have aligned themselves with the existing field. Thus, a positive anomaly is produced above the ridge crest.

Further out on either side of the ridge, however, the rocks were formed during the previous polarity state. Thus the subtractive effect tends to slightly weaken the overall magnetic field above them, producing a negative anomaly. Overall, the result is a series of linear magnetic anomalies, parallel to the ridge.

Unfortunately, at the time that Vine, Matthews, and Morley proposed their hypothesis, they apparently did not know that a magnetic field survey of the Red Sea was readily available to test their idea. It was known at the time that an oceanic ridge runs down the center of the Red Sea, and a published map of the magnetic pattern clearly shows a series of linear anomalies paralleling the ridge, exactly as their hypothesis predicts.

Furthermore, although we now know of oceanic-ridge segments off the Oregon and Washington coast, where the *Pioneer* survey was made, those segments were unknown at that time. Thus, the VMM hypothesis was not tested until 1965–1966 in the way that you will be testing it in this exercise.

A proper test had to wait, not only until the necessary profiles became available, but also until all reversals of the polar-reversal time scale became known for the last 4.5 million years. These conditions were met in 1965–1966, and the VMM hypothesis and seafloor spreading hypothesis were readily accepted. The theory of plate tectonics followed in 1967–1968.

TESTING THE VINE-MATTHEWS-MORLEY (VMM) HYPOTHESIS

Fortunately, testing the VMM hypothesis can be undertaken in steps. The test itself gives you new skills which you can adapt to other situations. The procedure also demonstrates how predictions made from scientific hypotheses can be used to test the validity of the hypotheses.

The VMM hypothesis makes a number of predictions about the nature of magnetic profiles. You will be testing four of them:

Prediction 1: The magnetic-anomaly pattern generally is symmetrical about the ridge, as located by topography.

Prediction 2: Magnetic-anomaly profiles can be *correlated* (matched) from place to place worldwide.

Prediction 3: Magnetic-anomaly profiles can be correlated with the polar-reversal time scale, determined from lava flows on the land.

Prediction 4: The spreading rates determined from the magnetic-anomaly profiles will approximate those required by the theory of continental drift.

QUESTIONS

This exercise is based on four magnetic profiles (Figures 18.1, 18.2, 18.3, 18.6). They were produced from raw data obtained from the National Geophysical Data Center in Boulder, Colorado. We selected these profiles based on descriptions and other versions of them made by W. C. Pitman III, J. R. Heirtzler, and E. M. Herron in 1966 and 1968.

Figure 18.1 shows bathymetric and magnetic-anomaly profiles across the Pacific-Antarctic Ridge. The ridge crest shows clearly on the bathymetric profile, and the broad central positive anomaly shows well on the magnetic-anomaly profile.

1. Visually compare the profile on one side of the ridge with that on the other side of the ridge, peak for peak and valley for valley. What does your visual comparison suggest about their similarity?

To help you make comparisons, we have manipulated the profile as follows: First, we enlarged the *left* side of Figure 18.1, *reversed* it from right to left, and reproduce it in Figure 18.2. Then we enlarged the *right* side of Figure 18.1 and reproduce it in Figure 18.3.

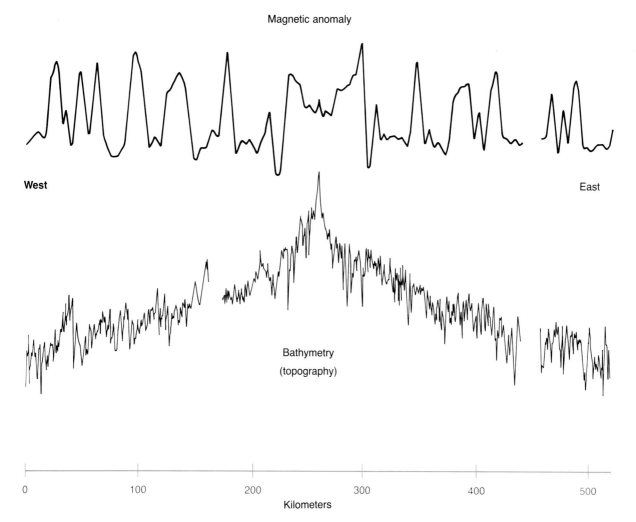

Magnetic anomaly

West   East

Bathymetry
(topography)

0   100   200   300   400   500
Kilometers

FIGURE 18.1 Magnetic anomaly (upper plot) and bathymetry (lower plot) across the Pacific-Antarctic Ridge, centered in the South Pacific Ocean at 51.6° S latitude, 118.1° W longitude. *Bathymetric profile:* the pronounced peak is the ridge crest. The seafloor topography appears very rough because the vertical dimension is exaggerated about 150 times, compared to the horizontal dimension. *Magnetic anomaly:* the vertical axis shows the difference between the average magnetic field intensity and the total field intensity. Thus, the peaks and troughs of the curve show incidents of magnetic anomaly. Note the broad "high," or positive anomaly, roughly centered at the bathymetric ridge crest.

Compare Figures 18.2 and 18.3. Note peak **B** on both figures. This peak corresponds between the two profiles, and so we can say that it is correlative. Try to match the two profiles visually, peak for peak and valley for valley.

2. Do the two profiles match, peak for peak and valley for valley? Describe the quality of correlation (correspondence between the two graphs), or the lack of it. Note other potential correlative points **A, C, D,** and **E** on Figure 18.2. We have labeled these to help you start matching the points and labeling them. Label as many correlative points as you can.

Then, measure the distance of each point from the ridge. Do so on both profiles, using the scales provided. Record the distances and letters on Figure 18.4. This already has been done for Point **B.**

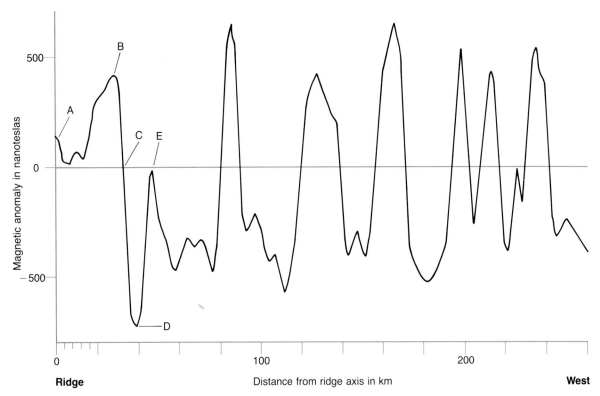

FIGURE 18.2 Profile of magnetic anomaly on the *west* side of the Pacific-Antarctic Ridge, starting at the crest (51.6° S, 118.1° W). This is the west half of the profile from Figure 18.1. To simplify comparison to other profiles, we have reversed it from left to right. Thus, the ridge axis now is to the *left*. Points **A, B, C, D,** and **E** you will be correlating with their equivalents on two other profiles (Figures 18.3 and 18.6). Point **C** records a reversal, from reversed polarity to normal.

Next, using graph paper with ten divisions to the inch, prepare a graph:

- Along the *X axis* (horizontal), plot the distances from the ridge to anomalies on the *west* side (summarized in Figure 18.4, second column).
- Along the *Y axis* (vertical), plot the distances from the ridge to anomalies on the *east* side (summarized in Figure 18.4, third column).

For example, Figure 18.5 shows how Point **B** is plotted on such a graph.

After plotting all points, use a straight edge (like a ruler) to draw a straight line through the origin of the graph (the 0,0 point), so that the line also passes through—or as close to—as many points as possible. This is called a **line-of-best-fit.**

3. Describe the relationship of the points to the line-of-best-fit.

4. VMM Prediction 1 states that the magnetic-anomaly pattern generally will be symmetrical about the ridge. Is this prediction verified? Explain. (Note: If the line you drew passes close to all of the points, then the two profiles correlate or match, and the pattern is symmetrical about the ridge.)

A second prediction made by the VMM hypothesis is that you should be able to correlate magnetic profiles from locality to locality. In fact, distance should make little difference. As magnetic reversals are global by nature, you should be able to correlate profiles from any part of the world to profiles from any other part of the world. You will make a more limited test.

Figure 18.6 is another magnetic profile from the south Pacific. It meets the Pacific-Antarctic Ridge about 560 km (350 miles) from where the profiles in Figures 18.2 and 18.3 meet the ridge. Compare the profile in Figure 18.2 with the profile in Figure 18.6.

5. Do the profiles correlate visually?

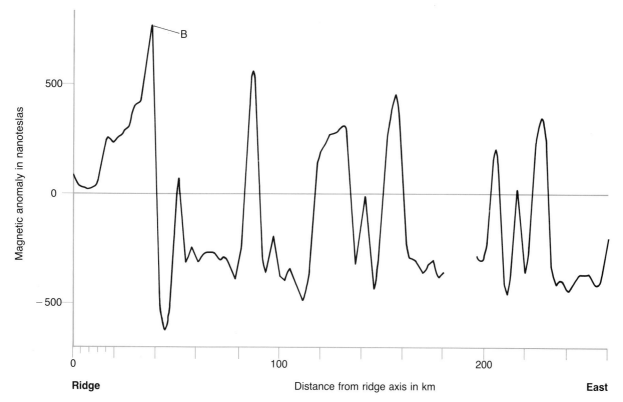

FIGURE 18.3 Profile of magnetic anomaly on the *east* side of the Pacific-Antarctic Ridge, starting at the crest (51.6° S latitude, 118.1° W longitude).

As before, match corresponding points on Figures 18.2 and 18.6. If you can, label any additional points between these two figures that you could not match between Figures 18.2 and 18.3 (there definitely are some). Then, measure the corresponding distances for Figure 18.6, and complete Figure 18.4 (fourth column). Finally, plot the same type of graph for Figures 18.2 and 18.6 that you did for Figures 18.2 and 18.3.

6. Do the points mostly plot close to a line-of-best-fit?

7. Can magnetic profiles be correlated from locality to locality, as predicted by the VMM hypothesis?

The crucial test of the VMM hypothesis is *whether the magnetic profiles can be correlated with the polar-reversal time scale* that was developed on the basis of data from lava flows on the land (Prediction 3). Figure 18.7 is a polar-reversal time scale covering the past 4.5 million years. See if you can correlate Figure 18.6 with this time scale, matching the positive magnetic anomalies with the times of

normal polarity and the negative anomalies with the times of reversed polarity.

Note that some peaks on the magnetic profile—those corresponding to relatively short intervals of normal polarity—*do not rise above the zero line.* This is not surprising, because the effect of a narrow band of normally polarized rock on the strength of the local magnetic field may be overridden by the effect of wide bands of reversely polarized rock on each side of it.

8. Does the polar-reversal time scale correlate with the magnetic profile? Describe the quality of the correlation or the lack of it.

Next, complete Figure 18.4 by filling in the "Age in Ma" column from the polar-reversal time scale (Figure 18.7). You will not be able to match every point you labeled on Figure 18.2 with a point on the polar-reversal time scale. Enter ages in Figure 18.7 only for the distances where the anomaly line on the profile crosses the zero line. These points clearly correspond to the times when reversals occurred.

FIGURE 18.4 Chart of equivalent points from Figures 18.2, 18.3, and 18.6, and the polar-reversal time scale (Figure 18.7). First column: write labels you choose for equivalent points. Next three columns: enter distances you measured for equivalent points from Figures 18.2, 18.3, and 18.6. Last column: write ages of equivalent points from polar-reversal time scale (Figure 18.7). (Note: You will not have ages for every point, only for those where the profile line crosses the 0 line. Ma = millions of years before the present.)

Point	Distance from ridge in km			Age in Ma
	Fig. 18.2 (west)	Fig. 18.3 (east)	Fig. 18.6	
A				0
B	27	37	30	—
C				0.73
D				—
E				—

FIGURE 18.5 Example of plotting onto a single graph the distances of equivalent points from two magnetic profiles. (1) In Figure 18.2, measure the distance from the ridge axis to point **B,** about 27 km. (2) Find 27 km on the horizontal axis here, and extend a vertical dashed line up from that point. (3) In Figure 18.3, measure the distance from the ridge axis to point **B,** about 37 km. Find 37 km on the vertical axis here, and extend a horizontal dashed line from that point. Where these two dashed lines intersect marks the location of point **B** on the graph.

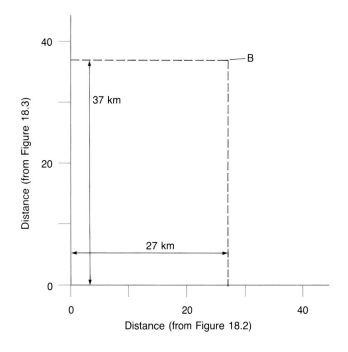

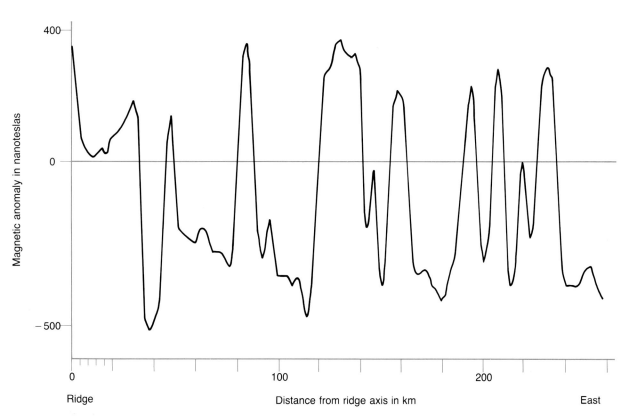

FIGURE 18.6 Profile of magnetic intensity on the east side of the Pacific-Antarctic Ridge, starting at 47.7° S latitude, 113.1° W longitude. The magnetic anomaly (vertical axis) is the difference between the average magnetic field intensity and the total field intensity. The total magnetic field intensity in the area is approximately 50 microteslas.

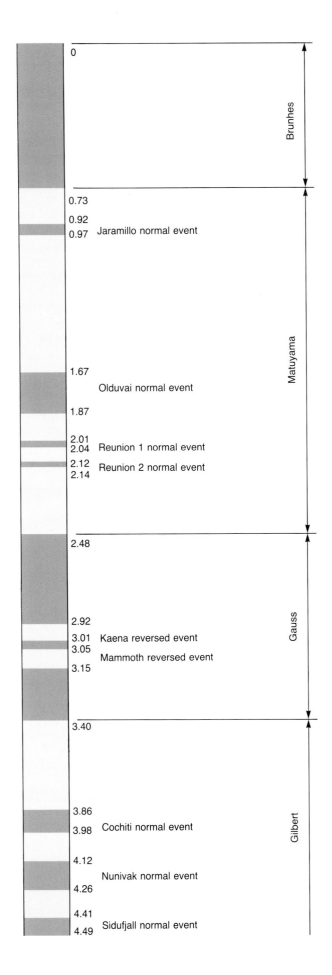

FIGURE 18.7 Polar-reversal time scale for the past 4.5 million years. This is the time period covered by the original scale developed in the 1960s. Times of normal polarity are green; times of reversed polarity are yellow. A change from green to yellow, or yellow to green, marks when a reversal occurred. Note that the pattern is irregular: the periods of constant polarity vary in duration. Numerals are in Ma, or millions of years before the present. (Data from Harland, W. B., and others, 1982, *A Geologic Time Scale*, Cambridge Univ. Press, Fig. 4.2 and Table 4.3.)

Now prepare a graph of distance from the ridge crest for Figure 18.2 (horizontal axis) with age as determined from the polar-reversal time scale (vertical axis). There will be many fewer points on this graph than on previous ones. After you have plotted the points, draw a line-of-best-fit that runs through the origin.

9. Describe the fit of the line-of-best-fit with the plotted points. What conclusion can you draw, based on your graph?

Seafloor Spreading Rates

Another useful aspect of magnetic anomalies is that they provide a way to determine the *rates* at which seafloor spreading has occurred, and the way in which rates have varied, both from place to place and through time. The rates are calculated by dividing the distance from the ridge of a particular reversal by the age of that reversal. For example, if a reversal is located 250 km from the ridge, and if its age is 5 million years, then the spreading rate during that time must have averaged 5 cm per year (250,000 m ÷ 5,000,000 years = 0.05 m, or 5 cm per year).

Determination of spreading rates is another check on the validity of the VMM hypothesis. The hypothesis holds that the spreading rates from oceanic ridges also are the drift rates for the continents. The rates of continental drift are known, from other evidence, to be a few centimeters per year. If the spreading rates differ greatly from the known continental-drift rates, then the hypothesis becomes questionable. Of course, the continental-drift rates could be in error, but that seems unlikely. Therefore, determination of the seafloor spreading rates is important.

Using the data from Figure 18.2 and the ages from the polar-reversal time scale, calculate the rate at which spreading has occurred on that section of ridge. Before selecting a reversal for this purpose, think about which reversal would be the best choice:

10. Should you choose a reversal recorded near the ridge, or one farther away? What label will you put on the reversal you choose? Use the distance and age recorded in Figure 18.4 for the reversal you choose to calculate the spreading rate.

11. What has the spreading rate averaged (in cm per year) during the time that has elapsed since the occurrence of the particular reversal you chose? (Show your work.)

Note that the spreading rate you determined actually is a *spreading half-rate.* Based on your earlier correlations, it is clear that the other side of the ridge spread at very nearly the same rate, so the *total spreading rate* for this section of ridge has been about twice the rate that you have just calculated.

12. Is the total spreading rate you calculated consistent with the aforementioned rates of continental drift determined on the basis of other evidence?

13. Is your spreading rate consistent with the rates shown on the map of relative plate motions in Figure 1.14 (showing full spreading rates)?

ADDITIONAL QUESTIONS

When the original polar-reversal time scale was worked out, it extended back only about 4.5 million years, because the accuracy of the dating method decreases with increasing age. The method could not separate even fairly long polarity intervals from one another if they were older than 4.5 million years. The magnetic anomalies, however, provide a solution to this problem.

Note that Figure 18.2 has a very distinct peak that lies just beyond the last reversal that you were able to correlate with the polar-reversal time scale. On Figure 18.4, record the distances of the points where the intensity curve crosses the 0 line on the

profile for that peak (both as the intensity curve rises and as it falls). Use those distances and the spreading rate that you just determined to calculate the ages of those two reversals.

14. What are the ages of those two reversals? (Show your work.)

What you have just done is to extend the polar-reversal time scale by using the magnetic profile and by assuming that the spreading rate was constant so far back in time. You must undertake such extrapolation with great care and with a full understanding that you are exceeding the limits of control. This is exactly how the rather short polar-reversal time scale, based on radiometric dating of solidified lava flows, was extended back beyond 4.5 million years, to about 165 million years (Jurassic Period). In this instance, fossils from ocean sediments cored up by the Deep Sea Drilling Project served as a check on the method, and were used to modify the results of straight-line extrapolation.

15. Discuss the hypothesis that the magnetic peaks and valleys are simply random magnetic "noise" or experimental error, and that they have no meaning in terms of tectonics. Which hypothesis, "magnetic noise" or "seafloor spreading," do you feel is the better interpretation of the data? Explain your answer.

SUMMARY

Whenever detailed predictions are borne out by data, there is little doubt that the original hypothesis has been confirmed. This is not to say that it has been "proven" in any rigorous sense. It merely has passed the test of observation in this instance. After a scientific hypothesis has passed a number of tests of this sort, it becomes a theory. By now, of course, the hypothesis of seafloor spreading and the VMM hypothesis have been incorporated into the more comprehensive "theory" of plate tectonics.

EXERCISE NINETEEN

Lunar Processes and History

Charles P. Walters
Kansas State University

PURPOSE

In this exercise you will examine rocks and common features of the Moon, and discuss their possible origins. We relate the *absolute* ages of lunar samples obtained by Apollo astronauts to the *relative* age relationships of lunar features, so that you can deduce the general—and fascinating—history of the Moon.

MATERIALS

Ruler, pencil, eraser.

INTRODUCTION

Earth's nearest neighbor in space, and its only natural satellite, is the Moon. It is not surprising that scientists long have sought answers to questions regarding the Moon's surface features and geologic history.

Most observations of the Moon have been made telescopically. Galileo viewed the Moon through a telescope for the first time in 1610 and noted types of surface features. From then until 1957, most observations of the Moon were made telescopically. Since then, other data about the Moon have been obtained by unmanned, remote-

controlled spacecraft, including the Russian *Luna 16* (1970) and *Luna 20* (1972), which returned with lunar samples.

The first people to land on the Moon, collect samples, and make direct observations were American *Apollo 11* astronauts Neil Armstrong and Michael Collins, on July 21, 1969. Similar Apollo landings were made later that year (*Apollo 12*), in 1971 (*Apollo 14, 15*), and in 1972 (*Apollo 16, 17*). Many direct observations about the Moon were made, instruments were stationed for long-term data collection, and samples of lunar rock materials were returned to Earth.

Some of these samples have been analyzed to obtain their absolute ages, allowing space scientists and geologists to better understand the chronology of events on the Moon. Other aspects have been analyzed, allowing us to piece together the Moon's geologic history. Nevertheless, many of the hypotheses and models used to explain lunar features remain as inferences, based on their similarity to igneous features or impact structures observed on Earth.

LUNAR FEATURES

The Moon has essentially no atmosphere, so there is no water or wind to produce surface features. Instead, the surface has been shaped mainly by

250

ancient volcanic processes (an internal cause) and impact cratering (an external cause). Seismic studies, based on data from seismographs placed on the Moon by Apollo astronauts, indicate that the Moon is solid (i.e., it has no liquid interior portions like Earth) and presently has no igneous activity. Earthquakes do occur, however, probably as fractured rocks respond to gravity and the extreme temperature changes caused by diurnal cycles of solar heating in the absence of an atmosphere.

The most obvious features of the Moon are the terrae and maria:

Terrae or **lunar highlands**   densely cratered, raised portions of the lunar surface (Figure 19.1). These areas are bright when viewed from Earth. (Plural of *terra*, Latin for land.)

Maria   flat lowland portions of the lunar surface (Figure 19.1). These areas appear dark when viewed from Earth. (Plural of *mare*, Latin for sea.)

Terrae and maria can be seen from Earth with the unaided eye. Their arrangement forms the well-known "man in the Moon" image. Their Latin names, meaning land and sea, came from early observers who believed that the Moon had continents and oceans, like Earth.

Many types of craters and other features exist on the lunar surface. Some of them are:

concentric craters   craters composed of wide rings of lunar rock material (Figure 19.1).

terraced craters   craters with distinct terraces adjacent to their outer edges, often having central peaks in their centers (Figure 19.1).

rayed craters   craters from which extend linear streaks resembling splash marks (Figure 19.1).

youthful craters   small, shallow craters with sharp edges and concave floors (Figure 19.1).

embayed craters   shallow craters with incomplete outer edges and level floors that are of the same elevation as adjacent level areas outside of the crater, usually a mare (Figure 19.1).

even-floored craters   shallow craters with complete outer edges and level (even) floors (Figure 19.1).

crater chains   series of craters arranged in linear fashion (Figures 19.1 and 19.7).

rilles   long, sinuous or linear, narrow valleys often having steep sides (Figures 19.1 and 19.4).

mare ridges   long, sinuous, slightly raised ridges on maria; they often branch like a tree (Figure 19.1).

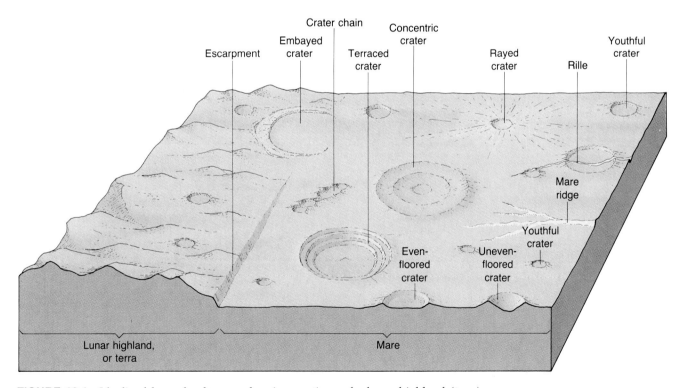

FIGURE 19.1   Idealized lunar landscape, showing portions of a lunar highland (*terra*) and "sea" (*mare*). Note the smaller features (see definitions in text).

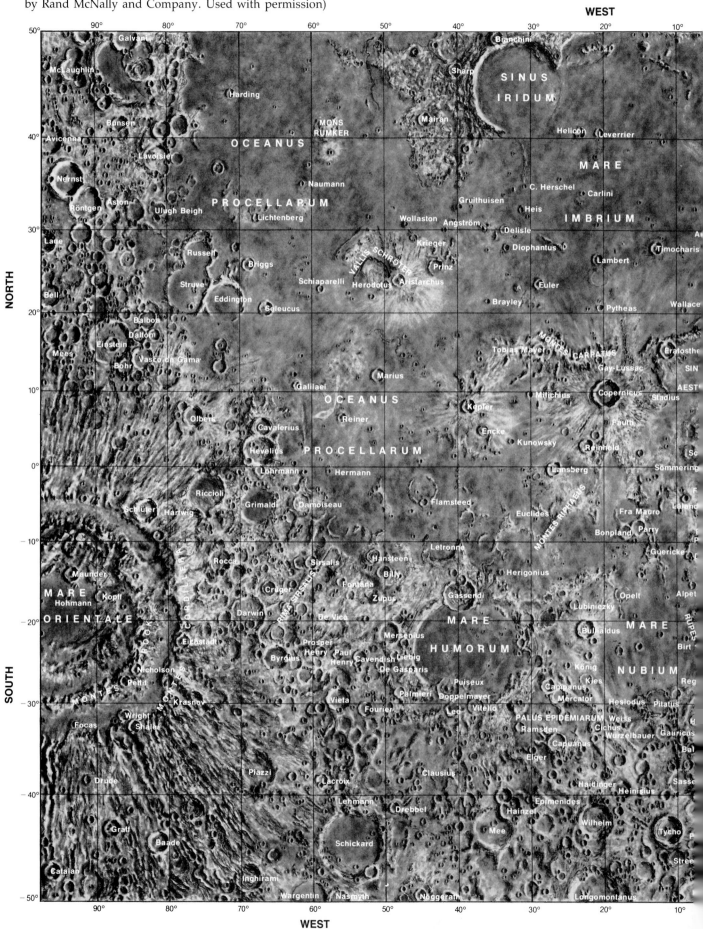

FIGURE 19.2 Near Side (the side that always faces Earth) Mercator image of the Moon, art-enhanced. (Mitchell Beazley Publishers, 1981, distributed in the U. S. A. by Rand McNally and Company. Used with permission)

FIGURE 19.3 Crater Copernicus, viewed from the south by *Orbiter II*. Distance from base of photo to horizon is about 290 km (180 miles). Crater Copernicus is 96 km in diameter (60 miles) and 3 km deep (2 miles). Peaks rise 300 m (1000 feet) from the crater floor, with slopes of 30° and loose blocks of rubble. Crater Fauth in the foreground is 21 km in diameter (13 miles) and 1370 m deep (4500 feet). (Photograph 66–H–1471, courtesy of NASA)

Crater Copernicus

Crater Fauth

escarpments long, steep slopes found at the boundaries between maria and terrae, or separating two level portions of a mare having different elevations (Figure 19.1).

scarps steep slopes located uphill from terraces or slumps, or located between adjacent terraces.

Some types of craters are combinations. For example, there are terraced rayed craters and concentric rayed craters. Many features also cut across, or overlie, one another. This aids in deducing relative age relationships.

LUNAR ROCK MATERIALS

Most of the Moon is covered with 0.02–10.0 m of loose, fragmented rock material called **regolith** or **"lunar soil."** The top part of this regolith generally is a powder that readily retains impressions, such as the bootprints of astronauts. Some of the regolith contains tiny glass spheres (0.1–0.2 mm in diameter) which are thought to be of impact origin (Figure 19.10).

All of the rocks collected from the Moon on Apollo and Luna missions were igneous rocks, or

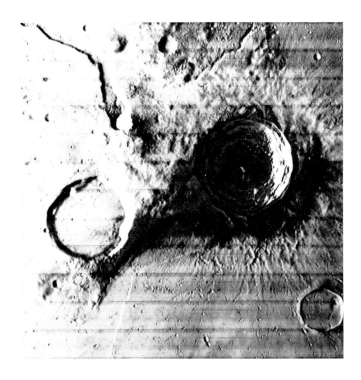

FIGURE 19.4 Orbiter photograph of lunar surface, showing two large craters. Crater Aristarchus on the right is about 40 km across (25 miles), at 24° N, 48° W in Figure 19.2. Crater Herodotus on the left is at 23.5° N, 50° W in Figure 19.2. The prominent rille in the upper-left corner is called Schroters Valley. (In Figure 19.2, its Latin name is used: Vallis Schroter). (Courtesy of NASA)

breccias composed of angular clasts from igneous rocks (Figure 19.11). The textures of lunar rocks are similar to those encountered in igneous rocks and breccias on Earth, as described in Exercise Five.

The igneous rocks are mostly basalts, plus some coarse-grained gabbros. Basalts from lunar highlands are commonly light colored, because they are rich in plagioclase and poor in dark ferromagnesian minerals (pyroxene). The mare basalts and gabbros are commonly dark colored, because they have a much higher proportion of ferromagnesian minerals, mainly pyroxene, olivine, or ilmenite (Figure 19.12). Some of the light-colored basalts have so few ferromagnesian minerals that they are essentially composed of plagioclase, and they are called anorthosites (Figure 19.13).

QUESTIONS

Locate the crater Copernicus in Figure 19.2 (10° N, 20° W). Also examine the photograph of Copernicus in Figure 19.3, and answer these questions:

1. What type of crater is this?

2. What is the probable origin of this type of crater? Explain.

3. Based on Figure 19.3, add a vertical and a horizontal scale to Figure 19.5, so that the crater in Figure 19.5 resembles Copernicus. What are the steep surfaces called that are located be-

tween the terraces in Figures 19.3 and 19.5? Label them on Figure 19.5.

4. How might the terraces in Figures 19.3 and 19.5 have formed? Complete the vertical sides of the block diagram in Figure 19.5 to show your hypothesis.

5. Based on your block diagram in Figure 19.5, how might the central peaks of Copernicus have formed?

Referring to Figure 19.4, note craters Aristarchus and Herodotus. Also note Schroters Valley, and answer these questions:

6. What kind of crater is Aristarchus?

7. What kind of crater is Herodotus?

8. How might crater Aristarchus have formed?

9. How might crater Herodotus have formed? Explain.

10. How might Schroters Valley have formed? Explain.

11. Consider the age of Herodotus and Schroters Valley relative to surrounding features. Are they older or younger than Aristarchus? What is your evidence?

12. Describe how conditions on or within the Moon have changed from the time that Herodotus and Schroters Valley formed to the time at which Aristarchus formed.

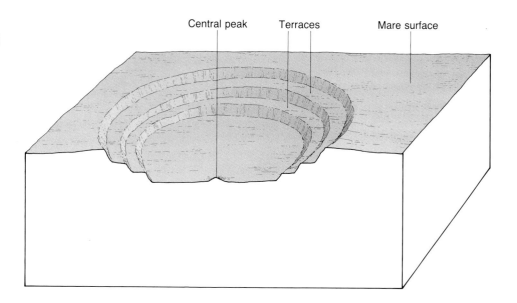

FIGURE 19.5 Hypothetical diagram (partially completed) of a terraced crater.

Central peak   Terraces   Mare surface

Refer to Figure 19.6 and answer these questions:

13. How might the escarpment have formed between the terra and the mare?

14. How might the rille have formed?

15. How might the flat, extensive, mare surface have formed? (Hint: cores and craters in maria that were examined by Apollo astronauts revealed that maria are composed of even layers of dark-colored basalt.)

16. How might the level-floored crater have formed, based upon your answer to Question 9?

17. Complete the vertical sides of the block diagram, based on your answers to Questions 13 to 16.

Refer to Figure 19.7 showing the Davey crater chain and answer the following questions.

18. How might this crater chain have formed? Explain.

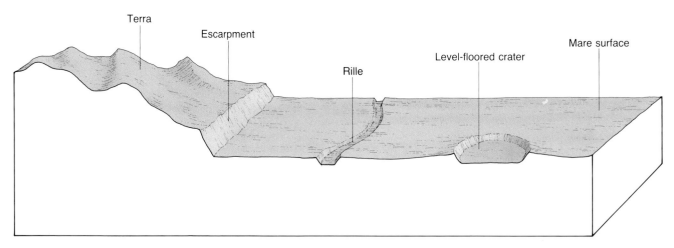

Terra   Escarpment   Rille   Level-floored crater   Mare surface

FIGURE 19.6 Hypothetical diagram (partially completed) of portion of a mare and adjacent terra.

FIGURE 19.7 View of lunar surface from *Apollo 14,* looking south. Note the Davey Crater Chain extending toward the horizon—12° S, 8° W in Figure 19.2. (Photograph 71–HC–300, courtesy of NASA)

24. Scientists regard the youngest features of the Moon to be less than a billion years old. List these features.

25. Based on information from Questions 22 to 24, how old are the rayed craters of the Moon?

FIGURE 19.8 "Mug shot" of *Apollo 16* lunar sample number 67015, collected by astronaut Charles M. Duke, Jr., on the rim of North Ray crater, 4.2 km west of the spacecraft's landing site (8.6° S, 15.5° E in Figure 19.2). Sample is 14 cm wide. (Photograph 72–HC–346, courtesy of NASA)

19. What is the age of the crater chain relative to the surface on which it is developed? Explain.

    Carefully examine Figures 19.2 through 19.7 to answer these questions:

20. Are lunar maria older or younger than lunar highlands (terrae)? Explain your reasoning.

21. Did most of the cratering on the Moon occur before or after the maria formed? What evidence is there for your answer?

22. Note the rayed craters Copernicus (10° N, 20° W in Figure 19.2), Langrenus (10° S, 60° E), Orientale (20° S, 90° W), and Aristarchus (24° N, 48° W and Figure 19.4).
    a. Are they older or younger than the lunar highlands? Explain your reasoning.
    b. Are they older or younger than the maria? Explain your reasoning.

23. Rocks from lunar maria, obtained during manned Apollo landings, have absolute ages of 3.2–4.0 billion years. How old are the lunar highlands?

FIGURE 19.9 "Mug shot" of *Apollo 16* lunar sample number 68815, a fragment from a large boulder some 1.5 m long and 1.2 m wide. Sample was collected by astronauts Duke and John W. Young near the spacecraft's landing site (8.6° S, 15.5° E in Figure 19.2). Sample is 19 cm wide, hard, and has metallic particles in the black portion. (Photograph 72–HC–340, courtesy of NASA)

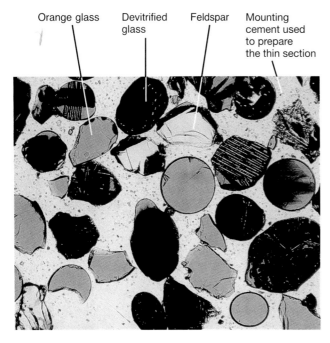

Orange glass   Devitrified glass   Feldspar   Mounting cement used to prepare the thin section

FIGURE 19.10 Photomicrograph of lunar regolith, magnified ×29. This particular regolith is known as "orange soil." The glass spheres are thought to be impact-related, and are orange because they contain titanium oxide. The dark spheres are devitrified (converted from glass to a microcrystalline state). NASA sample 74220/289, collected by *Apollo 17* astronauts. (Photo by Omni Resources, Inc. formerly Geoscience Resources)

Refer to Figures 19.8 and 19.9, and answer these questions:

26. Figure 19.8 shows what type of rock, based on its texture?

27. How did the rock in Figure 19.8 probably form?

28. Angular clasts in lunar rocks are common, as in Figure 19.8. Why are the clasts not rounded?

29. What might the metallic particles in the rock of Figure 19.9 be? Why?

30. Detail the steps of how the rock in Figure 19.9 probably formed.

ADDITIONAL QUESTIONS

List the four major intervals of lunar geologic history that you described in your answers to Questions 11, 12, 15, and 19 to 25.

31. What is the absolute duration (in years) of each interval?

32. What happened during each interval?

33. The lunar highlands commonly are composed of light-colored basalts or anorthosites, whereas maria are composed of dark-colored basalts and gabbros. What is a reasonable explanation for this phenomenon, considering your answers in Question 32?

34. Some portions of the surface of Mars (Figure 1.8) are densely cratered, much like the lunar highlands. What do you suspect is the age of such portions of Mars? Explain.

35. Is it likely that Earth once was heavily cratered like the Moon and Mars? If so, why are there so few craters now visible on Earth's surface?

36. Examine the photomicrograph of lunar regolith in Figure 19.10. Explain step-by-step how it formed. Start with a step involving the eruption of a volcano, and end with a step involving collection of the sample by *Apollo 17* astronauts.

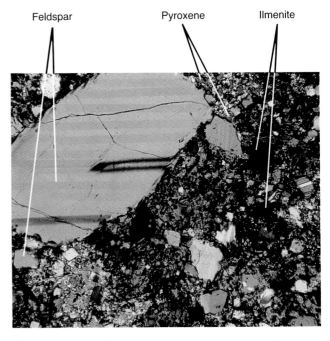

Feldspar   Pyroxene   Ilmenite

FIGURE 19.11 Thin-section photomicrograph of lunar breccia, magnified ×72.5. This breccia is composed of large plagioclase feldspar clasts in a fine-grained matrix of plagioclase and pyroxene, with minor ilmenite (ferrotitanium oxide). NASA sample 65015/142, collected by *Apollo 16* astronauts. (Photo by Omni Resources, Inc. formerly Geoscience Resources)

37. Examine the photomicrograph of lunar regolith in Figure 19.13. Suppose that the identification data for this sample were lost.

  a. What type of lunar landform would you suspect this sample to be from?

  b. How old might this sample be? (Give a range in years.)

  c. How might this sample have gotten its cataclastic texture?

38. Examine the photomicrograph of a lunar breccia sample in Figure 19.11.

  a. Give a likely provenance (place of origin) for the constituents of this rock.

  b. Why are the sedimentary grains so fresh and unweathered?

Crushed feldspar crystals

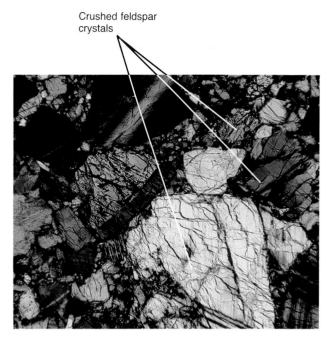

FIGURE 19.13 Thin-section photomicrograph of anorthosite, magnified ×58. Note the cataclastic (shattered) texture, due to impacts. NASA sample 60025/231 collected by *Apollo 16* astronauts from the Cayley Plain. (Photo by Omni Resources, Inc. formerly Geoscience Resources)

Pyroxene   Ilmenite   Feldspar

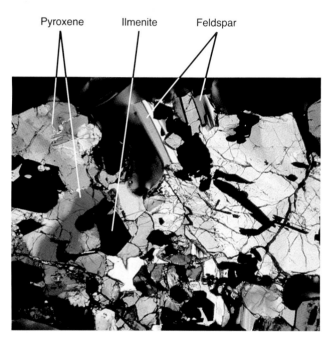

FIGURE 19.12 Thin-section photomicrograph of a mare basalt, magnified ×26.1. This basalt contains ilmenite blades enclosed within pyroxene, with minor plagioclase feldspar. NASA sample 70017/196, collected by *Apollo 17* astronauts in Taurus Lithow between Camelot and Steno craters. (Photo by Omni Resources, Inc. formerly Geoscience Resources)

The Geologic Time Scale

Eon	Era	Period**		Epoch		Approximate Ages (In millions of years)
Phanerozoic: The Eon of Visible Life	Cenozoic: The Age of Mammals	Quaternary (Q)		Recent / Pleistocene	Neogene*	
						—1.6—
		Tertiary (T)		Pliocene / Miocene / Oligocene / Eocene / Paleocene	Paleogene*	—24—
						—65—
	Mesozoic: The Age of Dinosaurs	Cretaceous (K)		Late / Early		
						—144—
		Jurassic (J)		Late / Middle / Early		
						—213—
		Triassic (Ŕ)		Late / Middle / Early		
						—248—
	Paleozoic: The Age of Trilobites	Permian (P)		Late / Early		
						—286—
		Carboniferous (C)*	Pennsylvanian (ℙ)	Late / Middle / Early		
						—320—
			Mississippian (M)	Late / Early		
						—360—
		Devonian (D)		Late / Middle / Early		
						—408—
		Silurian (S)		Late / Middle / Early		
						—438—
		Ordovician (O)		Late / Middle / Early		
						—505—
		Cambrian (Ͼ)		Late / Middle / Early		
						—590—
	Precambrian (PͼCͼ)	Locally divided into Early, Middle, and Late				—4500+—

*European names

**Symbols in parentheses are abbreviations commonly used to designate the age of rock units on geologic maps.

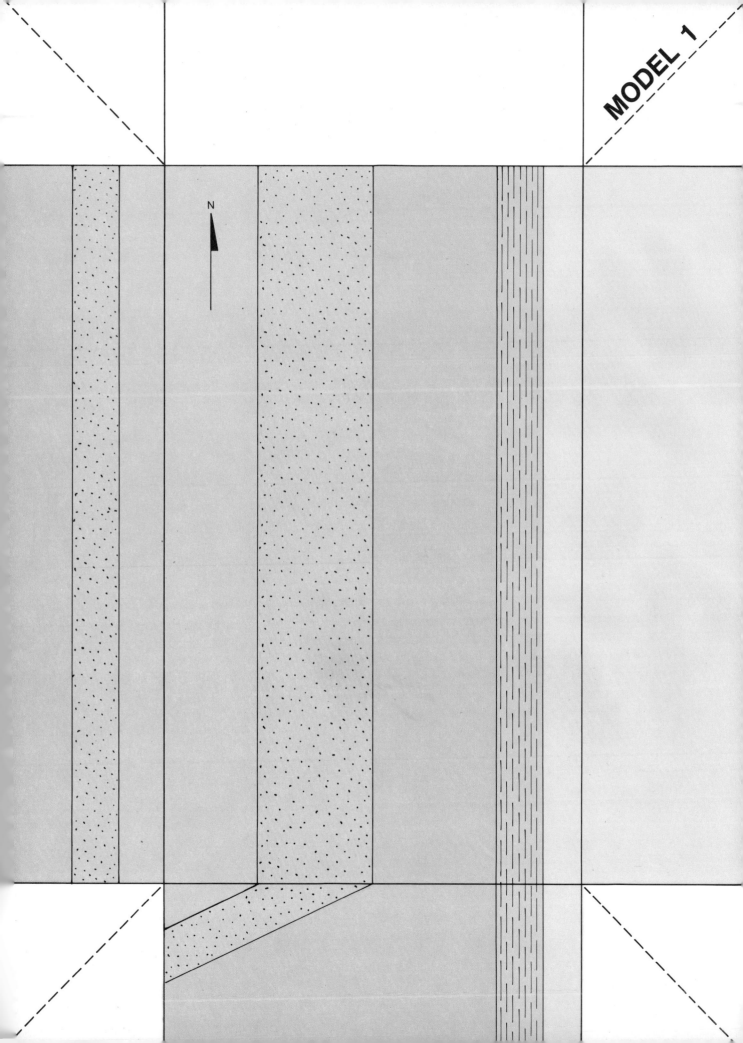

MODEL 1

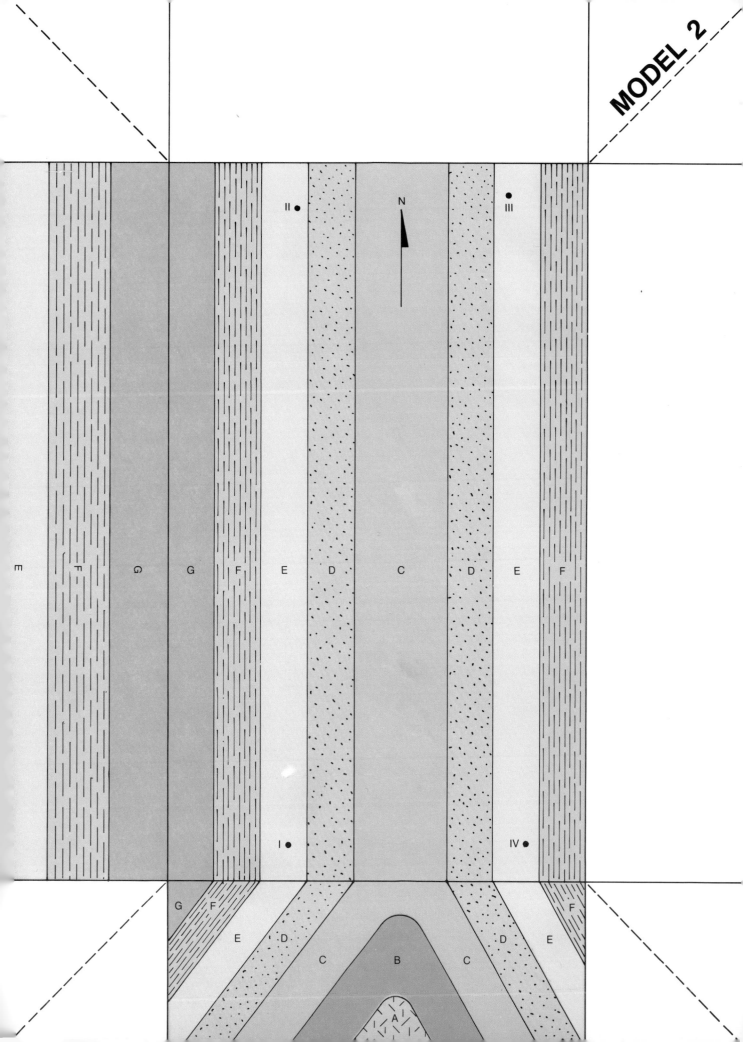

MODEL 2

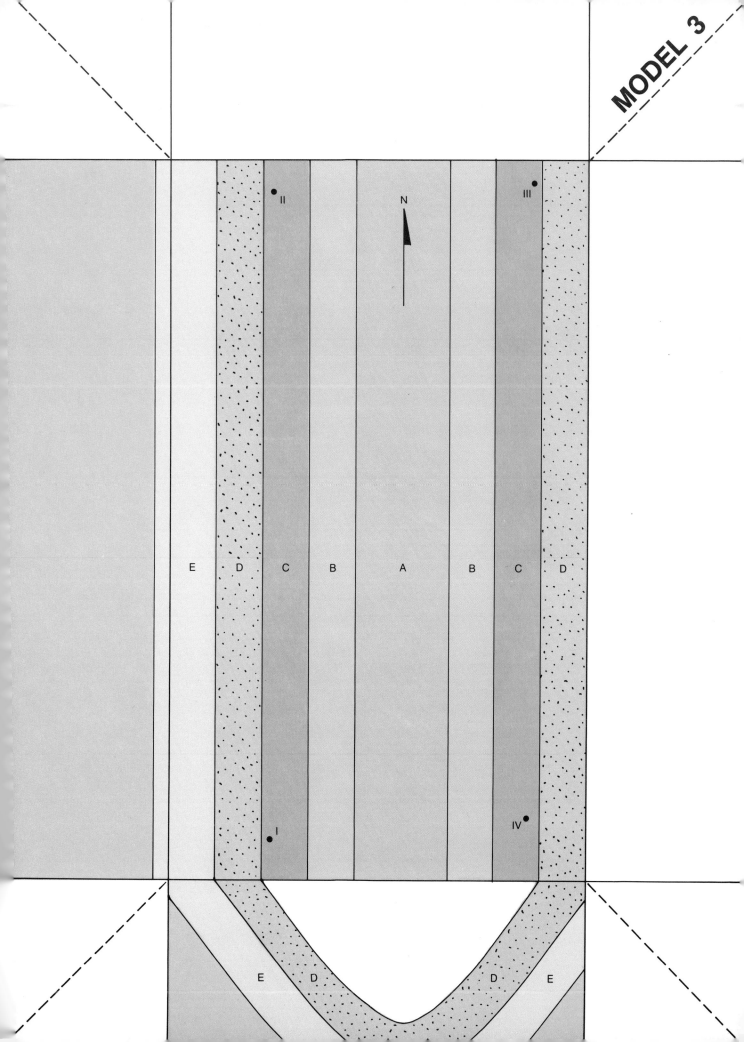

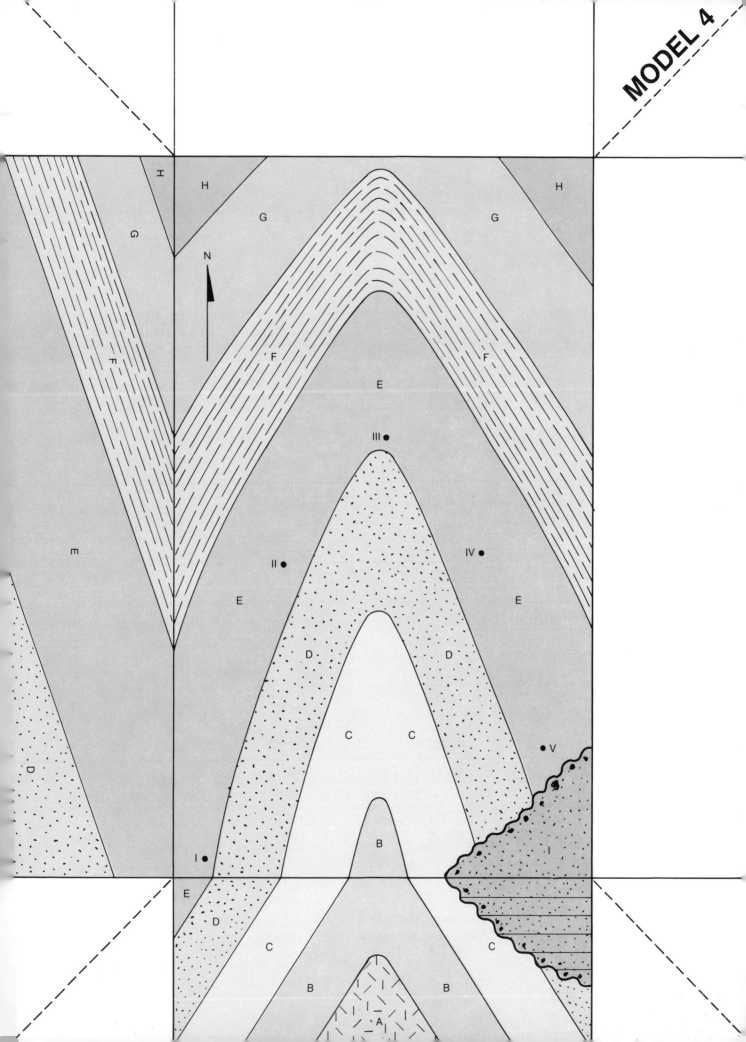

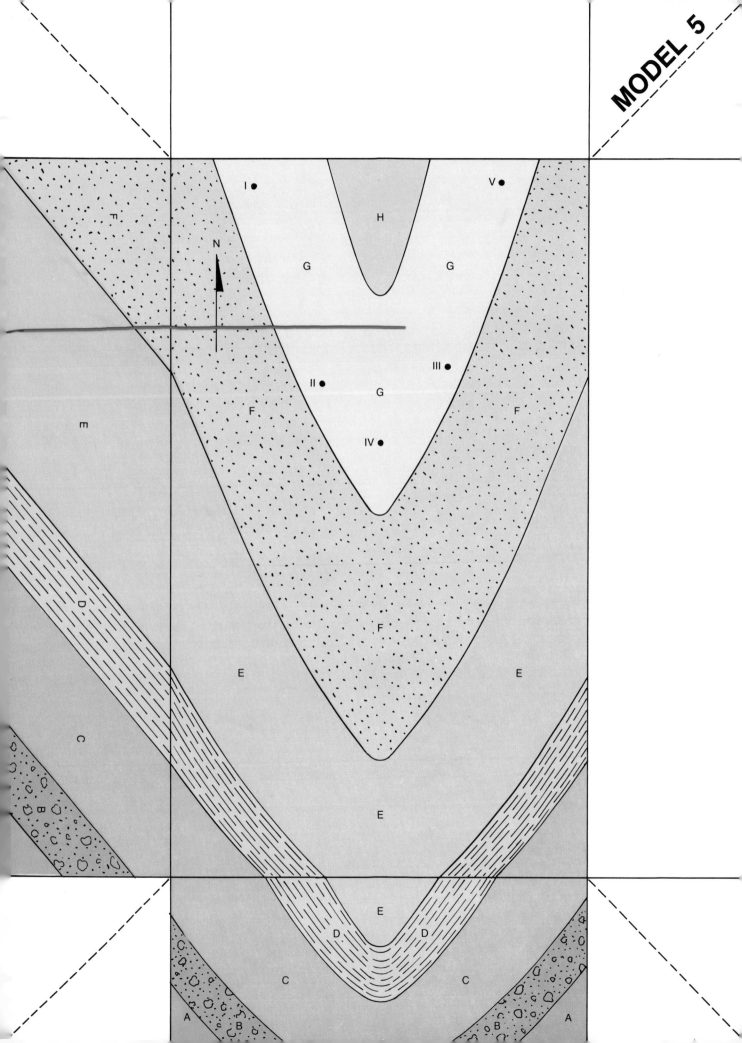

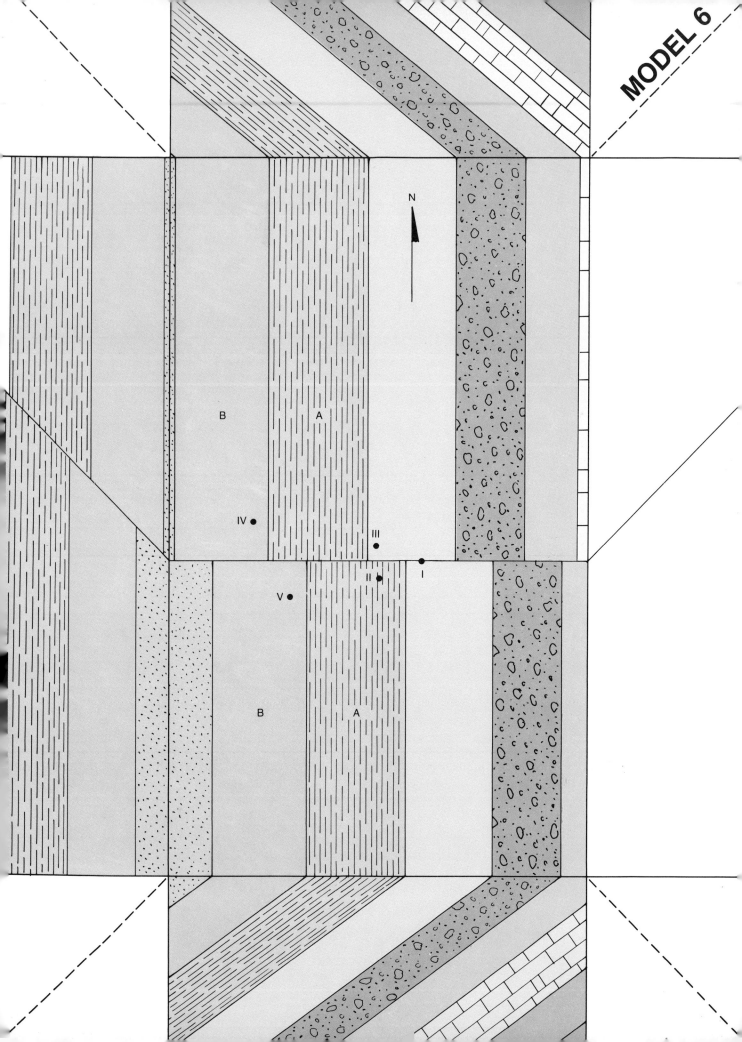

MODEL 6

N